# RIGHTSTART™ MATHEMATICS

by Joan A. Cotter, Ph.D.
with Kathleen Cotter Lawler

## LEVEL E LESSONS
### Second Edition

*A Activities for Learning, Inc.*

A special thank you to Maren Ehley and Rebecca Walsh for their work in the final preparation of this manual.

Note: Levels are used rather than grades. For example, Level A is kindergarten and Level B is first grade and so forth.

Printed in the United States of America

**www.RightStartMath.com**

For more information: info@RightStartMath.com
Supplies may be ordered from: www.RightStartMath.com

Activities for Learning, Inc.
321 Hill Street
Hazelton, ND 58544-0468
United States of America
888-775-6284 or 701-782-2000
701-782-2007 fax

ISBN 978-1-942943-11-2

April 2018

# RightStart™ Mathematics Objectives for Level E

| | Quarter 1 | Quarter 2 | Quarter 3 | Quarter 4 |
|---|---|---|---|---|
| **Numeration** | | | | |
| Understands and finds prime numbers | N/A | | | |
| Factors numbers | N/A | | | |
| Reads, writes, rounds, and compares numbers to the billions | | | | |
| **Addition and Subtraction** | | | | |
| Adds and subtracts multi-digit numbers in multiple ways | | | | |
| **Multiplication and Division** | | | | |
| Knows multiplication facts to $10 \times 10$ | N/A | | | |
| Knows division facts, including remainders | N/A | N/A | | |
| Applies commutative, associative, and distributive properties | N/A | | | |
| Multiplies multiples of 10, e.g. $80 \times 7$ | N/A | | | |
| Multiplies multi-digit numbers by a 2-digit number | N/A | N/A | | |
| Does short division to divide multi-digit number by a single digit | N/A | N/A | | |
| **Problem Solving** | | | | |
| Solves two-step problems involving four operations | | | | |
| Writes equations to represent story problems | | | | |
| Solves division story problems with remainders | | | | |
| Solves elapsed time, distance, money, and capacity problems | N/A | N/A | N/A | |
| **Measurement** | | | | |
| Understands square units: cm², dm², sq ft, and sq yd | N/A | N/A | | |
| Finds perimeter and area in customary and metric units | N/A | N/A | | |
| Converts measurements in same system (e.g., g to kg) | N/A | N/A | N/A | |
| **Fractions** | | | | |
| Adds and subtracts simple fractions and mixed numbers | N/A | | | |
| Understands $a/b$ as $1/b$ multiplied by $a$ | N/A | | | |
| Understands $n\frac{a}{b}$ as a whole number plus a fraction | N/A | | | |
| Compares and finds equivalences on the fraction chart | N/A | | | |
| Multiplies fractions times a whole number | N/A | | | |
| **Decimals and Percents** | | | | |
| Understands decimals as fractions of tenths or hundredths | N/A | N/A | | |
| Converts decimal fractions from tenths to hundredths and back | N/A | N/A | | |
| Adds, subtracts, and compares decimals to two decimal places | N/A | N/A | | |
| Understands and uses simple percents | N/A | N/A | | |
| **Patterns** | | | | |
| Recognizes and continues numeric and geometric patterns | N/A | N/A | N/A | |
| Uses algebraic thinking to write a pattern symbolically | | | | |
| Solves simple equations | N/A | | | |
| **Data** | | | | |
| Makes line plots and interprets data | N/A | N/A | N/A | |
| **Geometry** | | | | |
| Locates lines of symmetry and draws reflections | N/A | N/A | N/A | |
| Knows angles 30°, 45°, 60°, 90°, 180°, and 360° | N/A | N/A | N/A | |
| Classifies shapes by attributes | N/A | N/A | N/A | |
| Constructs equilateral triangle and other shapes | N/A | N/A | N/A | |

## Materials needed that are not included in the RS2 Math Set

Occasionally, the materials needed for a lesson have items listed in boldface type, indicating that these items are not included in the RS2 Math Set. Below is a list of theses items and the lesson number where they are needed.

Lesson 14     An empty corner in the room, 3 ft (1 m) in all three directions

Lesson 38     Tape*, sharp pencil (preferably mechanical) and eraser
  * The best tape is 3M's Removable Tape, which can be reused several times and doesn't tear the corners of the paper.

Lesson 39     Tape

Lesson 41     Tape

Lesson 42     Tape

Lesson 55     Objects for the child to measure, such as books or boxes

Lesson 63     Scissors

Lesson 80     A blank check, optional

Lesson 96     Scissors

Lesson 104    Scissors and a protractor, if available

Lesson 109    Two rulers

Lesson 123    Colored pencils, optional

Lesson 127    Colored pencils: blue, yellow, black, green, red

Lesson 133    Scissors

Lesson 134    7 strips of paper about 11" (30 cm) × 1" (2 to 3 cm) wide, scissors, and tape

# How This Program Was Developed

We have been hearing for years that Japanese students do better than U.S. students in math in Japan. The Asian students are ahead by the middle of first grade. And the gap widens every year thereafter.

Many explanations have been given, including less diversity and a longer school year. Japanese students attend school 240 days a year.

A third explanation given is that the Asian public values and supports education more than we do. A first grade teacher has the same status as a university professor. If a student falls behind, the family, not the school, helps the child or hires a tutor. Students often attend after-school classes.

A fourth explanation involves the philosophy of learning. Asians and Europeans believe anyone can learn mathematics or even play the violin. It is not a matter of talent, but of good teaching and hard work.

Although these explanations are valid, I decided to take a careful look at how mathematics is taught in Japanese first grades. Japan has a national curriculum, so there is little variation among teachers.

I found some important differences. One of these is the way the Asians name their numbers. In English we count ten, eleven, twelve, thirteen, and so on, which doesn't give the child a clue about tens and ones. But in Asian languages, one counts by saying ten-1, ten-2, ten-3 for the teens, and 2-ten 1, 2-ten 2, and 2-ten 3 for the twenties.

Still another difference is their criteria for manipulatives. Americans think the more the better. Asians prefer very few, but insist that they be imaginable, that is, visualizable. That is one reason they do not use colored rods. You can imagine the one and the three, but try imagining a brown eight–the quantity eight, not the color. It cannot be done without grouping.

Another important difference is the emphasis on non-counting strategies for computation. Japanese children are discouraged from counting; rather they are taught to see quantities in groups of fives and tens.

For example, when an American child wants to know 9 + 4, most likely the child will start with 9 and count up 4. In contrast, the Asian child will think that if he takes 1 from the 4 and puts it with the 9, then he will have 10 and 3, or 13. Unfortunately, very few American first-graders at the end of the year even know that 10 + 3 is 13.

I decided to conduct research using some of these ideas in two similar first grade classrooms. The control group studied math in the traditional workbook-based manner. The other class used the lesson plans I developed. The children used that special number naming for three months.

They also used a special abacus I designed, based on fives and tens. I asked 5-year-old Stan how much is 11 + 6. Then I asked him how he knew. He replied, "I have the abacus in my mind."

The children were working with thousands by the sixth week. They figured out how to add 4-digit numbers on paper after learning how on the abacus.

Every child in the experimental class, including those enrolled in special education classes, could add numbers like 9 + 4, by changing it to 10 + 3.

I asked the children to explain what the 6 and 2 mean in the number 26. Ninety-three percent of the children in the experimental group explained it correctly while only 50% of third graders did so in another study.

I gave the children some base ten rods (none of them had seen them before) that looked like ones and tens and asked them to make 48. Then I asked them to subtract 14. The children in the control group counted 14 ones, while the experimental class removed 1 ten and 4 ones. This indicated that they saw 14 as 1 ten and 4 ones and not as 14 ones. This view of numbers is vital to understanding algorithms, or procedures, for doing arithmetic.

I asked the experimental class to mentally add 64 + 20, which only 52% of nine-year-olds on the 1986 National test did correctly; 56% of those in the experimental class could do it.

Since children often confuse columns when taught traditionally, I wrote 2304 + 86 = horizontally and asked them to find the sum any way they liked. Fifty-six percent did so correctly, including one child who did it in his head.

The following year I revised the lesson plans and both first grade classes used these methods. I am delighted to report that on a national standardized test, both classes scored at the 98th percentile.

*Joan A. Cotter, Ph.D.*

# Some General Thoughts on Teaching Mathematics

1. Only five percent of mathematics should be learned by rote; 95 percent should be understood.

2. Real learning builds on what the child already knows. Rote teaching ignores it.

3. Contrary to the common myth, "young children can think both concretely and abstractly. Development is not a kind of inevitable unfolding in which one simply waits until a child is cognitively 'ready.'" —*Foundations for Success* NMAP

4. What is developmentally appropriate is not a simple function of age or grade, but rather is largely contingent on prior opportunities to learn." —Duschl & others

5. Understanding a new model is easier if you have made one yourself. So, a child needs to construct a graph before attempting to read a ready-made graph.

6. Good manipulatives cause confusion at first. If a new manipulative makes perfect sense at first sight, it is not needed. Trying to understand and relate it to previous knowledge is what leads to greater learning. —Richard Behr & others.

7. According to Arthur Baroody, "Teaching mathematics is essentially a process of translating mathematics into a form children can comprehend, providing experiences that enable children to discover relationships and construct meanings, and creating opportunities to develop and exercise mathematical reasoning."

8. Lauren Resnick says, "Good mathematics learners expect to be able to make sense out of rules they are taught, and they apply some energy and time to the task of making sense. By contrast, those less adept in mathematics try to memorize and apply the rules that are taught, but do not attempt to relate these rules to what they know about mathematics at a more intuitive level."

9. Mindy Holte puts learning the facts in proper perspective when she says, "In our concern about the memorization of math facts or solving problems, we must not forget that the root of mathematical study is the creation of mental pictures in the imagination and manipulating those images and relationships using the power of reason and logic." She also emphasizes the ability to imagine or visualize, an important skill in mathematics and other areas.

10. The only students who like flash cards are those who do not need them.

11. Mathematics is not a solitary pursuit. According to Richard Skemp, solitary math on paper is like reading music, rather than listening to it: "Mathematics, like music, needs to be expressed in physical actions and human interactions before its symbols can evoke the silent patterns of mathematical ideas (like musical notes), simultaneous relationships (like harmonies) and expositions or proofs (like melodies)."

12. "More than most other school subjects, mathematics offers special opportunities for children to learn the power of thought as distinct from the power of authority. This is a very important lesson to learn, an essential step in the emergence of independent thinking." —*Everybody Counts*

13. The role of the teacher is to encourage thinking by asking questions, not giving answers. Once you give an answer, thinking usually stops.

14. Putting thoughts into words helps the learning process.

15. Help the children realize that it is their responsibility to ask questions when they do not understand. Do not settle for "I don't get it."

16. The difference between a novice and an expert is that an expert catches errors much more quickly. A violinist adjusts pitch so quickly that the audience does not hear it.

17. Europeans and Asians believe learning occurs not because of ability, but primarily because of effort. In the ability model of learning, errors are a sign of failure. In the effort model, errors are natural. In Japanese classrooms, the teachers discuss errors with the whole class.

18. For teaching vocabulary, be sure either the word or the concept is known. For example, if a child is familiar with six-sided figures, we can give him the word, hexagon. Or, if he has heard the word, multiply, we can tell him what it means. It is difficult to learn a new concept and the term simultaneously.

19. Introduce new concepts globally before details. This lets the children know where they are headed.

20. Informal mathematics should precede paper and pencil work. Long before a child learns how to add fractions with unlike denominators, she should be able to add one half and one fourth mentally.

21. Some pairs of concepts are easier to remember if one of them is thought of as dominant. Then the non-dominant concept is simply the other one. For example, if even is dominant over odd, an odd number is one that is not even.

22. Worksheets should also make the child think. Therefore, they should not be a large collection of similar exercises, but should present a variety. In RightStart™ Mathematics, they are designed to be done independently.

23. Keep math time enjoyable. We store our emotional state along with what we have learned. A person who dislikes math will avoid it and a child under stress stops learning. If a lesson is too hard, stop and play a game. Try the lesson again later.

24. In Japan students spend more time on fewer problems. Teachers do not concern themselves with attention spans as is done in the U.S.

25. In Japan the goal of the math lesson is that the student has understood a concept, not necessarily has done something (a worksheet).

26. The calendar must show the entire month, so the children can plan ahead. The days passed can be crossed out or the current day circled.

27. A real mathematical problem is one in which the procedures to find the answer are not obvious. It is like a puzzle, needing trial and error. Emphasize the satisfaction of solving problems and like puzzles, of not giving away the solution to others.

# RightStart™ Mathematics

Ten major characteristics make this research-based program effective:

1. Refers to quantities of up to 5 as a group; discourages counting individually. Uses fingers and tally sticks to show quantities up to 10; teaches quantities 6 to 10 as 5 plus a quantity, for example 6 = 5 + 1.

2. Avoids counting procedures for finding sums and differences. Teaches five- and ten-based strategies for the facts that are both visual and visualizable.

3. Employs games, not flash cards, for practice.

4. Once quantities 1 to 10 are known, proceeds to 10 as a unit. Temporarily uses the "math way" of naming numbers; for example, "1 ten-1" (or "ten-1") for eleven, "1-ten 2" for twelve, "2-ten" for twenty, and "2-ten 5" for twenty-five.

5. Uses expanded notation (overlapping) place-value cards for recording tens and ones; the ones card is placed on the zero of the tens card. Encourages a child to read numbers starting at the left and not backward by starting at the ones.

6. Proceeds rapidly to hundreds and thousands using manipulatives and place-value cards. Provides opportunities for trading between ones and tens, tens and hundreds, and hundreds and thousands with manipulatives.

7. Teaches mental computation. Investigates informal solutions, often through story problems, before learning procedures.

8. Teaches four-digit addition on the abacus, letting the child discover the paper and pencil algorithm.

9. Introduces fractions with a linear visual model, including all fractions from 1/2 to 1/10. "Pies" are not used initially because they cannot show fractions greater than 1. Later, the tenths will become the basis for decimals.

10. Teaches short division (where only the answer is written down) for single-digit divisors, before long division.

## Second Edition

Many changes have occurred since the first RightStart™ lessons were begun in 1994. First, mathematics is used more widely in many fields, for example, architecture, science, technology, and medicine. Today, many careers require math beyond basic arithmetic. Second, research has given us new insights into how children learn mathematics. Third, kindergarten has become much more academic, and fourth, most children are tested to ensure their preparedness for the next step.

This second edition is updated to reflect new research and applications. Topics within each level are always taught with the most appropriate method using the best approach with the child and teacher in mind.

# Daily Lessons

***Objectives.*** The objectives outline the purpose and goal of the lesson. Some possibilities are to introduce, to build, to learn a term, to practice, or to review.

***Materials.*** The Math Set of manipulatives includes the specially crafted items needed to teach RightStart™ Mathematics. Occasionally, common objects such as scissors will be needed. These items are indicated by boldface type.

***Warm-up.*** The warm-up time is the time for quick review, memory work, and sometimes an introduction to the day's topics. The dry erase board makes an ideal slate for quick responses.

***Activities.*** The Activities for Teaching section is the heart of the lesson; it starts on the left page and continues to the right page. These are the instructions for teaching the lesson. The expected answers from the child are given in square brackets.

Establish with the children some indication when you want a quick response and when you want a more thoughtful response. Research shows that the quiet time for thoughtful response should be about three seconds. Avoid talking during this quiet time; resist the temptation to rephrase the question. This quiet time gives the slower child time to think and the quicker child time to think more deeply.

Encourage the child to develop persistence and perseverance. Avoid giving hints or explanations too quickly. Children tend to stop thinking once they hear the answer.

***Explanations.*** Special background notes for the teacher are given in Explanations.

***Worksheets.*** The worksheets are designed to give the children a chance to think about and to practice the day's lesson. The children are to do them independently. Some lessons, especially in the early levels, have no worksheet.

***Games.*** Games, not worksheets or flash cards, provide practice. The games, found in the *Math Card Games* book, can be played as many times as necessary until proficiency or memorization takes place. They are as important to learning math as books are to reading. The *Math Card Games* book also includes extra games for the child needing more help, and some more challenging games for the advanced child.

***In conclusion.*** Each lesson ends with a short summary called, "In conclusion," where the child answers a few short questions based on the day's learning.

***Number of lessons.*** Generally, each lesson is to be done in one day and each manual, in one school year. Complete each manual before going on to the next level.

***Comments.*** We really want to hear how this program is working. Please let us know any improvements and suggestions that you may have.


*Joan A. Cotter, Ph.D.*

info@RightStartMath.com
www.RightStartMath.com

# LEVEL E TABLE OF CONTENTS

# LEVEL E TABLE OF CONTENTS

# LEVEL E TABLE OF CONTENTS

# LEVEL E TABLE OF CONTENTS

# REVIEW LESSON 1: THE AL ABACUS AND ADDITION STRATEGIES

## OBJECTIVES:

1. To learn (or review) the term *subitizing*
2. To construct quantities 1 to 10 on fingers
3. To enter quantities 1 to 10 on the abacus
4. To identify quantities 1 to 10 on the abacus
5. To review addition strategies

## MATERIALS:

1. AL Abacus
2. *Math Card Games* book,* A44
3. Math journal, found in the back of the child's worksheets

## ACTIVITIES FOR TEACHING:

***Exploring the AL Abacus.*** Give the child the abacus. Ask: Are the two sides of the abacus the same? [no] Tell her: On the first side each bead has a value of one. On the second side, a bead's value depends upon what column it is in.

Tell her to lay her abacus flat with the wires horizontal and the logo in the top right. Then tell her to *clear* her abacus by lifting the left edge allowing the beads to slide to the right. See the figure on the right.

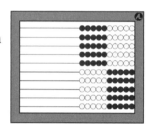
**Abacus cleared.**

***Quantities 1 to 5.*** Tell the child to enter 2 on the abacus by moving the beads as a group. Then tell her to clear her abacus.

Repeat for 3, 4, 5, and 1. Explain: Showing or recognizing quantities without counting is called *subitizing*.

***Quantities 6 to 10.*** Tell the child to subitize 6 with her fingers, 5 with the left hand and 1 with the right hand, as shown below.

 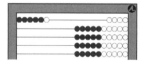
**6 subitized as 5 and 1.**

Then tell her to enter 6 on her abacus without counting. Ask: How does the abacus compare to your hands? [Blue is left hand; yellow is right hand.] Give her quantities 6–10 at random to enter on the abacus. Then give her numbers 1–10 to enter. Also enter numbers on the abacus from 1–10 at random for her to read.

***Two-Fives Strategy.*** Tell her: We can use the abacus to show strategies for addition facts. Tell her: The Two-Fives Strategy works when both numbers are 5 or more. Have the child enter 9 and 6 on the top two wires of her abacus. See the left figure on the next page.

## EXPLANATIONS:

These review lessons are designed for the child who has had no previous RightStart™ instruction or for the child needing a quick review.

*The Fifth Edition of the *Math Card Games* book is needed for this manual.

The book is arranged in chapters as follows:
1. Number Sense (N)
2. Addition (A)
3. Clocks (C)
4. Multiplication (P)
5. Money (M)
6. Subtraction (S)
7. Division (D)
8. Fractions (F)

The games are numbered sequentially within each chapter. For example, A2 is the second game in the Addition chapter. Within each chapter the games get progressively harder.

Quantities 1–5 are always shown on the left hand; 6–10, on the right hand. Which fingers to use on a hand is unimportant.

Subitizing beyond five by grouping is called *conceptual subitizing.*

**ACTIVITIES FOR TEACHING CONTINUED:**

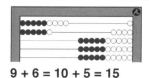 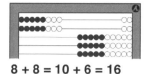

9 + 6 = 10 + 5 = 15    8 + 8 = 10 + 6 = 16

Ask: Do you see the two fives? [the dark-colored beads] How much is left over? [4 + 1] So, how much is 9 + 6? [10 + 5 = 15] Tell her to use the Two-Fives Strategy to find 8 + 8. [8 + 8 = 10 + 6 = 16] See the right figure above. Repeat for 6 + 7. [6 + 7 = 10 + 3 = 13]

**Make Ten Strategy.** Say: There is another good addition strategy, the Make Ten Strategy. Enter 9 on the first wire and 4 on the next wire. We want to make a 10, so take one bead from the 4 and give it to the 9. See the figures below.

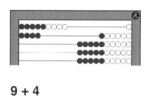 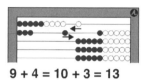

9 + 4    9 + 4 = 10 + 3 = 13

Once she has done it once, challenge her to move that bead in her mind. Tell her to use the Make Ten Strategy to add 8 + 7, where 2 is taken from 7 and given to 8 to make 10.

**Addition War game.** Play the following variation of Addition War game found in *Math Card Games* book, A44. Tell the child to write the two strategies in her math journal as shown below.

Addition Strategies

Two-Fives          ⳾⳾⳾ |

Make Ten          | | |

Explain that for each turn, she writes a tally mark for either of the strategies that could be used. Many facts can be found with both strategies. She can use her abacus to find the appropriate sums.

At the end of the game, there is a second winner: the player with the greater number of tally marks.

**In conclusion.** Ask: Which strategies can you use to find 6 + 7? [Two Fives] What strategies can you use to find 9 + 8? [Two Fives and Make Ten]

**EXPLANATIONS CONTINUED:**

See page iii, numbers 15 and 23 of "Some General Thoughts on Teaching Mathematics," for additional information.

When a child learns to read, she can practice those skills by reading for pleasure. In the same way, these card games combine practice with pleasure. Although learning math requires hard work, it can be enjoyable. When a person is interested in and loves her work, she can more easily tackle the distasteful segments found in any activity.

These games allow adults and children of various ages and abilities to play together. It does away with anxiety-producing flash cards, which cast the parent or teacher in the role of judge. The only person who enjoys flash cards is the person who doesn't need them. Games create a stress-free atmosphere that allows all to learn at their own pace. Then the parent or teacher becomes a partner in the learning process.

There is another reason to make mathematics enjoyable for children. Along with the information recorded in our memories are the feelings we experienced when we learned it. These feelings are often recalled along with the fact or experience. For this reason, information stored with negative feelings tends to be forgotten. Children who associate math with feelings of failure and inadequacy will find learning difficult, and worse yet, they will ignore applications to daily life. When children recall feelings of discovery and success, they will want to continue learning and will apply that knowledge to other areas. Therefore, it is important that learning be a pleasant experience.

Conclusions may be a summary of the day's lesson or an expansion of the lesson to challenge higher level thinking.

# REVIEW LESSON 2: THE MATH BALANCE

## OBJECTIVES:

1. To introduce the math balance
2. To review writing addition and multiplication equations

## MATERIALS:

1. AL Abacus
2. Math balance* and weights
3. Dry erase board

## ACTIVITIES FOR TEACHING:

***Warm-up.*** Give the child the abacus. Tell her to show on her fingers and her abacus the quantities that you say as fast as she can. Say: Show and enter 3. Show and enter 5. Show and enter 6. Continue with 1, 8, 2, 7, 4, 10, and 9.

Ask: Which strategies can you use to find 6 + 7? [Two Fives] What is 6 + 7? [13] What strategies can you use to find 8 + 8? [Two Fives and Make Ten] What is 8 + 8? [16] What strategies can you use to find 8 + 9? [Make Ten] What is 8 + 9? [17]

***Math balance.*** Present the math balance. Give the child two weights and ask her to make it balance. Avoid giving hints.

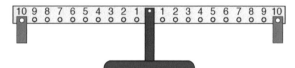

**The math balance balanced with two weights.**

Remove the two weights and ask her to find another way to make it balance.

Next give the child three weights and ask her to make it balance. One possibility is shown below. Ask: Why does it balance? [because the sides equal the same amount]

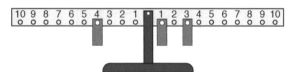

**Balancing with three weights; 4 is 1 + 3.**

***Ways to make 10.*** Place a weight on the left 10. Give the child two weights and ask her to make it balance. See the figure below for one solution. Ask her to write the equation on her dry erase board. [10 = 3 + 7]

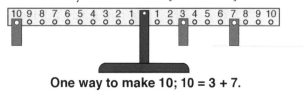

**One way to make 10; 10 = 3 + 7.**

## EXPLANATIONS:

*After the math balance is assembled, check to be sure it is level. If necessary, adjust it by moving the little white weights under the yellow beam.

The first half of these RightStart™ Mathematics lessons refers to the child as a female and the second half refers to the child as a male.

A person can make this discovery only once so do not let anyone else spoil it.

For a person's first attempt, children usually choose the 10s, while adults usually choose a low number.

All the weights are the same; ignore the numbers embossed on them.

The white peg in the center is not a solution.

| ACTIVITIES FOR TEACHING CONTINUED: | EXPLANATIONS CONTINUED: |

Ask the child to find a different solution to make it balance with 10. [10 = 1 + 9, 10 = 2 + 8, 10 = 4 + 6, or 10 = 5 + 5] Tell her to write it down on her dry erase board. Continue until all five ways are found and recorded. Tell her to end with two weights on one peg.

Tell the child to write it as a multiplication equation:

10 = 5 × 2

An explanation of the meaning of 5 × 2 vs. 2 × 5 will be discussed in Lesson 6.

**Multiplying on the math balance.** Tell the child to put one more weight on the right 5. Ask: How can you make it balance by adding one more weight? [put the weight on the left 5] See below.

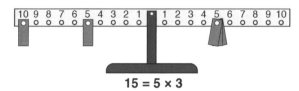

15 = 5 × 3

Tell her to write the new multiplication equation:

15 = 5 × 3

Tell the child to put two weights on the left 10 and one weight on the left 8. Next ask her to keep putting weights on the right 7 until it balances. [four] See below.

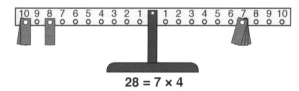

28 = 7 × 4

Ask: Why does it balance? [28 = 7 × 4] Tell her to write the equation. [28 = 7 × 4]

**Commutative example.** Tell the child to put four weights on the right 3. Ask: How many weights do you need on the left 4 to make it balance? [three] See below.

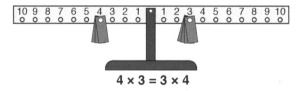

4 × 3 = 3 × 4

**Practice.** Say: Make up your own multiplication problems to solve on the math balance and write them down. If you are multiplying by more than five, put the extra weights on the peg on the back side of the balance.

**In conclusion.** Ask: What does it mean when the math balance is level? [It is balanced; the two sides are equal.] What does an equal sign mean in an equation? [The two sides are equal.]

Conclusions may be a summary of the day's lesson or an expansion of the lesson to challenge higher level thinking.

# REVIEW LESSON 3: MENTAL ADDING

## OBJECTIVES:

1. To enter tens on the abacus
2. To practice mental addition
3. To learn to play the Corners™ game

## MATERIALS:

1. AL Abacus
2. *Math Card Games* book, A9
3. Math journal, found in the back of the child's worksheets

## ACTIVITIES FOR TEACHING:

***Warm-up.*** Give the child the abacus. Tell the child to show on her fingers and her abacus the quantities that you say as fast as she can. Say: Show and enter 4. Show and enter 6. Show and enter 9. Continue with 2, 10, 7, 3, 5, and 8.

Ask: Which strategies can you use to find 9 + 7? [Make Ten] What is 9 + 7? [16] What strategies can you use to find 6 + 8? [Two Fives and Make Ten] What is 6 + 8? [14] What strategies can you use to find 7 + 7? [Two Fives] What is 7 + 7? [14]

***Tens on the abacus.*** Tell the child to enter 10 on her abacus. Then tell her to enter another 10 on the second wire. Ask: How many beads are entered? [twenty] Say: If you lived in Asia, you would call it 2-ten. Today we will use these Asian names, or math names, for the numbers.

Tell her to enter another 2-ten. Ask: How much do you have now? [4-ten] Tell her to enter another 2-ten. Ask: How much do you have now? [6-ten] See the figure on the right. How can you tell it is 6-ten without counting? [Five rows have the same color pattern and one row is reversed.] Repeat for 8-ten.

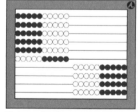

**6-ten (60) entered.**

Enter various tens on the abacus and ask the child to name them. Focus especially on 6-ten to 10-ten.

Ask: What is 4 + 1? [5] What is 40 + 10? [50] What is 8 + 1? [9] What is 80 + 10? [90] What is 6 + 1? [7] What is 60 + 10? [70] What is 9 + 1? [10] What is 90 + 10? [100]

***Mentally adding 5, 10, and 15.*** Tell the child that today she will be playing the game Corners™. First she needs to practice mental adding. Ask the following:

What is 60 + 10? [70]

What is 75 + 10? [85]

## EXPLANATIONS:

If possible, use the name of an Asian country the child is familiar with.

It is more difficult for children to see the beads color change vertically after 5-ten than the color change horizontally after five in a row.

| ACTIVITIES FOR TEACHING CONTINUED: | EXPLANATIONS CONTINUED: |
|---|---|

What is 105 + 10? [115]

What is 60 + 15? [75] Tell her a good way to add 15 is to first add the 10 and then the 5, 60 + 10 = 70 + 5 = 75.

What is 85 + 15? [100]

What is 135 + 15? [150]

**Corners™ game.** Play the Corners™ game found in *Math Card Games* book, A9.

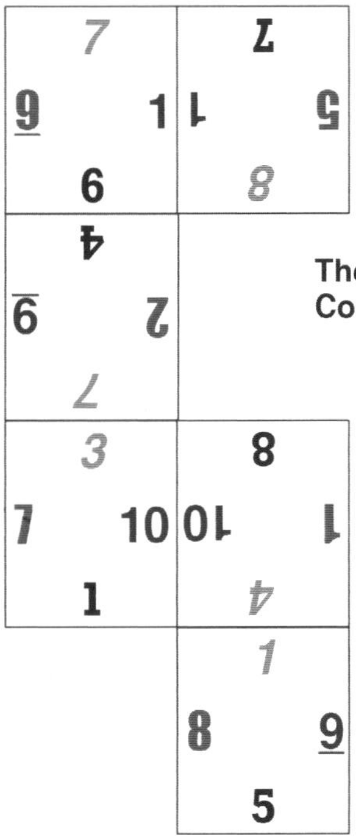

**The beginning of a Corners™ game.**

Instructions for the Corners™ game can also be found on the DVD inside the back cover of the *Math Card Games* book or at RightStartMath.com.

Note that the numbers touching must either be the same or have a sum of 5, 10, 15, or 20. However, only the sums that are a multiple of 5 are added to the score. In other words, matching numbers, such as 3 + 3, that are not a multiple of 5 are valid plays, but result in no points.

Other Corners™ games will be played throughout the year.

See page ii, number 11 of "Some General Thoughts on Teaching Mathematics," for additional information.

Tell the child to write her scores in her math journal. She is to write down only the result of the latest addition with no intermediate step.

A scoring sample is shown below.

**Scoring for the Corners™ game.**

**In conclusion.** Ask: In the Corners™ game, what three numbers can you join with 9? [1, 6, and 9] How many points would a 1 give you? [10] How many points would a 6 give you? [15] How many points would a 9 give you? [0]

# REVIEW LESSON 4: SUBTRACTION STRATEGIES

**OBJECTIVES:**
1. To review part-whole circles
2. To review subtraction strategies
3. To practice the strategies

**MATERIALS:**
1. AL Abacus
2. *Math Card Games* book, S24

---

**ACTIVITIES FOR TEACHING:**

***Warm-up.*** Ask: What is 9 + 6? [15] What is 8 + 7? [15] What do you need with 6 to make 10? [4] With 6 to make 15? [9] What do you need with 8 to make 10? [2] With 8 to make 15? [7] What do you need with 7 to make 10? [3] With 7 to make 15? [8]

***Part-whole circles.*** Draw a part-whole circle, shown below on the left. Write "whole" in the large circle and "part" in the smaller circles.

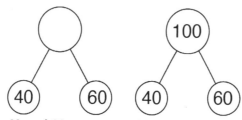

**Part-whole circles**   **40 and 60 as parts.**   **40 + 60 = <u>100</u>**

Write 40 and 60 in the smaller circles as shown in the second figure above. Ask: If 40 and 60 are parts, what is the whole? [100] Write 100 in the large circle. See the right figure above.

***Going Up Strategy.*** Write 14 in the whole-circle and 9 in a part-circle as shown below in the left figure.

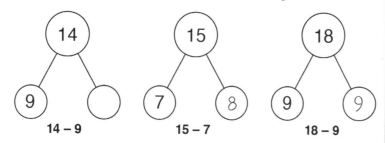

**14 – 9**     **15 – 7**     **18 – 9**

Ask: How can you find the other part? [subtract] Can you think of a strategy to find the answer if you did not know it? What do you need to get to 10? [1] Then how many more to 14? [4] So, how much is needed to go from 9 to 14? [5] Tell her: This is the Going Up Strategy. Repeat for 15 – 7, [8] and 18 – 9. [9]

**EXPLANATIONS:**

If the child struggles with these problems, let her use the abacus.

See page ii, numbers 7 and 8 of "Some General Thoughts on Teaching Mathematics," for additional information.

It is best to avoid the term "take away" when referring to subtraction. The term emphasizes the going back aspect of subtraction, ignoring other meanings such as going up and differences, making it difficult for children to develop a deeper understanding of subtraction.

## ACTIVITIES FOR TEACHING CONTINUED:

***Subtracting Part from Ten Strategy.*** Give the child the abacus and write:

$$15 - 7 =$$

Tell the child: Enter 15 on your abacus. Ask: How could you subtract 7? [Subtract 5 from second wire and 2 from first wire.] See the figures below.

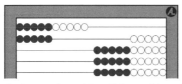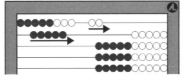

**Subtracting 15 – 7 by taking 5 from 5 and 2 from 10.**

Say: So to subtract the 7, you subtract 5 from the 5 and 2 from the 10, giving 8. We can call this Subtracting Part from Ten Strategy. Tell her to use the Subtracting Part from Ten Strategy to find 13 – 4, [9] and 16 – 9. [7]

***Subtracting All from Ten Strategy.*** Say: There is another strategy for subtracting 15 – 7, the Subtracting All from Ten Strategy. Tell her to enter 15 on the abacus. Next tell her to subtract the whole 7 from the 10, as shown in the figures below.

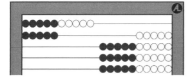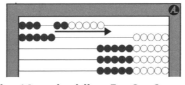

**15 – 7 by subtracting 7 from the 10 and adding 5 + 3 = 8.**

Ask: What is left? [3 plus 5, 8] Tell her to use the Subtracting All from Ten Strategy for 11 – 4, [7] and 13 – 5. [8]

***Subtraction Bingo game.*** Play the Subtraction Bingo game, found in the *Math Card Games* book, S24. Tell her to use her abacus as she is playing the game.

***In conclusion.*** Ask the child to explain several ways to subtract 14 – 8. [Going Up: 2 to get to 10; 2 + 4 = 6. Taking Part from Ten: 4 from 4 and 4 from 10 gives 6. Taking All from Ten: 8 from 10 is 2; 2 + 4 = 6.]

## EXPLANATIONS CONTINUED:

Flash cards are not a good way to drill the number facts. The only people who like flash cards are those who do not need them. Many adults today, because they could not respond fast enough to flash cards or time tests, became convinced as children that they have no math "ability." These people often develop math anxiety.

Flash cards are abstract; they require associating a symbol with two other symbols. On the other hand, a child familiar with the abacus thinks about the concrete beads when asked for a fact.

Another problem with flash cards is the false impression they give that mathematics is a subject that doesn't require thinking, or that it is just a tidy collection of "facts" that everyone must memorize.

The theory behind flash cards, going back to 1910, is based on the erroneous concept that a person learns these facts by associating a third symbol with two symbols. For example, if you see 8 and 7, you think 15. Brain research now tells us our brains do not work well that way. Rather, it is more natural to use a strategy. In this case they might take 2 from the 7, combine it with the 8 and change it into 10 and 5, which is 15.

Also, even if the child did memorize 8, 7, 15, a few years later, the unfortunate child is expected to memorize 8, 7, 56. Many children find this very difficult.

Facts practice should always provide a strategy for the learner to figure out a forgotten answer. The AL Abacus provides a good way through visual representation, based on 5s and 10s.

Another reason to provide the abacus is to discourage counting. Counting is slow, unreliable, and habit forming. Those adding by counting dots on numerals are still counting dots decades later, although now it might be in her head.

A 5-year-old was asked how much is 11 and 6. After he said 17 without counting, he was asked how he knew. He replied with a grin, "I have the abacus in my mind."

# REVIEW LESSON 5: TRADING ON SIDE 2 OF THE ABACUS

## OBJECTIVES:

1. To review trading on side 2 of the abacus

## MATERIALS:

1. AL Abacus
2. Place-value cards
3. *Math Card Games* book, A7.1

---

## ACTIVITIES FOR TEACHING:

***Warm-up.*** Give the child the abacus and ask her to explain several ways to subtract 16 – 7. [Going Up: 3 to get to 10; 3 + 6 = 9. Taking Part from Ten: 6 from 6 and 1 from 10 gives 9. Taking All from Ten: 7 from 10 is 3; 3 + 6 = 9.]

Ask the child to explain several ways to subtract 15 – 8. [Going Up: 2 to get to 10; 2 + 5 = 7. Taking Part from Ten: 5 from 5 and 3 from 10 gives 7. Taking All from Ten: 8 from 10 is 2; 2 + 5 = 7.]

***Side 2 of the abacus.*** Tell the child to turn her abacus to side 2, with 1000, 100, 10, 1 on top. Ask: How many wires do you see under the 1000? [2] How many wires for the hundreds? [2] The tens? [2] The ones? [2]

Stress that on this side of the abacus we do not enter actual tens, but only the number of tens. This is also true with the hundreds and thousands.

***Trading ones on the abacus.*** Tell her to clear her abacus by sliding all the beads to the bottom. Say: Enter 8 ones by sliding up 8 beads, 4 on each wire under the 1. Then add 6. See the left figure below.

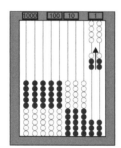 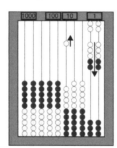 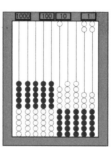

**Entering 8 + 6.**    **Trading 10 ones for 1 ten.**    **8 + 6 = 14**

Ask: What is the sum? [14] How do you know? [There are 10 light-colored and 4 dark-colored beads.] Say: We have a problem: we cannot have 10 or more ones. Ask: What can we do? [Trade 10 ones for 1 ten.]

## EXPLANATIONS:

It is important to keep the two wires as even as possible to make trading easier. See the figures below, both showing 12 ones entered. The right figure clearly identifies the sum is over 10, therefore needs trading.

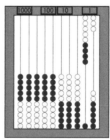 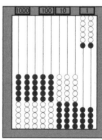

**Incorrectly entering 9 + 3.**    **Correctly entering 9 + 3.**

---

| **ACTIVITIES FOR TEACHING CONTINUED:** | **EXPLANATIONS CONTINUED:** |

Demonstrate trading as shown in the second figure on the previous page, using the left hand for the ten and the right hand for the ones, moving both at the same time. The final sum is shown in the third figure on the previous page. Tell her to do the trading on her abacus.

*Trading tens on the abacus.* Tell the child to add 80 and 60. See the left figure below. Ask: How many tens do you have? [14 tens] What do you need to do? [Trade 10 tens for 1 hundred.] Tell her to do the trading. Then ask: Now what is the sum? [140]

Trading is best done using both hands simultaneously.

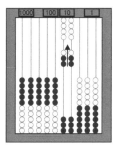
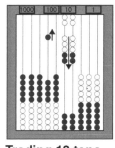
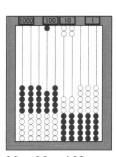

**Entering 80 + 60.**   **Trading 10 tens for 1 hundred.**   **80 + 60 = 140**

*Trading hundreds on the abacus.* Tell her to add 800 and 600 on her abacus. Ask the child to explain how to do it. [8 hundred and 6 hundred is 14 hundred, then trade 10 hundreds for 1 thousand. Sum is 1 thousand 4 hundred.]

*Adding twos.* Tell her to clear her abacus and then add the even numbers from 2 to 30. Start with 2, then add 4 and then add 6. Here she can trade. Then she continues with 8 to 30, trading when needed. The final sum will be 240.

*Bead Trading game.* Give the child the place-value cards. Tell her to set aside the six place-value cards that are greater than 3000. Play this variation of the Bead Trading game found in *Math Card Games*, A7.1.

Tell her to add the value of all the remaining place-value cards on side 2 of her abacus. First pick up any one of the place-value cards and enter that quantity on the abacus. Next she picks up another card and adds it to the amount on the abacus, trading when necessary. Continue until all the place-value cards have been added. The final sum will be 10,995.

*In conclusion.* Ask: How much is 30 + 70? [100] What is another name for 16 ten? [1 hundred sixty] What is another name for 87 ten? [8 hundred seventy] What is another name for 30 hundred? [3 thousand] What is another name for 59 hundred? [5 thousand 9 hundred]

See page iii, number 25 of "Some General Thoughts on Teaching Mathematics," for additional information.

# REVIEW LESSON 6: MULTIPLICATION STRATEGIES

## OBJECTIVES:
1. To review multiplication strategies
2. To practice the strategies

## MATERIALS:
1. AL Abacus
2. Dry erase board
3. Short Multiplication Table, Appendix p. 1
4. *Math Card Games* book, P32

## ACTIVITIES FOR TEACHING:

***Warm-up.*** Ask: How much is 40 + 60? [100] How much is 80 + 90? [170] What is another name for 17 tens? [1 hundred seventy] What is another name for 54 tens? [5 hundred forty] What is another name for 70 hundred? [7 thousand] What is another name for 27 hundred? [2 thousand 7 hundred]

***Arrays on the abacus.*** Give the child the abacus and dry erase board. Ask the child to enter 6 on the first three rows of her abacus as shown below. Ask: How can you tell how much it is? [15 dark-colored beads and 3 light-colored beads equaling 18] Tell her to write the addition equation on her dry erase board and then turn it toward you to check. [6 + 6 + 6 = 18]

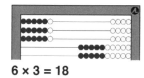

**6 × 3 = 18**

Repeat for the multiplication equation. [6 × 3 = 18] Ask: How can you read this equation? [6 times 3 = 18, or 6 multiplied by 3 = 18, or 6 taken 3 times = 18]

***Finding 9 × 4.*** Tell the child to enter the 9 × 4 on the abacus. See the figure at the right.

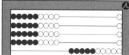

**9 multiplied by 4.**

Ask her to think of as many ways as possible to find the amount, the product. [36] Some possibilities include:

1. The dark-colored beads are 2 tens, or 20, and the light-colored beads are 8 + 8 = 16; 20 + 16 is 36.

2. The first two rows are 18; 18 + 18 is 36.

3. Four 10s is 40; 40 − 4 is 36.

4. Take and Give Strategy, shown on the next page, also ends up with 36.

## EXPLANATIONS:

Sometimes 6 × 3 is thought of as "6 groups of 3." However, consistency with the other arithmetic operations requires a second look. When adding 6 + 3, we start with 6 and transform it by adding 3. When subtracting 6 − 3, we start with 6 and transform it by removing 3. When dividing 6 ÷ 3, we start with 6 and transform it by dividing it into 3 groups or into groups of 3s. Likewise, 6 × 3 means we start with 6 and transform it by duplicating it a total of 3 times.

In the array (an arrangement of quantities in rows and columns) model, 6 × 3, 6 represents the horizontal quantity and 3 the vertical quantity. This is also consistent with the coordinate system; in (6, 3), the first number, 6, indicates the horizontal number and 3, the vertical number.

**ACTIVITIES FOR TEACHING CONTINUED:**

**EXPLANATIONS CONTINUED:**

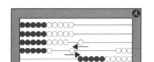

**Take 1 from row 4 and Give 1 to row 1.**

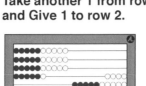

**Take another 1 from row 4 and Give 1 to row 2.**

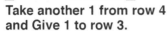

**Take another 1 from row 4 and Give 1 to row 3.**

**9 × 4 = 36.**

***Finding 8 × 7.*** Tell her to enter 8 × 7 on the abacus. See the figure. Ask: How can you find the product? One way is to see 10 fives, five dark-colored groups of five and 5 light-colored groups, making 50 and then adding the last 3 × 2, giving 56.

Another way is to think of 10 × 7 and then subtract 14 to get 56.

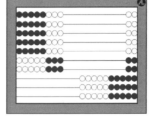

**8 × 7 = 10 × 5 + 6 = 56 or 70 − 14 = 56.**

***The short multiplication table.*** Give the child the short multiplication table. Tell her to find the row and the column for the following, which are shown in the left figure below.

5 × 4 [20, fifth row, fourth cell]

5 × 5 [25, fifth row, fifth cell]

5 × 6 [30, sixth row, fifth cell]

The child should have a copy of the short multiplication table for her use. The table will not become a "crutch," but will help the child see relationships in multiplication and division, similar to a dictionary.

Ask her to find 6 × 8 and explain it. [Go to row 6 and down to row 8.] See the table below on the right. Repeat for 8 × 9. [Go to row 6 and down to row 8.]

No counting is necessary because the cells are grouped in fives.

See page iii, number 10 of "Some General Thoughts on Teaching Mathematics," for additional information.

This table provides a great visual tool for organizing and memorizing the multiplication facts.

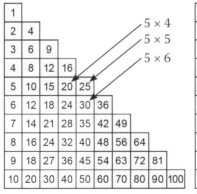
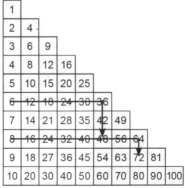

**Finding 6 × 8 and 8 × 9.**

***Ring around the Products game.*** Play the Ring around the Products game found in the *Math Card Games* book, P32.

***In conclusion.*** Ask: Since 8 × 4 is 32, how can you find 8 × 8? [64, double 32] If 9 × 10 = 90, how can you find 9 × 9? [81, subtract 9]

# REVIEW LESSON 7: DIVISION STRATEGIES

**OBJECTIVES:**
1. To review division strategies
2. To practice the strategies

**MATERIALS:**
1. AL Abacus
2. Short Multiplication Table, Appendix p. 1
3. *Math Card Games* book, P29

| ACTIVITIES FOR TEACHING: | EXPLANATIONS: |
|---|---|
| ***Warm-up.*** Ask: What is $8 \times 3$? [24] So what is $8 \times 6$? [48] What is $6 \times 3$? [18] So what is $6 \times 6$? [36] What is $7 \times 4$? [28] So what is $7 \times 8$? [56] | If the child struggles with these equations, let her use the abacus. |
| Ask: What is $10 \times 7$? [70] So what is $9 \times 7$? [63] What is $10 \times 4$? [40] So what is $9 \times 4$? [36] What is $10 \times 6$? [60] So what is $9 \times 6$? [54] | |
| ***Dividing on the abacus.*** Give the child the abacus. Ask: What is the inverse, or opposite, of addition? [subtraction] What is the inverse of subtraction? [addition] What is the inverse of multiplication? [division] What is the inverse of division? [multiplication] | |
| ***Finding the number of groups.*** Write: $$4 \times 3 = 12$$ and ask: What does the 4 mean? [size of the group] What does the 3 mean? [number of groups] | Writing these equations as missing factors emphasizes the size of the group and the number of groups aspect of multiplication and division that the division equation ignores. |
| Write: $\qquad 6 \times n = 48$ | |
| Tell her to enter 48 on her abacus and to find *n*, the number of groups of 6s, in 48. See the figures below. | |

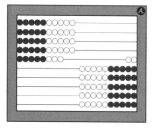
**48 entered.**

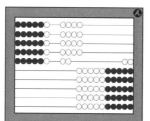
**Forming groups of 6.**

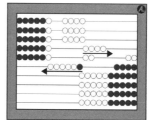
**Using Take and Give.**

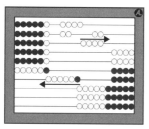
**Using Take and Give.**

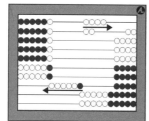
**Using Take and Give.**

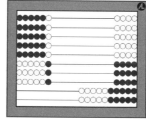
$6 \times n = 48, n = 8$

There are a variety of ways to use Take and Give to get the number of groups.

Ask: What is the size of the group? [6] How many groups? [8]

| ACTIVITIES FOR TEACHING CONTINUED: | EXPLANATIONS CONTINUED: |
|---|---|

***The short multiplication table.*** Give the child the short multiplication table. Tell her to figure out how to find 48 ÷ 6 on the table and explain it. [Start at 6 until reaching 48, which is 8 cells. Note 48 is also in row 8.] See the arrows in the figure on the right.

| 1 | | | | | | | | | |
|---|---|---|---|---|---|---|---|---|---|
| 2 | 4 | | | | | | | | |
| 3 | 6 | 9 | | | | | | | |
| 4 | 8 | 12 | 16 | | | | | | |
| 5 | 10 | 15 | 20 | 25 | | | | | |
| 6 | 12 | 18 | 24 | 30 | 36 | | | | |
| 7 | 14 | 21 | 28 | 35 | 42 | 49 | | | |
| 8 | 16 | 24 | 32 | 40 | 48 | 56 | 64 | | |
| 9 | 18 | 27 | 36 | 45 | 54 | 63 | 72 | 81 | |
| 10 | 20 | 30 | 40 | 50 | 60 | 70 | 80 | 90 | 100 |

**6 × n = 48, n = 8**

Division tables do exist, but by using the multiplication table for division, the child is more likely to see the relationship between multiplication and division.

Say: There is another way to write the equation. We can write it as a division equation:

$$48 ÷ 6 = n$$

Ask: What is *n*? [8]

Tell her to find 72 ÷ 8 = *n*. [*n* = 9]

***Finding the size of the group.*** Write:

$$s × 6 = 48$$

Tell her to enter 48 on her abacus and find the size of the group when there are 6 groups in 48. See below.

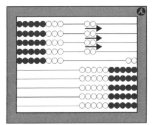 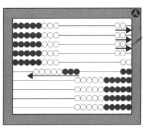

**48 entered.**   **Forming group size of 8.  s × 6 = 48, s = 8.**

Then ask: What is the size of the group? [8] How many groups? [6] Say: This time we can write the equation as:

$$48 ÷ 6 = s$$

Ask: What is *s*? [8]

Tell her to find the equation on the multiplication table. See the figure at the right.

***Find the Two Factors game.*** Play the Find the Two Factors game found in *Math Card Games* book, P29. Players take five basic number cards and replace a card played after a turn.

| 1 | | | | | | | | | |
|---|---|---|---|---|---|---|---|---|---|
| 2 | 4 | | | | | | | | |
| 3 | 6 | 9 | | | | | | | |
| 4 | 8 | 12 | 16 | | | | | | |
| 5 | 10 | 15 | 20 | 25 | | | | | |
| 6 | 12 | 18 | 24 | 30 | 36 | | | | |
| 7 | 14 | 21 | 28 | 35 | 42 | 49 | | | |
| 8 | 16 | 24 | 32 | 40 | 48 | 56 | 64 | | |
| 9 | 18 | 27 | 36 | 45 | 54 | 63 | 72 | 81 | |
| 10 | 20 | 30 | 40 | 50 | 60 | 70 | 80 | 90 | 100 |

**s × 6 = 48, s = 8**

***In conclusion.*** Ask: Which two questions can division answer? [size of a group and number of groups] What is opposite of division? [multiplication]

# LESSON 8: FINDING REMAINDERS

**OBJECTIVES:**

1. To review (or learn) the term *remainder*
2. To find remainders after dividing

**MATERIALS:**

1. AL Abacus
2. Short Multiplication Table, Appendix p. 1
3. Math balance
4. *Math Card Games* book, D7

**ACTIVITIES FOR TEACHING:**

***Warm-up.*** Ask: What is 4 × 3? [12] So what is 4 × 6? [24] What is 24 ÷ 6? [4] What is 24 ÷ 4? [6]

Ask: What is 7 × 4? [28] So what is 7 × 8? [56] What is 56 ÷ 7? [8] What is 56 ÷ 8? [7]

Ask: What is 8 × 4? [32] What is 8 × 8? [64] What is 8 × 9? [72] What is 72 ÷ 8? [9] What is 64 ÷ 8? [8]

***Introducing remainders.*** Give the child the abacus and short multiplication table. Give her this problem:

> Thirty people come into the cafeteria. Four people can sit around a table. How many tables do they need?

Tell her to solve it on the abacus and the multiplication table. Ask her to explain it. Both are shown below.

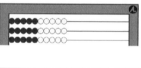

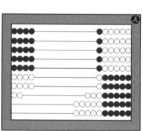

**30 ÷ 4 = 7 r2**

| 1 | | | | | | | | | |
|---|---|---|---|---|---|---|---|---|---|
| 2 | 4 | | | | | | | | |
| 3 | 6 | 9 | | | | | | | |
| 4 | 8 | 12 | 16 | | | | | | |
| 5 | 10 | 15 | 20 | 25 | | | | | |
| 6 | 12 | 18 | 24 | 30 | 36 | | | | |
| 7 | 14 | 21 | 28 | 35 | 42 | 49 | | | |
| 8 | 16 | 24 | 32 | 40 | 48 | 56 | 64 | | |
| 9 | 18 | 27 | 36 | 45 | 54 | 63 | 72 | 81 | |
| 10 | 20 | 30 | 40 | 50 | 60 | 70 | 80 | 90 | 100 |

**30 ÷ 4 = 7 r2**

To solve the equation on the abacus, enter 30. Then use Take and Give to find how many groups. The *quotient*, or answer, is 7 and the 2 that is left over is called the *remainder*.

To solve the equation on the short multiplication table, go down the fours column to 28, the greatest number not more than 30. Get the remainder by finding the difference between 28 and 30, using the Going Up Strategy going from 28 to 30. [2]

Show her how to write the equation:

$$t = 30 ÷ 4 = 7 \text{ r2}$$

**EXPLANATIONS:**

The first half of these RightStart™ Mathematics lessons refers to the child as a female and the second half refers to the child as a male.

Give the child a copy of the short multiplication table for her personal use. The table will not become a "crutch," but will help her see relationships in multiplication and division, similar to a dictionary.

| ACTIVITIES FOR TEACHING CONTINUED: | EXPLANATIONS CONTINUED: |
|---|---|

Ask: How many tables are needed for the 30 people? [8] Ask for an explanation. Be sure the child understands why 8 tables, not 7 tables are needed. [The remaining two people need to sit at a table.] Write the answer:

$$t = 8 \text{ tables}$$

**Remainders on the math balance.** Give the child the math balance and tell her to solve this problem. Start by putting three weights on the left 10. Then put weights on the 7-peg until it is too many, then remove one. [four] Ask: How can you make it balance? [Put an additional weight on the on 2-peg.] See below.

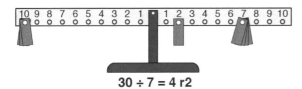

**30 ÷ 7 = 4 r2**

**Problem variation.** Say: Let's change the problem so 34 people come into the cafeteria. Ask: How many tables of four are needed now? Tell her to solve it two ways. One way is to think that 34 is 4 more than 30, so one more table is needed. Another way is divide 34 by 4 to get the quotient of 8 and a remainder of 2.

Write:  34 ÷ 4 = 7 r6

Ask: Is this correct? [no, the remainder cannot be equal to or greater than 4.] How should the equation be written? [34 ÷ 4 = 8 r2]

**Quotient and Remainder game.** Play this variation of the Quotient and Remainder game from *Math Card Games* book, D7. The variation is the card layout. Place the dividend card, the multiplication card, first in the row as shown on the right.

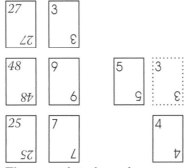

The completed row is
48 ÷ 9 = 5 r3.

***In conclusion.*** Ask: What will the remainder be when you divide an even number by 2? [zero] What will the remainder be when you divide an odd number by 2? [1]

Conclusions may be a summary of the day's lesson or an expansion of the lesson to challenge higher level thinking.

# LESSON 9: REMAINDERS AFTER DIVIDING BY NINE

## OBJECTIVES:

1. To find remainders after dividing by 9
2. To discover that remainders can be combined

## MATERIALS:

1. Worksheet 1, Remainders after Dividing by Nine
2. *Math Card Games* book, D8

| ACTIVITIES FOR TEACHING: | EXPLANATIONS: |
|---|---|
| **Warm-up.** Ask: What will the remainder be when you divide 16 by 2? [zero] What will the remainder be when you divide 42 by 2? [zero] | |

**Warm-up.** Ask: What will the remainder be when you divide 16 by 2? [zero] What will the remainder be when you divide 42 by 2? [zero]

What will the remainder be when you divide 13 by 2? [1] What will the remainder be when you divide 49 by 2? [1] What will the remainder be when you divide an odd number by 2? [1]

**Remainders after dividing by 9.** Give the child the worksheet. Tell the child to read the first problem:

See page iii, number 13 of "Some General Thoughts on Teaching Mathematics," for additional information.

> 1. Kaitlyn is selling tickets for a sporting event. Nine people can sit in a row in the bleachers. A group of 12 people are attending. How many full rows of nine do they need? [1] How many people will be sitting in the row that is not full, the partial row? [3] Write your answers in the left chart below.

Tell her to solve the problem and record the answer in Kaitlyn's chart. See the chart below.

| Kaitlyn's Ticket Sales | | |
|---|---|---|
| Number of People | Full Rows with 9 People | People in Partial Row |
| 12 | 1 | 3 |
| 22 | 2 | 4 |
| 28 | 3 | 1 |
| 62 | 6 | 8 |

Tell her to do the next three problems:

> 2. Next Kaitlyn sells tickets to a group of 22 people. How many full rows of nine will they need? How many will sit in the partial row? Write your answers in the left chart.

> 3. Kaitlyn then sells tickets to a group of 28 people. How many full rows will they need? How many will sit in the partial row? Write your answers in the left chart.

> 4. At halftime the three groups left, returned, and sat together. What is the fewest number of rows they need now? Write your answers in the left chart.

| ACTIVITIES FOR TEACHING CONTINUED: | EXPLANATIONS CONTINUED: |
|---|---|

Ask: How did you find the total number of people? [added the numbers in the groups] What are the two ways to find the number of full rows? [Add the numbers of full rows, 1 + 2 + 3, or divide 62 by 9 to get 6.]

Ask: What are the two ways to find the number of people in the partial rows? [Add the number of people in the partial rows, 3 + 4 + 1, or find the remainder after dividing 62 by 9, which is 8.]

Tell her to read and solve the Problems 5 and 6.

5. Kurt is also selling tickets. His first group has 15 people, the second group has 23 people, and the third group has 30 people. Find the number of full rows and the number of people sitting in partial rows per group. Write your answers in the right chart above.

6. At halftime the three groups left, returned, and sat together. What is the fewest number of rows Kurt's groups need now? Write your answers in the right chart.

The answers are shown in the chart below.

| Kurt's Ticket Sales | | |
|---|---|---|
| Number of People | Full Rows with 9 People | People in Partial Row |
| 15 | 1 | 6 |
| 23 | 2 | 5 |
| 30 | 3 | 3 |
| 68 | 7 | 5 |

Ask: How did you find the total number of people? [added the numbers in the groups] How many full rows were needed before the three groups combined? [6] How many full rows are needed after the groups combine? [7] Where did the extra row come from? [Two of the partial rows, the 6 and the 3, created a new full row.]

Ask: What are the two ways to find the number of people in the partial rows? [Add the number of partial rows, 6 + 5 + 3, combine the 6 and 3 to get 9, another full row, leaving 5 in a partial row, or find the remainder after dividing 68 by 9, which is 5.] Tell her to answer the remaining two questions on the worksheet. Answers will vary.

**Remainders game.** Play the Remainders game from *Math Card Games* book, D8. Use a divisor of 9. For two players, use half of the multiplication cards; for three or four players, use all the cards.

**In conclusion.** Ask: What is the remainder when 24 is divided by 9? [6] What is the remainder when 71 is divided by 9? [8] What is the remainder when 43 is divided by 9? [7]

# LESSON 10: FINDING CHECK NUMBERS

**OBJECTIVES:**
1. To learn the term *check number*
2. To practice finding check numbers

**MATERIALS:**
1. AL Abacus
2. *Math Card Games* book, A63

| ACTIVITIES FOR TEACHING: | EXPLANATIONS: |
|---|---|

**Warm-up.** Ask: What is 9 × 3? [27] What is the remainder when 30 is divided by 9? [3] What is 9 × 8? [72] What is the remainder when 79 is divided by 9? [7] What is 9 × 6? [54] What is the remainder when 55 is divided by 9? [1]

**History of check numbers.** Tell the child: In the last lesson, you found that adding the remainders of a group of numbers is the same as the remainder of the sum of the numbers.

Write:                      23 + 19 + 38 =
and ask: What is the sum? [80]

Say: Let's write the remainders of each number divided by 9. We will use parentheses to show the remainders. Ask for the remainders for each number divided by 9 in the equation.

Write:            (5)   (1)   (2)   (8)
                  23 + 19 + 38 = 80
and ask: Does 5 + 1 + 2 = 8? [yes]

Tell her: Over 600 years ago, people thought that checking those remainders would be a good way to check their answers.

**Finding check numbers.** Say: Using remainders for checking arithmetic is a good idea only if there is an easy way to find the remainders.

Write:                      36  63  72  99
and ask: What is special about these numbers? [multiples of 9] What happens when you add their digits? [9 and 18, which is a multiple of 9]

Enter 70 on the abacus, as shown in the left figure on the next page. Say: We can show dividing by 9 by moving one bead from each row. See the right figure on the next page.

Say: Look at the abacus. Ask: What is 70 divided by 9? [7] What is the remainder? [7] What is the sum of the digits for 70? [7, 7 + 0] This sum is called the *check number*.

*EXPLANATIONS:*

See page iii, number 19 of "Some General Thoughts on Teaching Mathematics," for additional information.

Check numbers are also referred to as "Casting out Nines," "Excess of Nines," "Digital Roots," and "Check Digits."

With the advent of calculators and computers, check numbers are taught less frequently today. Since they do provide a rapid and simple check on the four arithmetic operations, they will be taught in this manual.

Why using the sum of the digits works to find a remainder after dividing by 9 can be demonstrated as follows:

Write the number 5671 in expanded form:
$$5000 = 999 \times 5 + 5$$
$$600 = 99 \times 6 + 6$$
$$70 = 9 \times 7 + 7$$
$$1 = \phantom{9 \times 7 +} 1$$
$$5671 = \text{a multiple of } 9, + 5 + 6 + 7 + 1.$$

Therefore, 5671 ÷ 9 has a remainder of 5 + 6 + 7 + 1, which is the sum of its digits.

Adapted from *The Teaching of Arithmetic* by David Eugene Smith, 1913.

| ACTIVITIES FOR TEACHING CONTINUED: | EXPLANATIONS CONTINUED: |
|---|---|

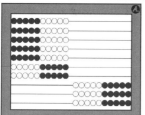

**70 entered.**

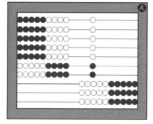

**Dividing 70 by 9 with remainder of 7.**

Change the number from 70 to 71 as shown in the left figure below. Ask: What is the remainder? [8] What is the sum of the digits? [8, 7 + 1] What is the check number? [8]

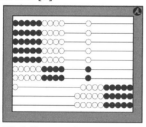

**Dividing 71 by 9 with remainder of 8.**

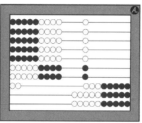

**Dividing 72 by 9 with remainder of 0.**

Add one more bead to change the number to 72. See the right figure above. Tell her to look carefully. Ask: What is the remainder? [0] Why is the remainder 0? [The 7 combined with the 2 makes another 9.] Does 72 ÷ 9 have a remainder? [no] What is the check number? [0] Say: A 9 is always a 0, so check numbers are always less than 9.

Ask: Do you remember the game that you played in the last lesson? Did you notice that you could find the remainders by adding the digits?

**Practice.** Write the following numbers and tell her find the check numbers:

16 (7)<br/>93 (3)

Tell her there are two ways to find the check number for 93. One way is to think the 9 is a 0, so the check number is 3. The other way is to add 9 + 3, getting 12, then add 1 + 2 to get 3.

Tell her check numbers also work for large numbers. Write: 475
and tell her to find the check number. [7] Here the 4 and 5 make 0, so the check number is 7. Or, 4 + 7 + 5 = 16, 1 + 6 = 7.

**Check Numbers game.** Play the Check Numbers game from *Math Card Games* book, A63.

**In conclusion.** Ask: What is the check number for 29? [2] What is the check number for 333? [0]

A calculator can be used to find check numbers. Enter the number and divide by 9. The check number will be the repeating digit following the decimal point.

For example, find the check number for 8167. Dividing 8167 by 9, gives 907.44444. The check number is 4.

To find the check numbers of several numbers in succession, use the constant feature. Press ⑨ ➗ ➗. Then enter each number followed by ⑤.

Check numbers are an example of modular arithmetic, also known as "clock arithmetic." For example, the time 4 hours after 9:00 is 1:00, not 13:00. The number where we start over is known as the *modulus*.

In check numbers, the modulus is 9.

# LESSON 11: USING CHECK NUMBERS TO CHECK ADDING

**OBJECTIVES:**

1. To practice using check numbers to check addition

**MATERIALS:**

1. Worksheet 2, Using Check Numbers to Check Adding

| ACTIVITIES FOR TEACHING: | EXPLANATIONS: |
|---|---|
| ***Warm-up.*** Ask: What is 9 × 4? [36] What is the remainder when 39 is divided by 9? [3] What is the check number for 39? [3] | |
| Ask: What is 9 × 5? [45] What is the remainder when 50 is divided by 9? [5] What is the check number for 50? [5] | |
| Ask: What is the check number for 9? [0] What is the check number for 18? [0] | |
| ***Using check numbers.*** Tell the child: Today you will practice using check numbers to check your adding. | |
| Ask: Do you think they will work for single digit numbers? | |
| Write: $6 + 7 =$ | |
| and tell the child to complete the equation and write the check numbers: | |
| (6) (7) (4)<br>$6 + 7 = 13$ | |
| Ask: Did it work? [yes] | |
| Write: $27 + 2 =$ | |
| and tell the child to complete the equation and write the check numbers: | |
| (0) (2) (2)<br>$27 + 2 = 29$ | |
| Ask: Did it work? [yes] How do you know? [0 + 2 = 2] Can 9 ever be a check number? [no] | The expression "(0) + (2) = (2)" can be read as "check number 0 + check number 2 equals check number 2." |
| Write: $84 + 84 =$ | |
| and tell the child to complete the equation and write the check numbers: | |
| (3) (3) (6)<br>$84 + 84 = 168$ | |
| Ask: Did it work? [yes] How do you know? [3 + 3 = 6] What is an easy way to find the check number for 168? [1 + 8 is 9, which is 0, so the check number is 6.] | |

| ACTIVITIES FOR TEACHING CONTINUED: | EXPLANATIONS CONTINUED: |
|---|---|

**Finding errors with check numbers.** Write this incorrect equation:

$$(8) \quad (5) \quad (3)$$
$$35 + 86 = 111$$

Ask: Do the check numbers add up? [no, (8) + (5) = (4)] What is wrong? [The sum of 35 and 86 is 121.] Correct it as follows:

$$(8) \quad (5) \quad (4)$$
$$35 + 86 = 121$$

Repeat for another equation with incorrect check numbers:

$$(2) \quad (7) \quad (1)$$
$$48 + 34 = 82$$

Ask: Do the check numbers add up? [no] What is wrong? [The check number for 48 is (3), not (2).] Correct it as follows:

$$(3) \quad (7) \quad (1)$$
$$48 + 34 = 82$$

**When check numbers do not find an error.** Ask: Do you think check numbers can find every mistake? Write the incorrect equation:

$$(4) \quad (2) \quad (6)$$
$$67 + 20 = 69$$

Ask: Do the check numbers add up? [yes] What is wrong? [The person added 2 instead of 20.] Correct it as follows:

$$(4) \quad (2) \quad (6)$$
$$67 + 20 = 87$$

Say: You must still look to see if the answer makes sense even if the check numbers are correct.

**Worksheet 2.** Give the child the worksheet and tell her to read the instructions, then to complete the worksheet. The solutions are below.

| (7) (0) (7) | (0) (3) (3) | (5) (6) (2) |
|---|---|---|
| 7 + 9 = **16** | 18 + 30 = **48** | 77 + 6 = **83** |
| (5) (3) (8) | (1) (8) (0) | (7) (2) (0) |
| 41 + 21 = **62** | 19 + 35 = **54** | 25 + 29 = **54** |
| (1) (1) (2) | (2) (6) (8) | (7) (4) (2) |
| 73 + 37 = **110** | 56 + 24 = **80** | 43 + 40 = **83** |
| (6) (2) (8) | (3) (8) (2) | (5) (6) (2) |
| 78 + 20 = **98** | 75 + 26 = **101** | 68 + 24 = **92** |
| (3) (6) (0) | (8) (8) (7) | (2) (5) (7) |
| 147 + 33 = **180** | 188 + 26 = **214** | 209 + 428 = **637** |
| (3) (7) (1) | (6) (8) (5) | (1) (1) (2) |
| 39 + **61** = 100 | 87 + **17** = 104 | 127 + **73** = 200 |

**In conclusion.** Ask: Can check numbers help a person find most mistakes? [yes] Can check numbers find every mistake? [no]

Continue playing games on a regular basis. If there is additional time following this lesson or more practice is needed, play the Check Numbers game, found in *Math Card Games* book, A63.

# REVIEW LESSON 12: ADDING ON SIDE 2 OF THE ABACUS

## OBJECTIVES:

1. To add 4-digit numbers with trading on side 2 of the abacus

## MATERIALS:

1. Worksheet 3, Adding on Side 2 of the Abacus
2. AL Abacus

| ACTIVITIES FOR TEACHING: | EXPLANATIONS: |
|---|---|

**Warm-up.** Give the child the worksheet. Tell her the warm-up today will be on her worksheet and to do just the warm-up equations. Solutions are:

**(5)  (5)  (1)       (2)  (5)  (7)       (6)  (3)  (0)**
14 + 23 = **37**       29 + 41 = **70**       78 + 21 = **99**

**Adding on side 2 of the abacus.** Give the child the abacus. Tell the child to turn her abacus to side 2, with 1000, 100, 10, 1 on top.

See page ii, number 4 of "Some General Thoughts on Teaching Mathematics," for additional information.

Write:                3876
                   + 2519

and tell her to watch while you perform the addition on the abacus. Involve the child as much as possible.

Enter 3 on the thousands wires, 8 on the hundreds wires, 7 on the tens wires, and 6 on the ones wires. See the left figure below.

Add 9 ones. See second figure below. Ask: Is trading necessary? [yes] Trade 10 ones for 1 ten. See the third figure below.

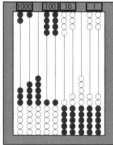

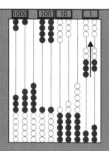

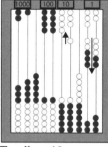

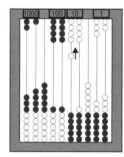

The "extra" bead can be in either on the left wire or the right wire.

**Entering 3876.**      **Adding 9 ones.**      **Trading 10 ones for 1 ten.**      **Adding 10.**

            1                1
        3876             3876
      + 2519           + 2519
            5               95

Ask: What do we write? [5] Did anything else change? [1 more ten] Write it as shown under the third figure.

Add 1 ten. See the fourth figure above. Ask: Do we need to trade? [no] What do we write? [9 ten] See the written work below the fourth figure.

| ACTIVITIES FOR TEACHING CONTINUED: | EXPLANATIONS CONTINUED: |

Add 5 hundred. See the first figure below. Ask: Do we need to trade? [yes] Trade 10 hundreds for 1 thousand. See the second figure below. Ask: How many hundreds do we write? [3] Did anything else change? [1 more thousand] Write it as shown under the second figure.

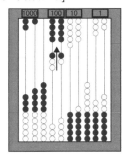 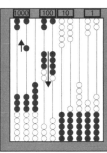 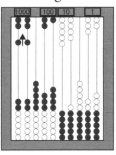

**Adding 5 hundred.** **Trading 10 hundred** **Adding 2 thousand.**
**for 1 thousand.**

$$\begin{array}{r} 1\phantom{0}1 \\ 3876 \\ + 2519 \\ \hline 395 \end{array} \qquad \begin{array}{r} 1\phantom{0}1 \\ 3876 \\ + 2519 \\ \hline \mathbf{6}395 \end{array}$$

Ask: What is next? [Add the 2 thousand.] Ask: Do we need to trade? [no] See the third figure above. Write the final 6 as shown under the third figure.

***Checking the addition.*** Tell the child to find the check numbers for the three numbers. Write them and ask: Do the check numbers add up correctly? [yes] Then write a check mark to show that the addition checks as shown.

$$\begin{array}{r} 1\phantom{0}1 \\ 3876\ \mathbf{(6)} \\ + 2519\ \mathbf{(8)} \\ \hline 6395\ \mathbf{(5)}\ \checkmark \end{array}$$

Tell the child to repeat the same addition problem on her abacus.

***Worksheet 3.*** Tell her to do the first problem on the worksheet.

Repeat for the next three problems and for the last three. The solutions are below.

$$\begin{array}{r} 1 \\ 4382\ \mathbf{(8)} \\ + 2576\ \mathbf{(2)} \\ \hline 6958\ \mathbf{(1)}\ \checkmark \end{array} \qquad \begin{array}{r} 11 \\ 5466\ \mathbf{(3)} \\ + 4078\ \mathbf{(1)} \\ \hline 9544\ \mathbf{(4)}\ \checkmark \end{array}$$

$$\begin{array}{r} 11 \\ 7862\ \mathbf{(5)} \\ + 1909\ \mathbf{(1)} \\ \hline 9771\ \mathbf{(6)}\ \checkmark \end{array} \qquad \begin{array}{r} 111 \\ 3909\ \mathbf{(3)} \\ + 4795\ \mathbf{(7)} \\ \hline 8704\ \mathbf{(1)}\ \checkmark \end{array}$$

$$\begin{array}{r} 1 \\ 4382\ \mathbf{(8)} \\ + 2576\ \mathbf{(2)} \\ \hline 6958\ \mathbf{(1)}\ \checkmark \end{array} \quad \begin{array}{r} 111 \\ 4567\ \mathbf{(4)} \\ + 7859\ \mathbf{(2)} \\ \hline 12{,}426\ \mathbf{(6)}\ \checkmark \end{array} \quad \begin{array}{r} 111 \\ 5997\ \mathbf{(3)} \\ + 3997\ \mathbf{(1)} \\ \hline 9994\ \mathbf{(4)}\ \checkmark \end{array}$$

***In conclusion.*** Ask: When you add, how can you tell that you need to trade? [the sum is 10 or more] Ask: What is 700 + 700? [1 thousand 4 hundred or 14 hundred]

Continue playing games on a regular basis. If there is additional time following this lesson or more practice is needed, play the Addition Bingo game, found in *Math Card Games* book, A50.

# LESSON 13: ADDING MULTI-DIGIT NUMBERS

## OBJECTIVES:

1. To practice add 4-digit numbers

## MATERIALS:

1. AL Abacus
2. *Math Card Games* book, A64
3. Math journal, found in the back of the child's worksheets

## ACTIVITIES FOR TEACHING:

***Warm-up.*** Write the following and ask the child to find the check numbers:

| | | |
|---|---|---|
| 14 [5] | 93 [3] | 74 [2] |
| 128 [2] | 5369 [5] | 7137 [0] |

Ask: When you add, how can you tell that you need to trade? [the sum is 10 or more] Ask: What is 600 + 600? [1 thousand 2 hundred or 12 hundred]

***Adding multi-digit numbers on the abacus.*** Give the child the abacus.

Write:

$$\begin{array}{r} 8396 \\ + 3475 \\ \hline \end{array}$$

and tell the child to help you add it on the abacus. Follow her directions, but occasionally make an error for her to correct. The procedure is as follows:

Enter 8 on the thousands wires, 3 on the hundreds wires, 9 on the tens wires, and 6 on the ones wires. See the left figure below.

Add 5 ones. See second figure below. Trade 10 ones for 1 ten. See the third figure below.

Write the 1 and the extra ten as shown under the third figure.

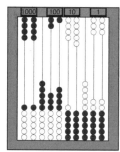
**Entering 8396.**

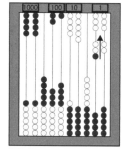
**Adding 5 ones.**

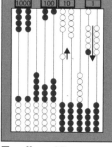
**Trading 10 ones for 1 ten.**

$$\begin{array}{r} \overset{1}{\phantom{0}} \\ 8396 \\ + 3475 \\ \hline 1 \end{array}$$

## EXPLANATIONS:

27

## ACTIVITIES FOR TEACHING CONTINUED:

Next add 7 tens. See the first figure below. Trade 10 tens for 1 hundred. See the second figure below. Write the 7 tens and the extra hundred as shown below the second figure.

## EXPLANATIONS CONTINUED:

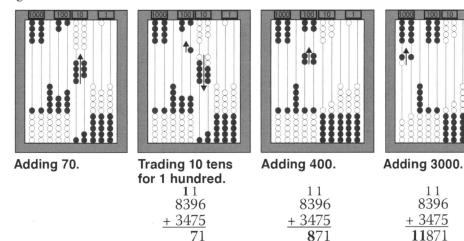

| Adding 70. | Trading 10 tens for 1 hundred. | Adding 400. | Adding 3000. |
|---|---|---|---|

$$\begin{array}{r} 1\,1 \\ 8396 \\ + 3475 \\ \hline 71 \end{array}$$

$$\begin{array}{r} 1\,1 \\ 8396 \\ + 3475 \\ \hline 871 \end{array}$$

$$\begin{array}{r} 1\,1 \\ 8396 \\ + 3475 \\ \hline 11871 \end{array}$$

Add 4 hundred. See the third figure above. Write the 800 as shown under the third figure.

Add 3 thousand. See the fourth figure above. Write the final 11 thousand as shown under the fourth figure.

***Checking the addition.*** Tell the child to use check numbers to see if the answer checks. See the figure on the right.

$$\begin{array}{r} 1\,1 \\ 8396\ (8) \\ + 3475\ (1) \\ \hline 11871\ (0)\ \checkmark \end{array}$$

***Column Addition game.*** Play the Column Addition game, found in *Math Card Games* book, A64. Tell her to use her abacus and to write the additions in her math journal. Also tell her to use check numbers.

If three children play, one child can add a diagonal, the three numbers above the diagonal, and the three numbers below it. If four play, one child can add the other diagonal, and the numbers above, and below it.

***In conclusion.*** Ask: When you played the game, why were the answers the same for everyone? [The order does not matter when adding.]

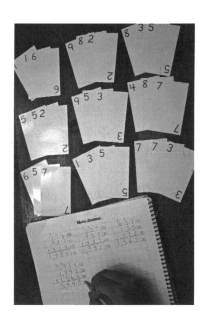

© Activities for Learning, Inc. 2016

28

# Lesson 14: On to the Millions

## OBJECTIVES:

1. To learn about number periods: simple, thousand, and million
2. To understand numbers to the millions
3. To construct a large cube to represent a million

## MATERIALS:

1. Geometry square panels*
2. Centimeter cubes, about 50
3. **A empty corner in the room, 3 ft (1 m) in all three directions**
4. Math journal

| ACTIVITIES FOR TEACHING: | EXPLANATIONS: |
|---|---|

**Warm-up.** Ask: What is 800 + 800? [1 thousand 6 hundred or 16 hundred] When you add, how can you tell that you need to trade? [the sum is 10 or more]

Ask: What is 300 + 400 + 500? [1200] What is 500 + 300 + 400? [1200] Why were the answers the same? [The order does not matter when adding.]

**The simple numbers.** Explain that today we are going to talk about thousands. Lots of them. Say: Numbers are grouped in *periods*. The first period has numbers from 1 to 999. They are called *simple* numbers.

Give the child the geometric panels and about 50 centimeter cubes. Tell her to make a cube with six panels, but to leave some of the rubber bands off so she can see inside. See figure below.

Say: Find out how many centimeter cubes will fit in the large cube. [1000] See the figures above for one solution.

Ask the child to explain how she knows. [There are ten cubes in a row. Ten rows will fit on the bottom, which makes one hundred. Ten stacks of one hundred makes ten hundreds, which is one thousand.]

Say: Any number of cubes up to 1000 that will fit in the large cube is a simple number. Ask: Is 79 a simple number? [yes] Is 213 a simple number? [yes] Is 2000 a simple number? [no]

Ask: How many simple numbers are there? [999] What is the greatest number of digits we need to write a simple number? [three]

**The thousands.** Say: The next period are the *thousands*. There are one thousand, ten thousands, and hundred thousands.

\* If the panels have not been used yet, the edges need to be creased. Bend the edges along the perforated lines toward the colored side. Place the panel on a hard surface and bend gently. Bending two panels at a time works well.

Sometimes the first period of numbers, those from 1 to 999, are called *ones*. Since many children are likely to confuse this additional meaning of the word *ones*, the term *simple* will be used.

Leave the rubber bands off most of the edges of the top and front faces to gain access inside.

| ACTIVITIES FOR TEACHING CONTINUED: | EXPLANATIONS CONTINUED: |

Tell the child to return the centimeter cubes to their container and to replace the side on her large cube.

Tell the child to place the large cube in an empty corner of the room. Tell her to make five more cubes, then to place the cubes in the row, spacing them so that she can see where the tenth cube would be if she had ten. See the left figure below. Ask: How many little centimeter cubes will fit in a large cube? [1 thousand] How many little centimeter cubes will fit in the whole row? [10 thousand]

Another possibility is lay down a single square panel to mark the places.

Tell the child to place large cubes to show 10 rows of ten. (She will need to use the remaining four cubes to estimate where the tenth cube would be.) See the left figure below. Ask: How many little centimeter cubes will fit in two rows? [20 thousand] How many little centimeter cubes will fit in all ten rows? [100 thousand]

Next tell the child to stack a large cube on top of the corner cube. See the right figure above. Ask: How many large cubes would we need to fill the whole level? [200] How many centimeter cubes are needed to fill the 200 large cubes? [200 thousand] Hold a cube on top of the second cube and ask the same questions. [300, 300 thousand]

Lastly, show where the tenth large cube would be as shown on the right. Ask: How many large cubes would be needed to fill in all the levels up to ten? [1000] How many centimeter cubes would be needed to fill the 1000 large cubes? [1000 thousand] What shape would we have if we had enough large cubes? [an even larger cube]

Say: The name for 1000 thousand is *one million*. If we had one million centimeter cubes, they would weigh a little more than 1 ton.

The actual weight is 1 metric ton, which is equal to 2205 pounds. In the U.S. Customary system, a ton is 2000 pounds.

Say: Million is the name for next period. There are millions, ten millions, and hundred millions.

See page iii, number 14 of "Some General Thoughts on Teaching Mathematics," for additional information.

**Written work.** Tell the child to explain in her math journal how much one million is.

**In conclusion.** Ask: What is the name for ten hundreds? [a thousand] What is the name for a thousand thousands? [a million]

Continue playing games on a regular basis. If there is additional time following this lesson, play the Go to the Dump game, found in *Math Card Games* book, A3, Old Main, A4, or Fish at the Dump, A5.

# LESSON 15: WRITING AND READING LARGE NUMBERS

## OBJECTIVES:

1. To introduce expanded forms and standard forms for writing numbers
2. To practice writing and reading numbers
3. To introduce billions

## MATERIALS:

1. Worksheet 4, Writing and Reading Large Numbers
2. Place-value cards

## ACTIVITIES FOR TEACHING:

**Warm-up.** Give the child the worksheet. Tell her to do just the warm-up equations. Solutions are:

|  |  |  |
|---|---|---|
| **11** | **111** | **111** |
| 4382  (8) | 2374  (7) | 2988  (0) |
| + 5948  (8) | + 5958  (0) | + 5247  (0) |
| 10,330  (7) ✓ | 8332  (7) ✓ | 8235  (0) ✓ |

**Composing hundreds.** Give the child the place-value cards. Tell her to set aside the thousand cards except for 1000.

Tell the child to spread out the remaining place-value cards face up. Tell her to find 3 hundred, 3 ten, and 3, and then lay them out in a row as shown below in the left figure. Say: This is the *expanded* form for writing a number. Now stack the cards and align them on the right edges. Say: This is the same number in *standard* form. See the right figure below.

| 3 0 0 | 3 0 | 3 | | 3 3 3 |
|---|---|---|---|---|
| **333 in expanded form.** | | | | **333 in standard form.** |

**Composing thousands.** Say: Find the card that says 1000. Ask: How could we change this to 3000 using the cards in front of you? [Put the 3 on the 1.] See below.

| 3 0 0 0 | 3 0 0 0 |
|---|---|
| **Composing 3 thousand.** | |

Now tell her we can change the number to 33 thousand. See the left figure below. Then tell her to change it to 333 thousand. See the right figure below.

| 3 3 0 0 0 | 3 3 3 0 0 0 |
|---|---|
| **33 thousand** | **333 thousand** |

Tell her to compose the following:

456 thousand    4 5 6 0 0 0

902 thousand    9 0 2 0 0 0

17 thousand    1 7 0 0 0

## EXPLANATIONS:

| ACTIVITIES FOR TEACHING CONTINUED: | EXPLANATIONS CONTINUED: |

Now tell her to set aside the 1000-card and to compose 333,444, leaving a space between the thousands and the simple numbers. See the figure below.

$$\boxed{3}\boxed{3|3}\;\boxed{4}\boxed{4|4}$$
**333,444**

Next tell her to change the number to 333,044. Show her how to do it by turning 400 upside down as shown below.

$$\boxed{3|3|3}\;\boxed{0\;4|4}\qquad\boxed{3|3|3}\;\boxed{0|4|4}$$
**Composing 333,044**

***Composing millions and billions.*** Say: Let's compose some numbers with three periods; they will be in the millions. Compose 22 million 333 thousand 444. See below.

$$\boxed{2|2}\;\boxed{3|3|3}\;\boxed{4|4|4}$$
**22,333,444**

See page iii, number 19 of "Some General Thoughts on Teaching Mathematics," for additional information.

Say: Remember the million cube we showed with centimeter cubes in the last lesson? Show with your arms about how wide it was. [about three-fourths of a typical child's arm span] If we made a thousand of the million cubes, we would have a billion. *Billion* is the name of the next period. The billion cube would be four stories high, wide, and deep.

Tell her to compose 11 billion 222 million 333 thousand 444. See below.

$$\boxed{1|1}\;\boxed{2|2|2}\;\boxed{3|3|3}\;\boxed{4|4|4}$$
**11,222,333,444**

Repeat for 40 billion 333 million 204 thousand 100.

$$\boxed{4|0}\;\boxed{3|3|3}\;\boxed{2|0|4}\;\boxed{1|0|0}$$
**40,333,204,100**

***Worksheet 4.*** Say: The worksheet has some important information on it, besides the directions. It is marked with the word "Information." Solutions are below.

The "Information" section is designed to encourage the child to learn about math topics through reading.

$\boxed{5}\;\boxed{4|3|1}\;\boxed{7|0|2}\;\boxed{8|6|9}$ **5,431,702,869**
$\boxed{3|2}\;\boxed{9|1|7}\;\boxed{5|8|4}\;\boxed{6\;0\;0}$ **32,917,584,600**
$\boxed{6|0}\;\boxed{2|9|8}\;\boxed{8|0|0}\;\boxed{1|3|4}$ **60,298,800,134**
$\boxed{1|1}\;\boxed{0|2|9}\;\boxed{8|5|5}\;\boxed{0|7|3}$ **11,029,855,073**

305,162,000 **three hundred five million one hundred sixty-two thousand**
200,064,014 **two hundred million sixty-four thousand fourteen**

***In conclusion.*** Ask: How many digits are in each period? [three] Say: Name the first four periods. [simple, thousands, millions, billions]

# LESSON 16: ROUNDING LARGE NUMBERS

**OBJECTIVES:**
1. To review rounding numbers
2. To practice rounding large numbers

**MATERIALS:**
1. Worksheet 5, Rounding Large Numbers
2. AL Abacus

---

**ACTIVITIES FOR TEACHING:**

**EXPLANATIONS:**

***Warm-up.*** Give the child the worksheet. Tell her to do just the warm-up equations. Solutions are:

|  | Quotient | Remainder |
|---|---|---|
| 49 ÷ 7 | **7** | **0** |
| 50 ÷ 7 | **7** | **1** |
| 51 ÷ 7 | **7** | **2** |
| 52 ÷ 7 | **7** | **3** |

|  | Quotient | Remainder |
|---|---|---|
| 27 ÷ 6 | **4** | **3** |
| 28 ÷ 6 | **4** | **4** |
| 29 ÷ 6 | **4** | **5** |
| 30 ÷ 6 | **5** | **0** |

***Rounding on side 2 of the abacus.*** Give the child the abacus. Tell her to turn the abacus to side 2 and enter 8396 as shown below on the left. Say: We are going to round this number. Think what rounding means. Rounding is changing a number into a new number that is close to the original number, but replaces the least important digits with zeros. This makes the number easier to talk about and easier to add or subtract.

When reviewing a term that has not been used for a while, avoid asking the child to guess the answer. Children with poor memories tend to remember the first response, even when it is wrong.

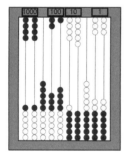 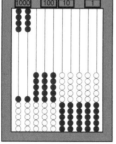 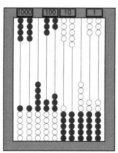 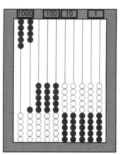

**Rounding 8396.**    **8396 rounded to nearest thousand.**    **Rounding 8596.**    **8596 rounded to nearest thousand.**

Say: We want to round the number on the abacus to the nearest thousand. Ask: Which two thousands is the number between? [8000 and 9000] What number is halfway between 8000 and 9000? [8500] Is 8396 nearer to 8000 or 9000? [8000] How do you know? [The number is less than halfway, so it is closer to 8000.]

Say: Now enter 8596 as shown above in the third figure. Ask: How would you round it to the nearest thousand? [8596 is closer to 8600 than to 8500, which is halfway.] See the fourth figure above.

Summarize: Tell her that the procedure for rounding a number is:

| ACTIVITIES FOR TEACHING CONTINUED: | EXPLANATIONS CONTINUED: |
|---|---|

- Point to the rounding digit.
- Look at the digit to the right. If it is 5 or more, add 1 to rounding digit; otherwise, don't change it.
- Change digits to the right of the rounded digit to 0s.

Tell her to enter 8596 again and this time to round it the nearest ten. Have her tell you what to do to round the number. [Point to the 9; look at the 6, which is more than 5; add another ten. This time the ten 10s must be traded for 100. So the answer is 8600.] See the figures.

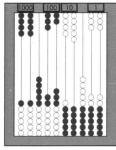 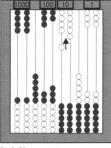 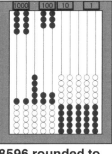

| **Rounding 8596.** | **Adding 1 ten.** | **8596 rounded to nearest ten.** |
|---|---|---|

***Rounding large numbers.*** Write the population of India:                    1,287,717,137

Ask: What is the population rounded to the nearest ten million? [1,290,000,000] Ask the child to go through the same procedure. [8 is the rounding digit. 7 is greater than 5, so 8 becomes 9. Change digits to the right to zeroes.]

Ask: How many billion people live in India? [1 billion]

***Worksheet 5.*** Tell the child to do the worksheet. The solutions are below.

This question is a practical everyday application of rounding.

See page iii, number 22 of "Some General Thoughts on Teaching Mathematics," for additional information.

| 12,300 | 12,400 | 12,500 | 12,600 |
|---|---|---|---|
| 12,323 | 12,399 | 12,491 | 12,603 |
| 12,290 | 12,424 | 12,470 | 12,567 |
| 12,287 | 12,400 | 12,461 | 12,599 |
| 12,250 | 12,356 | 12,546 | |

**7376 million**

**7 billion**

| 24 million | |
| **36 million** | **Australia** |
| **1405 million** | **Canada** |
| **100 million** | **United Kingdom** |
| **65 million** | **Ethiopia** |
| **326 million** | **United States** |
| **7376 million** | **China** |

***In conclusion.*** Ask: What are the steps for rounding? [Point to rounding digit. Add 1 if next digit is greater than or equal to 5. Change all digits to the right to zero.]

Continue playing games on a regular basis. If there is additional time following this lesson or more practice is needed, play the Rounding War game, found in *Math Card Games* book, N46.

# LESSON 17: ROUNDING ACTIVITIES

| OBJECTIVES: | MATERIALS: |
|---|---|
| 1. To observe the number periods on a calculator | 1. Casio SL-450S calculator |
| 2. To practice rounding | 2. *Math Card Games* book, A64 |
| 3. To multiply a number by 10 several times | 3. Math journal |

| ACTIVITIES FOR TEACHING: | EXPLANATIONS: |
|---|---|
| ***Warm-up.*** Ask: How many digits are in each period? [three] What are the first four periods? [simple, thousands, millions, billions]<br><br>Ask: What are the steps for rounding? [Point to rounding digit. Add 1 if next digit is greater than or equal to 5. Change all digits to the right to zero.] What is 4723 rounded to the nearest thousand? [5000] What is 4723 rounded to the nearest hundred? [4700] What is 4723 rounded to the nearest ten? [4720]<br><br>***Large numbers on a calculator.*** Give the child the calculator. Tell her to turn her calculator on by pressing the (AC) button.<br><br>Write without commas:  2678400 and tell the child that is the number of seconds in the month of October. Tell her to enter it on her calculator as you read the number, digit by digit.<br><br>Ask: How did the calculator separate the number periods? [with an apostrophe (')] Is the number easier to read with the marks? [yes] Tell her to read it. [2 million 678 thousand 4 hundred] | <br><br><br><br><br><br><br><br><br><br><br><br><br><br><br><br><br><br><br><br>Other calculators may use a different symbol. |
| ***Column Addition Rounding game.*** Play the Column Addition Rounding game, which is a variation of Column Addition, found in *Math Card Games* book, A64. The game is for two players. Use half the basic number cards deck, but no 10s.<br><br>Tell her that she is to make nine numbers each with five digits. See the layout on the next page. One player writes the numbers in her math journal and adds them on the calculator and rounds the final answer. The other player rounds each number to the nearest thousand and adds them on paper. Then the players compare their answers. See the calculations below the layout on the next page.<br><br>Players reverse roles and play the game again. | |

| ACTIVITIES FOR TEACHING CONTINUED: | EXPLANATIONS CONTINUED: |

| 5 6 1 6 3 — 3 | 8 5 3 1 4 — 4 | 6 2 1 2 3 — 3 |
| 3 8 4 0 2 — 2 | 5 4 3 7 5 — 5 | 2 1 6 0 9 — 6 |
| 7 0 5 6 8 — 8 | 1 0 6 9 8 — 8 | 2 7 9 0 7 — 7 |

**A layout for the Column Addition Rounding game.**

| | | |
|---|---|---|
| 56,163 | | 56,000 | |
| 85,314 | **Numbers** | 85,000 | **Numbers** |
| 62,123 | **added** | 62,000 | **rounded** |
| 38,402 | **and then** | 38,000 | **and then** |
| 54,375 | **rounded.** | 54,000 | **added.** |
| 21,609 | | 22,000 | |
| 70,568 | | 71,000 | |
| 10,698 | | 11,000 | |
| 27,907 | | 28,000 | |
| 427,159 | | 427,000 | |
| rounded 427,000 | | | |

The final answers should be very close, if not exactly the same.

***Using the constant key feature to add.*** Tell the child to clear the calculator by pressing ( C ). Then press 10 and ( + ) ( + ). Ask: What letter now shows on the display? [*K*] Explain: That *K* stands for *constant* and means the calculator is set for doing something special with 10. Ask: What sign shows on the right side of the display? [the plus sign (+)]

Tell her to press ( = ) over and over. Ask: What happened? [10, 20, 30, . . .] What did the calculator do? [added 10 to the previous number]

Say: Without clearing your calculator, press 4 and ( = ). Ask: What happened? [It added 10 and 4 to get 14.]

***Using the constant key feature to multiply.*** Say: Let's try something different. Press 10 and ( × ) ( × ) and then press ( = ) five times, reading the answer each time. [1 hundred, 1 thousand, 10 thousand, 100 thousand, 1 million] Ask: What did the calculator do? [multiplied by 10] Say: Press ( = ) once more and read the answer. [10 million] Press ( = ) once more and see what happens. [An *E* appears.] That *E* means *error*. To get rid of it, press ( C ).

When the answer exceeds the capacity of the calculator, the *E* appears.

Tell her to enter 27 without clearing. Press ( = ) repeatedly and read the answers. [270, 2,700, 27,000, 270,000, 2,700,000, 27,000,000] Ask: What was the calculator doing? [multiplying by 10]

If there is additional time following this lesson, have the child choose a game to play.

***In conclusion.*** Ask: Is it easier to add then round to the thousands or to round first then add? [Round first.]

# LESSON 18: REVIEW AND GAMES 1

## OBJECTIVES:

1. To review recent topics
2. To develop skills through playing math card games

## MATERIALS:

1. Worksheet 6-A or 6-B, Review 1
2. *Math Card Games* book, P34
3. Short Multiplication Table, Appendix p.1, if needed

## ACTIVITIES FOR TEACHING:

**Worksheet 6-A.** Give the child the worksheet. Tell her to listen to the problems and write the answers. Read each problem twice.

$$70 \times 10 \qquad 69 + 22 \qquad 50 \times 6$$

Tell her to complete the worksheet. Solutions are below.

Write only the answers.

**700**

**91**

**300**

Add. Use check numbers.

4928 (**5**)

+ 2566 (**1**)

**7494 (6)**

Write the answers.

$318 + 87 =$ **405**

$43 +$ **157** $= 200$

$(6 \times 3) + (6 \times 4) =$ **42**

Write these numbers using digits and commas.

39 million 24 thousand 718 **39,024,718**

1 billion 319 thousand 679 **1,000,319,679**

623 million 381 **623,000,381**

Fill in the table.

|  | Round to nearest hundred. | Round to nearest thousand. | Round to nearest million. |
|---|---|---|---|
| 6,083,140 | **6,083,100** | **6,083,000** | **6,000,000** |
| 18,945,562 | **18,945,600** | **18,946,000** | **19,000,000** |
| 65,709,697 | **65,709,700** | **65,710,000** | **66,000,000** |
| 2,376,450,712 | **2,376,450,700** | **2,376,451,000** | **2,376,000,000** |

Write >, <, or = on the lines.

6 million **=** 3,000,000 × 2

10,000 × 10 **<** 1,000,000

29 × 1000 **=** 29,000

3 hundred 6 **<** 3006

40 × 9 **=** 6 × 60

30 × 20 **>** 30 + 2

Fill in the table.

|  | Quotient (answer) | Remainder |
|---|---|---|
| 42 ÷ 2 | **21** | **0** |
| 24 ÷ 7 | **3** | **3** |
| 73 ÷ 9 | **8** | **1** |
| 60 ÷ 9 | **6** | **6** |
| 24 ÷ 10 | **2** | **4** |
| 102 ÷ 10 | **10** | **2** |

## EXPLANATIONS:

The Review worksheets each have two versions. The second version can be used in various ways: as a quiz, as a test, as a check after tutoring, and so forth.

Ask the child to correct any errors during the lesson.

See page iii, number 17 of "Some General Thoughts on Teaching Mathematics," for additional information.

## ACTIVITIES FOR TEACHING CONTINUED:

**EXPLANATIONS CONTINUED:**

***Multiply and Add game.*** Play the Multiply and Add game found in the *Math Card Games* book, P34. Tell her to use the short multiplication table if she needs it.

***Worksheet 6-B.*** Give the child the worksheet. Tell her to listen to the problems and write the answers. Read each problem twice.

$90 \times 10$        $58 + 17$        $40 \times 8$

Tell her to complete the worksheet. Solutions are below.

Write only the answers.

__**900**__

__**75**__

__**320**__

Write the answers.

$453 + 87 =$ **540**

$64 +$ **136** $= 200$

$(7 \times 5) + (7 \times 2) =$ **49**

Add. Use check numbers.

3786 (**6**)
+ 5492 (**2**)
**9278 (8)**

Write these numbers using digits and commas.

73 million 853 thousand 37  **73,853,037**

18 million 46 thousand 679  **18,046,679**

2 billion 840 million 7 thousand 832  **2,840,007,832**

Fill in the table.

|  | Round to nearest hundred. | Round to nearest thousand. | Round to nearest million. |
|---|---|---|---|
| 5,935,899 | **5,935,900** | **5,936,000** | **6,000,000** |
| 56,057,619 | **56,057,600** | **56,058,000** | **56,000,000** |
| 89,767,846 | **89,767,800** | **89,768,000** | **90,000,000** |
| 3,587,123,777 | **3,587,123,800** | **3,587,124,000** | **3,587,000,000** |

Write >, <, or = on the lines.

6 million **=** $2,000,000 \times 3$

100,000 **<** $10,000 \times 100$

$74 \times 1000$ **=** 74,000

5009 **>** 5 hundred 9

$30 \times 8$ **=** $6 \times 40$

$500 + 20$ **<** $500 \times 2$

Fill in the table.

|  | Quotient (answer) | Remainder |
|---|---|---|
| $28 \div 2$ | **14** | **0** |
| $37 \div 5$ | **7** | **2** |
| $73 \div 10$ | **7** | **3** |
| $98 \div 10$ | **9** | **8** |
| $80 \div 9$ | **8** | **8** |
| $70 \div 9$ | **7** | **7** |

# LESSON 19: ADDING AND SUBTRACTING SHORTCUTS

## OBJECTIVES:

1. To learn some shortcuts for adding and subtracting
2. To practice some shortcuts
3. To practice adding and subtracting in some special cases

## MATERIALS:

1. Worksheet 7, Adding and Subtracting Shortcuts

| ACTIVITIES FOR TEACHING: | EXPLANATIONS: |
|---|---|
| **Warm-up.** Ask: What is 43 + 10? [53] 43 + 9? [52] 43 + 11? [54] | |
| Ask: What is 89 + 10? [99] 89 + 9? [98] 89 + 11? [100] What is 57 + 10? [67] 57 + 9? [66] 57 + 11? [68] | |
| **Adding and subtracting in groups.** Say: Today's lesson is about shortcuts. Here is a shortcut that sometimes is helpful. Write: | These methods are in addition to the "traditional" algorithm. They do not need to be mastered. |

$$\begin{array}{r} 25\,76 \\ +\ 25\,13 \\ \hline [50\,89] \end{array}$$

and say: Look at the numbers in groups. You know what 25 and 25 hundred are and you can quickly add 76 and 13. So the sum is 5089. Tell her to try the following:

$$\begin{array}{r} 32\,58 \\ +\ 24\,27 \\ \hline [56\,85] \end{array} \qquad \begin{array}{r} 88\,40 \\ -\ 65\,38 \\ \hline [23\,02] \end{array}$$

**Adding shortcuts.** Say: Let's try another shortcut.

Write:          75 + 39 =

and tell the child to find the sum. Tell her to explain how she did it. One way is to add the tens, 70 and 30 to get 100, then add 5 and 9 to get 14. The sum is 114.

Another way is to think of 39 as 40 − 1. Add 75 + 40 to get 115 and then subtract 1, giving 114.

Write:          783 + 999 =

and tell her to use a shortcut to find the sum. [1782] Add 1000 to 783 and then subtract 1.

Repeat for:          4082 + 998 =

Again adding 1000 to 4082 gives 5082, subtracting 2 gives the sum of 5080.

**Adding from the left.** Say: You have been adding numbers with four digits by starting at the right.

Write:          
$$\begin{array}{r} 4865 \\ +\ 2619 \\ \hline [7484] \end{array}$$

See page ii, number 2 of "Some General Thoughts on Teaching Mathematics," for additional information.

| ACTIVITIES FOR TEACHING CONTINUED: | EXPLANATIONS CONTINUED: |
|---|---|

Ask: Could you start instead at the left? How can you tell when you will need to do a trade? [by looking at the next digits] Give her time to work it out.

Then ask the child to explain. One possible explanation is as follows: 4 thousand and 2 thousand is 6 thousand, but 8 hundred and 6 hundred will need a trade, so write 7 thousand. Next, 8 hundred and 6 hundred is 14 hundred; the tens don't need a trade, so write 4 hundred. For the tens, 6 and 1 is 7, but the ones will need a trade so write 8. Lastly, 5 and 9 is 14; write 4.

**Worksheet 7.** Give the child the worksheet. Tell her to only do the addition problems in the top rectangle. The solutions are below.

27 + 69 = **96**

354 + 78 = **432**

898 + 326 = **1224**

$$\begin{array}{r} 191 \\ + 323 \\ \hline \textbf{514} \end{array} \qquad \begin{array}{r} 10{,}298 \\ + 4{,}375 \\ \hline \textbf{14{,}673} \end{array} \qquad \begin{array}{r} 6537 \\ + 5948 \\ \hline \textbf{12{,}485} \end{array}$$

**Subtracting by compensating.** Write:

$$75 - 39 =$$

and tell the child to find the difference. Tell her to explain how she did it. One way is to subtract 40, giving 35, but we need to change it to 36 because we subtracted 1 too many. Another way is to change the problem to 76 − 40. Tell her to try it for:

$$500 - 199 =$$

Here 500 − 200 is 300, but we need to add 1, so the difference is 301. Or, add 1 to both numbers, getting 501 − 200 = 301.

**Worksheet 7.** Tell her to complete the worksheet. Tell her to discuss her solutions as shown below.

Write a 3-digit number with consecutive digits.

67 − 18 = **49**

46 − 37 = **9**

234 − 135 = **99**

$$\begin{array}{r} 787 \\ - 768 \\ \hline \textbf{19} \end{array} \qquad \begin{array}{r} 238 \\ - 209 \\ \hline \textbf{29} \end{array} \qquad \begin{array}{r} 845 \\ - 547 \\ \hline \textbf{298} \end{array}$$

**All examples will have a difference of 198.**

**With 4 consecutive digits, the difference will always be 3087; with 5 digits, the difference will be 41,976.**

Write any 3-digit number.

**The final sum will always be 1089.**

*The patterns on the worksheet are adapted from The Teaching of Arithmetic pp. 115-6 by David Eugene Smith, 1913.*

*If there is additional time following this lesson or more practice is needed, play the Zero Corners game, found in Math Card Games book, S9.*

*Using this procedure for 4-digit numbers gives either 9999 or 10,890 for the answer. For 5-digit numbers, the answer will be either 99,099 or 109, 890.*

**In conclusion.** Ask: Is there only one way to add? [no] Is there only one way to subtract? [no]

# LESSON 20: SUBTRACTING ON SIDE 2 OF THE ABACUS

**OBJECTIVES:**

1. To learn (or review) subtraction from left to right on side 2 of the AL Abacus

**MATERIALS:**

1. Worksheet 8, Subtracting on Side 2 of the Abacus
2. AL Abacus

## ACTIVITIES FOR TEACHING:

***Warm-up.*** Give the child the worksheet. Tell her to do just the warm-up equations. Solutions are:

| | | |
|---|---|---|
| 72 + 19 = **91** | 453 + 48 = **501** | 129 + 33 = **162** |
| 72 − 19 = **53** | 453 − 48 = **405** | 129 − 33 = **96** |

Ask: Is there only one way to add? [no]

***Subtracting on side 2.*** Give the child the abacus. Tell the child to turn her abacus to side 2.

Write:

$$\begin{array}{r} 6829 \\ -\ 2637 \end{array}$$

and tell her to watch while you perform the subtraction on the abacus. Involve the child as much as possible.

Enter 6829 on the abacus. See the left figure below.

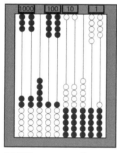 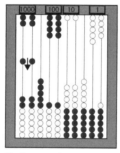 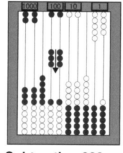

**6829 entered.**   **Subtracting 2000.**   **Subtracting 600.**

$$\begin{array}{r} 6829 \\ -\ 2637 \\ \hline 4 \end{array} \qquad \begin{array}{r} 6829 \\ -\ 2637 \\ \hline 4\mathbf{1} \end{array}$$

Say: We will start with the thousands. Ask: What do we subtract first? [2000] See the second figure above.

Say: Before we write the 4000, we need to see if the hundreds will need a trade. Ask: Are there enough hundreds to subtract 600? [yes] Say: No trade is needed. Write the 4 as shown under the second figure above.

Ask: What do we subtract next? [600] See the third figure above. Say: Before we write the 200, we need to see if the tens will need a trade. Ask: Are there enough tens to subtract 30? [no] Say: A trade will be needed, so we write 100 instead of 200. Do the trade as shown in the first figure above. Then ask: How many tens do we have

## EXPLANATIONS:

There are at least eight different ways to subtract multi-digit numbers. Even though a person has learned one method, it is good to explore other methods to enhance understanding.

See page iii, number 13 of "Some General Thoughts on Teaching Mathematics," for additional information.

The subtraction shown here proceeds from left to right like division. It was first taught in RightStart Mathematics Level C.

If the child has an accurate and efficient method of subtraction, do not insist that the child change to a new method.

## ACTIVITIES FOR TEACHING CONTINUED:   |   ## EXPLANATIONS CONTINUED:

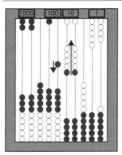 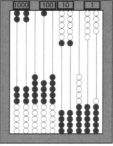 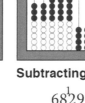

**Trading 1 hundred for 10 tens.**

**After the trade.**

$$6\overset{1}{8}29$$
$$-\;2637$$
$$\overline{\phantom{000}41}$$

**Subtracting 30.**

$$6\overset{1}{8}29$$
$$-\;2637$$
$$\overline{\phantom{00}419}$$

**Difference 4192.**

$$6\overset{1}{8}29$$
$$-\;2637$$
$$\overline{\phantom{0}4192}$$

Writing the little
1s is optional.

now? [12] Write a little 1 before the 2 as shown under the second figure above. Ask: What is 12 – 3? [9] Do we need to do a trade before subtracting the ones? [no] Write the 9 tens then subtract the ones. Tell her to do the same problem on her abacus by herself.

**Example 2.** Write:        7094
                          – 3528

Tell her to do the subtraction problem on her abacus. The steps are shown in the figures below.

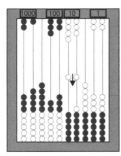 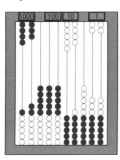 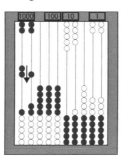 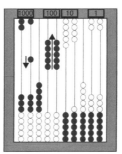 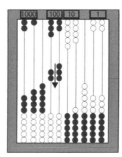

**7094 entered.**    **Subtracting 3000.**    **Trading 1 thousand for 10 hundreds.**    **Subtracting 500.**

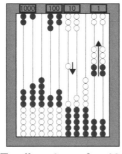 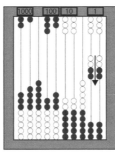 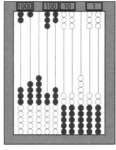

**Subtracting 20.**    **Trading 1 ten for 10.**    **Subtracting 8.**    **Difference 3566.**

**Worksheet 8.** Tell the child to do the first six subtraction problems. The solutions are:

| | | |
|---|---|---|
| 3073 | 1455 | 1432 |
| 1708 | 1479 | 3916 |

**In conclusion.** Ask: How do you know when you need to trade? [when the number being subtracted is more than the starting number]

The remainder of this worksheet will be completed in the next lesson.

If there is additional time following this lesson or more practice is needed, play the Zero Corners game, found in *Math Card Games* book, S9.

# LESSON 21: TRADITIONAL SUBTRACTING ON THE ABACUS

## OBJECTIVES:
1. To learn (or review) subtraction from right to left on side 2 of the AL Abacus

## MATERIALS:
1. AL Abacus
2. Worksheet 8, Subtracting on Side 2 of the Abacus

## ACTIVITIES FOR TEACHING:

***Warm-up.*** Ask: Is there only one way to add? [no] Is there only one way to subtract? [no] How do you know when you need to trade? [when the number being subtracted is more than the starting number]

Ask: What is 10 – 7? [3] What is 30 – 7? [23] What is 140 – 7? [133] What is 10 – 8? [2] What is 40 – 8? [32] What is 120 – 8? [112]

***Subtracting on side 2.*** Say: Today you will be subtracting large numbers, but starting at the right. Write the following subtraction in the vertical format:

$$\begin{array}{r} 9062 \\ -\,5146 \\ \hline \end{array}$$

Tell the child to enter the larger number, 9062, on her abacus. See the left figure below.

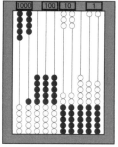 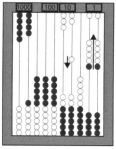 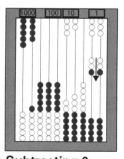

| **9062 entered.** | **Trading 1 ten for 10 ones.** | **Subtracting 6.** |

Say: First subtract the ones. Ask: Do you have enough ones to do the subtraction? [no] How can you get more ones? [Trade 1 ten for 10 ones.] Tell her to do the trade and subtraction. See the second and third figures above.

Tell her to finish the subtraction. See the figures on the next page. Tell her to read the difference. [3916]

Tell her to compare this equation to Problem 6 on her worksheet. [same]

## EXPLANATIONS:

If the child has not learned the traditional subtraction algorithm by subtracting from right to left, this lesson may be omitted.

Here subtraction proceeds from right to left, as in the traditional method used in the U.S. and Canada.

Subtracting on side 2 of the abacus makes it virtually impossible to subtract 2 from 6 as some children want to do in the following example:

$$\begin{array}{r} 62 \\ -\,46 \\ \hline \end{array}$$

| ACTIVITIES FOR TEACHING CONTINUED: | EXPLANATIONS CONTINUED: |

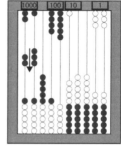

**Subtracting 40.**   **Trading 1 thousand for 10 hundreds.**   **Subtracting 100.**

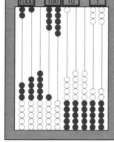

**Subtracting 5000.**   **Difference 3916.**

***Double trade.*** Write:

$$400$$
$$- 222$$
$$[178]$$

Tell her to enter 400 on her abacus. Ask: How can you get the ones you need to subtract? [trade twice] The trading steps are shown in the figures below.

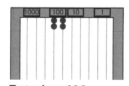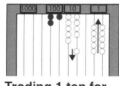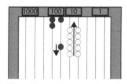

**Entering 400.**   **Trading 1 hundred for 10 tens.**   **Trading 1 ten for 10 ones.**

Tell her to finish subtracting 222. Ask the child to read the difference. [178]

***Worksheet 8.*** Tell the child to do the subtraction problems 7–12. The problems and solutions are given below.

| | | |
|---|---|---|
| 3079 | 8625 | 9162 |
| − 1836 | − 6632 | − 4585 |
| **1243** | **1993** | **4577** |
| 9468 | 4883 | 2728 |
| − 8273 | − 1709 | − 1859 |
| **1195** | **3174** | **869** |

***In conclusion.*** Ask: How much is 100 − 37? [63]

See page ii, number 12 of "Some General Thoughts on Teaching Mathematics," for additional information.

If there is additional time following this lesson or more practice is needed, play the Difference War game, found in *Math Card Games* book, S12, or Subtracting Nines on the Abacus, S14.

# LESSON 22: CHECKING SUBTRACTION BY ADDING UP

**OBJECTIVES:**

1. To check subtraction by adding up
2. To introduce the term *inverse*
3. To use check numbers to find errors

**MATERIALS:**

1. Worksheet 9, Checking Subtraction by Adding Up

| ACTIVITIES FOR TEACHING: | EXPLANATIONS: |
|---|---|
| **Warm-up.** Give the child the worksheet. Tell her to do just the warm-up equations. Solutions are: | |

$$
\begin{array}{ccc}
143 & 587 & 847 \\
-\,29 & -\,392 & -\,598 \\
\hline
\mathbf{114} & \mathbf{195} & \mathbf{249}
\end{array}
$$

**Adding the difference.** Write:

$$15 - 9 = 6$$

and ask the child: What happens if I add 9 back to the 6? [15, the same number we started with] Write it as:

$$9 + 6 = 15$$

Say: Think about entering 10 on the abacus and then subtracting 6. Ask: What will you have if you put the 6 back on? [10 again]

Summarize by saying: When two operations are opposites, like adding and subtracting, they are called *inverses*.

**Adding up.** Tell the child many people use adding to check their subtraction work. Write:

$$
\begin{array}{r}
4853 \\
-\,2936 \\
\hline
1917
\end{array}
$$

Say: Usually, they do it in their heads. They would think something like this: 7 + 6 is 13. Yes, the 3 is there. Then 1 + 1 + 3 is 5. Yes, the 5 is right. Next, 9 and 9 is 18. The 8 is there. And 1 and 1 and 2 is 4. My subtraction is correct.

Say: Sometimes they write down the addition like this:

$$
\begin{array}{r}
4853 \\
-\,2936 \\
\hline
\underline{1917} \\
4853
\end{array}
$$

**Checking with check numbers.** Say: Check numbers work when we subtract them or add them. Include the check numbers for the same example:

| ACTIVITIES FOR TEACHING CONTINUED: | EXPLANATIONS CONTINUED: |
|---|---|

$$4853\ (2)$$
$$-\ 2936\ (2)$$
$$1917\ (0)$$

Ask: Did the check numbers work? [yes, 2 − 2 = 0]

Say: Let's change the 3 in the minuend, the top number, to 2. Let's see what happens.

$$4852\ (\mathbf{1})$$
$$-\ 2936\ (2)$$
$$191\mathbf{6}\ (\mathbf{8})$$

Say:: We can use the check numbers by adding up: 8 and 2 equal 10, which has 1 as the check number.

**Practice.** Write the incorrect equation and check numbers shown below on the left:

| 3807 (0) | 3807 (0) |
|---|---|
| − 1234 (1) | − 1234 (1) |
| 1633 (4) | ~~1633 (4)~~ |
|  | 2573 (8) |

and ask the child: Is the difference correct? [No] How do you know? [When you add the tens, it should be 6, not a 0. Also, the check numbers do not add up, 4 + 1 is not 0.] Cross out the wrong answer and write the correction as shown above on the right.

**Worksheet 9.** Tell the child to do the worksheet. The solutions are below.

| 8449 (7) | 9427 (4) | 6966 (0) |
|---|---|---|
| − 4177 (1) | − 7921 (1) | − 4138 (7) |
| ~~4372~~ (7) | ~~1596~~ (3) | ~~2838~~ (2) |
| **4272 (6)** | **1506** (3) | **2828** (2) |
| 3443 (5) | 8194 (4) | 4912 (7) |
| − 1088 (8) | − 5532 (6) | − 3134 (2) |
| 2355 (7) | ~~2552~~ (2) | 1778 (5) |
| **2355 (6)** | **2662 (7)** | |
| 5129 (8) | 9095 (5) | 5660 (8) |
| − 3186 (0) | − 4697 (8) | − 3496 (4) |
| ~~2043~~ (0) | ~~4498~~ (7) | 2164 (4) |
| **1943 (8)** | **4398 (6)** | |
| 7797 (3) | 6595 (7) | 6042 (**3**) |
| − 843 (**6**) | − 5456 (2) | − 3537 (**0**) |
| **6954 (6)** | **1139 (5)** | **2505 (3)** |
| 2275 (7) | 7890 (6) | 4175 (**8**) |
| − 757 (**1**) | − 4362 (**6**) | − 1802 (**2**) |
| **1518 (6)** | **3528 (0)** | **2373 (6)** |

**In conclusion.** Ask: What are two ways to check subtraction? [adding up and check numbers]

An advanced child might realize that there is another way to check this example with check numbers. Instead of adding up 8 + 2 = 10 and 1 + 0 = 1, add 9 (which is the same as zero) to the 1. Nine plus the check number, 1, makes 10; then 10 − 2 = 8, which checks.

If there is additional time following this lesson or more practice is needed, play the Top and Bottom Corners game, found in *Math Card Games* book, S11, or On the Number Ten, S25.

# LESSON 23: MAGIC SQUARES

## OBJECTIVES:

1. To learn about magic squares and their magic sums
2. To review rotations and reflections

## MATERIALS:

1. Worksheet 10, Magic Squares
2. *Math Card Games* book, A60
3. AL Abacus

## ACTIVITIES FOR TEACHING:

**Warm-up.** Give the child the worksheet. Tell her to do just the warm-up equations. Solutions are:

$$543\ (3) \qquad 752\ (5) \qquad 947\ (2)$$
$$\underline{-435\ (3)} \qquad \underline{-527\ (5)} \qquad \underline{-479\ (2)}$$
$$108\ (0) \qquad 225\ (0) \qquad 468\ (0)$$

**Worksheet 10.** Tell the child to read the information on the worksheet and to do the first row of magic squares. The information and solutions are below.

INFORMATION: A magic square is a special array of numbers. In a magic square, the sum of each row, column, and diagonal is the same. This sum is the *magic sum.*

| 2 | 9 | 4 |
|---|---|---|
| 7 | 5 | 3 |
| 6 | 1 | 8 |

**15**

| 8 | 1 | 6 |
|---|---|---|
| 3 | 5 | 7 |
| 4 | 9 | 2 |

**15**

| 16 | 3 | 2 | 13 |
|----|---|---|----|
| 5 | 10 | 11 | 8 |
| 9 | 6 | 7 | 12 |
| 4 | 15 | 14 | 1 |

**34**

| 9 | 6 | 3 | 16 |
|---|---|---|----|
| 4 | 15 | 10 | 5 |
| 14 | 1 | 8 | 11 |
| 7 | 12 | 13 | 2 |

**34**

Ask: How did you find the number that is missing in the top row of the second magic square? [$8 + c + 6 = 15$ or $9 + 5 + c = 15$, so $c = 1$]

For the third magic square, either the 10 or the 7 must be found before the last column could be completed.

**Magic square sums.** Ask: How many different ways do the numbers in the $3 \times 3$ magic squares add up to the magic sum? [8: 3 horizontal, 3 vertical, and 2 diagonal]

Ask: How many different ways do the numbers in the $4 \times 4$ magic squares add up to the magic sum? [10, including, 4 horizontal, 4 vertical, and 2 diagonal]

**Magic Squares Memory.** Play the Magic Squares Memory game, found in *Math Card Games* book, A60. It may not be necessary to use blank cards for place holders.

**Worksheet 10.** Tell her to complete the worksheet. The solutions are shown on the next page.

## EXPLANATIONS:

Magic squares belong to a branch of mathematics called Recreational Mathematics. Benjamin Franklin worked on an $8 \times 8$ magic square when he was bored in long meetings.

Some magic squares have consecutive numbers starting with 1; these are often referred to as "normal" magic squares.

This lesson will include normal magic squares. Other magic squares will be discussed in future lessons.

See page iii, number 27 of "Some General Thoughts on Teaching Mathematics," for additional information.

| **ACTIVITIES FOR TEACHING CONTINUED:** | **EXPLANATIONS CONTINUED:** |

**A**

| 2 | 9 | 4 |
|---|---|---|
| 7 | **5** | 3 |
| 6 | 1 | 8 |

**B**

| 6 | 7 | 2 |
|---|---|---|
| **1** | **5** | **9** |
| 8 | 3 | 4 |

**C**

| 8 | 1 | **6** |
|---|---|---|
| 3 | 5 | **7** |
| 4 | 9 | **2** |

**D**

| **4** | 3 | 8 |
|---|---|---|
| 9 | **5** | 1 |
| 2 | 7 | **6** |

**E**

| 6 | 1 | **8** |
|---|---|---|
| 7 | 5 | 3 |
| **2** | 9 | **4** |

**F**

| 4 | **9** | 2 |
|---|---|---|
| **3** | 5 | **7** |
| 8 | **1** | 6 |

**G**

| 2 | **7** | 6 |
|---|---|---|
| 9 | **5** | 1 |
| **4** | 3 | **8** |

**H**

| 8 | 3 | **4** |
|---|---|---|
| 1 | 5 | **9** |
| **6** | **7** | **2** |

Ask: What is special about these squares? Tell her to find as many patterns as possible. Some possibilities are:

1. They include all the numbers from 1 to 9.
2. All even numbers are in the corners.
3. Each row, column, and diagonal adds to 15.
4. Opposite corners and sides equal 10.
5. One diagonal is 4, 5, 6; the other diagonal is 2, 5, 8.

***Rotations.*** Enter 10 on the top wire of the abacus. Lay it on a flat surface where the child can see it. Explain that you are going to rotate the abacus 90° at a time. Tell her to watch what happens to the 10. [on top, at the right side, at the bottom, at the left side.] See below.

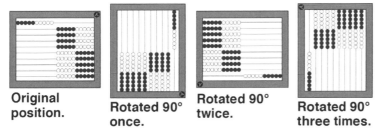

**Original position.** **Rotated 90° once.** **Rotated 90° twice.** **Rotated 90° three times.**

Tell her to look at numbers 2, 9, 4 in the magic squares A to D on the worksheet. Ask: Do you see any rotations? [B, C, and D are rotations of A.]

***Reflections.*** Explain that besides rotations, the abacus can be flipped, or reflected four different ways. See below.

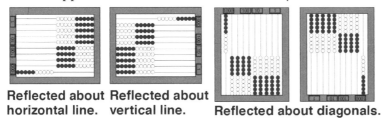

**Reflected about horizontal line.** **Reflected about vertical line.** **Reflected about diagonals.**

Tell her to look at numbers 2, 9, 4 in magic squares E to H on the worksheet. Ask: Do you see any reflections? [yes]

Ask: Do you see any rotations or reflections in the two 4 × 4 magic squares in the middle of the worksheet? [no]

***In conclusion.*** Ask: What is magic about magic squares? [answers will vary]

Encourage the child to think of finding the missing numbers as solving a puzzle. Planning ahead often helps.

Although these magic squares all have a 5 in the center and 15 as the magic number, many other combinations exist.

# LESSON 24: MODIFYING MAGIC SQUARES

**OBJECTIVES:**

1. To informally review or learn adding negative numbers

2. To learn about magic square relationships

**MATERIALS:**

1. Worksheet 11, Modifying Magic Squares

---

**ACTIVITIES FOR TEACHING:**

***Warm-up.*** Give the child the worksheet. Tell her to do just the warm-up equations. Solutions are:

$$
\begin{array}{ccc}
872\ (\mathbf{8}) & 734\ (\mathbf{5}) & 429\ (\mathbf{6}) \\
-728\ (\mathbf{8}) & -347\ (\mathbf{5}) & -294\ (\mathbf{6}) \\
\hline
144\ (\mathbf{0}) & 387\ (\mathbf{0}) & 135\ (\mathbf{0})
\end{array}
$$

***Adding a number to a magic square.*** Draw the following magic square and a blank magic square as shown below.

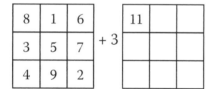

Adding the same number to each cell in a magic square gives a new magic square.

Tell the child to add 3 to each cell in the magic square and write it in the blank array. Ask: Is the new array a magic square? [yes] How do you know? [Rows, columns, and diagonals add to 24.]

***Subtracting a number from a magic square.*** Now change the + sign to a − sign. Ask: What is 8 − 3? [5] Write it in the first cell as shown below.

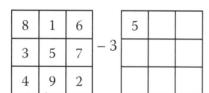

Subtracting the same number to each cell in a magic square gives a new magic square.

Draw the number line shown on the right. Ask: How would you find

$$-4\ \ -3\ \ -2\ \ -1\ \ 0\ \ 1\ \ 2\ \ 3\ \ 4$$

4 − 3 [1] on the number line? [Start at 4 and move to the left three spaces.] Say: Do the same thing to find 1 − 3, start at 1 and move to the left three spaces. We read the answer as negative 2.

**EXPLANATIONS:**

Do NOT attempt to teach any rules for working with negative numbers.

A negative number can also be read as "minus 2."

---

| ACTIVITIES FOR TEACHING CONTINUED: | EXPLANATIONS CONTINUED: |
|---|---|

Ask the child to find 0 − 2, [−2] 3 − 4, [−1] and −2 + 2. [0]

Complete the magic square, using the number line where necessary. See the answer on the previous page.

**Worksheet 11.** Tell her to do the first four problems on the worksheet. The solutions are below.

1.   **yes**

| 9 | 16 | 11 |
|---|----|----|
| 14 | 12 | 10 |
| 13 | 8 | 15 |

15        36

2.   **yes**

| 3 | −2 | 5 |
|---|----|---|
| 4 | 2 | 0 |
| −1 | 6 | 1 |

15        6

3.   **yes**

| 44 | 99 | 22 |
|----|----|----|
| 33 | 55 | 77 |
| 88 | 11 | 66 |

15        165

4.   **yes**

| 1 | 4 | 4 |
|---|---|---|
| 6 | 3 | 0 |
| 2 | 2 | 5 |

0      9      9

Ask: When you add or subtract the same number to each cell in a magic square, do you get a new magic square? [yes] When you add two magic squares together, do you get a new magic square? [yes]

Multiplying corresponding cells of two magic squares does not result in a new magic square.

Next tell her to complete the worksheet. The remaining solutions are below.

5. **The magic sum is 3 times the middle number.**

6.

| 3 | 5 | 10 |
|---|---|----|
| 13 | 6 | −1 |
| 2 | 7 | 9 |

| 13 | 3 | 5 |
|----|---|---|
| −1 | 7 | 15 |
| 9 | 11 | 1 |

| 10 | 4 | 10 |
|----|---|----|
| 8 | 8 | 8 |
| 6 | 12 | 6 |

For a 5 × 5 magic square, the magic sum is 5 times the middle number.

Ask the child to explain how she found the 7 in the first square in Problem 6. [First find the magic sum, 18, by either 6 × 3 or adding the second row. Then do the top row to get 5 and the middle column to get 7.]

**In conclusion.** Ask: What do we call numbers that are less than zero? [negative numbers] What is 0 − 2? [−2] What is −2 + 3? [1] What plus 2 equals −1? [−3]

If there is additional time following this lesson or more practice is needed, play the Magic Squares Memory game, found in *Math Card Games* book, A60.

# LESSON 25: LARGER MAGIC SQUARES

## OBJECTIVES:

1. To learn about 4 × 4 magic squares
2. To practice mental arithmetic
3. To practice working with negative numbers

## MATERIALS:

1. Worksheet 12, Larger Magic Squares

## ACTIVITIES FOR TEACHING:

***Warm-up.*** Give the child the worksheet. Tell her to do just the warm-up equations. Solutions are:

| | | |
|---|---|---|
| 6 − 3 = **3** | 5 − 6 = **−1** | −1 + 5 = **4** |
| 2 − 3 = **−1** | 9 − 11 = **−2** | −3 + 2 = **−1** |
| 7 − 9 = **−2** | 1 − 5 = **−4** | −1 + 8 = **7** |

***Historical note.*** Tell the child that since the year 650 B.C., the Chinese knew about the 3 × 3 magic square with the numbers 1 to 9. They called it the Lo Shu.

People in the Middle Ages knew about larger magic squares, which they thought brought good luck. They were especially interested in magic squares that had consecutive numbers starting with 1, called normal magic squares.

There is only one 3 × 3 normal magic square that is not a rotation or reflection. There are 880 different 4 × 4 normal magic squares and 275,305,224 different 5 × 5 normal magic squares. No one knows how many 6 × 6 normal magic squares are possible; it is millions of millions.

***The Durer 4 x 4 magic square.*** Draw the Durer 4 × 4 magic square as shown below. Tell the child that this magic square is in a famous painting completed in the year 1514.

| 16 | 3 | 2 | 13 |
|----|----|----|----|
| 5 | 10 | 11 | 8 |
| 9 | 6 | 7 | 12 |
| 4 | 15 | 14 | 1 |

**A 4 × 4 normal magic square, found in a painting by Durer in the year 1514. See the year in the last row.**

Ask: What numbers does the Durer magic square have? [1 to 16] Does that make it a normal magic square? [yes] Do you see the year it was painted in the square? [bottom row]

## EXPLANATIONS:

**ACTIVITIES FOR TEACHING CONTINUED:** | **EXPLANATIONS CONTINUED:**

*Worksheet 12.* Tell her to do the worksheet. The solutions are below.

| 7 | 12 | 1 | 14 |
|---|----|---|----|
| **2** | 13 | 8 | 11 |
| 16 | 3 | **10** | 5 |
| 9 | **6** | 15 | 4 |

| 12 | 1 | 14 | 7 |
|----|---|----|---|
| **13** | **8** | **11** | **2** |
| 3 | 10 | 5 | 16 |
| 6 | 15 | 4 | 9 |

| 4 | 14 | 15 | **1** |
|---|----|----|---|
| 9 | 7 | 6 | **12** |
| 5 | 11 | 10 | **8** |
| 16 | 2 | 3 | **13** |

| **0** | 3 | 4 | 13 |
|---|---|----|----|
| 10 | **0** | **10** | 0 |
| 17 | 4 | **6** | −7 |
| −7 | 13 | 0 | 14 |

| **1** | 12 | 8 | **13** |
|---|----|---|----|
| 15 | 6 | 10 | 3 |
| 14 | 7 | 11 | 2 |
| 4 | 9 | 5 | **16** |

| 6 | **15** | **4** | 9 |
|---|----|---|---|
| 3 | 10 | 5 | 16 |
| 13 | 8 | 11 | 2 |
| 12 | **1** | 14 | 7 |

| **10** | **−1** | −2 | 8 |
|----|----|----|---|
| 9 | 1 | 2 | 3 |
| −2 | 7 | 5 | 5 |
| −2 | 8 | **10** | **−1** |

| 1 | 14 | 14 | **4** |
|---|----|----|---|
| 11 | 7 | **6** | 9 |
| 8 | **10** | 10 | 5 |
| **13** | 2 | 3 | 15 |

1. Which two magic squares are reflections of each other? **B & F**
2. Which two magic squares are rotations of each other? **C & E**
3. Which three magic squares are not normal? **D, G, H**
4. What is special about the sum of the 4 corners? **magic sum**
5. What is special about the sum of the inner squares? **magic sum**
6. Top middle numbers + **bottom middle numbers** = magic sum.
7. Left middle numbers + **right middle numbers** = magic sum
8. Add the corresponding cells in magic squares G and H. Write it in the square at the right. What is its magic sum? **48**

| 11 | 13 | 12 | 12 |
|----|----|----|----|
| 20 | 8 | 8 | 12 |
| 6 | 17 | 15 | 10 |
| 11 | 10 | 13 | 14 |

Discuss the answers to the questions with the child.

*In conclusion.* Ask: Why do you think people find magic squares so interesting? [Answers will vary.]

If there is additional time following this lesson, play the Mixed Multiplication Cards game, found in *Math Card Games* book, P7.

# LESSON 26: TERRY'S WAY TO SUBTRACT

**OBJECTIVES:**

1. To review subtracting
2. To learn another way to subtract

**MATERIALS:**

1. Worksheet 13, Terry's Way to Subtract

**ACTIVITIES FOR TEACHING:**

***Warm-up.*** Give the child the worksheet. Tell her to do just the warm-up equations. Solutions are:

| | | |
|---|---|---|
| $27 - 21 = $ **6** | $114 - 115 = $ **-1** | $10 - 30 = $ **-20** |
| $27 - 29 = $ **-2** | $128 - 130 = $ **-2** | $40 - 50 = $ **-10** |
| $27 - 30 = $ **-3** | $497 - 500 = $ **-3** | $200 - 300 = $ **-100** |

***Worksheet 13.*** Tell the child: Read the explanation on the worksheet several times. Say: Be sure it makes sense to you, so you can explain it to someone else.

Give her 5 minutes or so of uninterrupted time. Then ask her to explain the first example.

$$87 - 49 = 40 - 2 = 38$$

Tell the child to explain it. [First subtract the tens, $80 - 40 = 40$. There are not enough ones to subtract the 9 from the 7. Two more are needed. So we write –2. Then combine the 40 and – 2 to get the answer of 38.]

Repeat for the second example:

$$516 - 394 = 200 - 80 + 2 = 122$$

Here there are enough hundreds and ones, but not enough tens. Combining it can be done by finding $200 - 80$, which is 120 and then adding 2 to get 122.

Repeat for the third example:

$$7365 - 5468 = 2000 - 100 - 3 = 1897$$

In this example, $7000 - 5000 = 2000$; $300 - 400 = -100$; and $5 - 8 = -3$. Combining $2000 - 100 - 3$ gives 1897.

***Practice.*** Write:     $724 - 357 = $

and ask her to solve it using Terry's way.

$$[724 - 357 = 400 - 30 - 3 = 367]$$

Repeat for:     $10,280 - 8367 = $

$$[10,280 - 8367 = 2000 - 100 + 20 - 7 = 1913]$$

**EXPLANATIONS:**

There are at least eight different ways to subtract multi-digit numbers. Even though a person has learned one method, it is good to explore other methods to enhance understanding.

| ACTIVITIES FOR TEACHING CONTINUED: | EXPLANATIONS CONTINUED: |
|---|---|

**Worksheet 13.** Tell her to complete the worksheet. The solutions are below.

$91 - 57 = \mathbf{40 - 6 = 34}$
$371 - 191 = \mathbf{200 - 20 = 180}$
$809 - 437 = \mathbf{400 - 30 + 2 = 372}$
$4792 - 3285 = \mathbf{1000 + 500 + 10 - 3 = 1507}$
$3141 - 893 = \mathbf{3000 - 700 - 50 - 2 = 2248}$ **or** $\mathbf{2300 - 50 - 2 = 2248}$
$7040 - 2769 = \mathbf{5000 - 700 - 20 - 9 = 4271}$

See page iii, number 21 of "Some General Thoughts on Teaching Mathematics," for additional information.

**In conclusion.** Ask: Is there more than one way to subtract? [yes]

If there is additional time following this lesson or more practice is needed, play the Equal Remainders game, found in *Math Card Games* book, S31. Tell the child to use Terry's Way to subtract.

# LESSON 27: TERRY'S OTHER WAY TO SUBTRACT

**OBJECTIVES:**

1. To practice another format for subtraction

**MATERIALS:**

1. Worksheet 14, Terry's Other Way to Subtract
2. *Math Card Games* book, S28

**ACTIVITIES FOR TEACHING:**

***Warm-up.*** Give the child the worksheet. Tell her to do just the warm-up equations. Solutions are:

$$\overset{(8)}{7}\overset{(8)}{1}9 - 521 = \mathbf{200 - 10 + 8 = 198}$$

$$\overset{(3)}{4}\overset{(5)}{6}2 - 293 = \mathbf{200 - 30 - 1 = 169}$$

***Worksheet 14.*** Tell the child: Read the explanation on the worksheet several times. Say: Be sure it makes sense to you, so you can explain it so anyone, even grandparents, could understand what she did to get the answer.

Give her 5 minutes or so of uninterrupted time. Then ask her to explain the first example, shown below.

$$\begin{array}{r} 54 \\ -\ 29 \\ \hline 30 \\ -5 \\ \hline 25 \end{array}$$

Tell the child to explain it. [50 − 20 is 30 and 4 − 9 is −5. Then add 30 and −5 to get the answer of 25.]

Repeat for the second example:

$$\begin{array}{r} 852 \\ -\ 375 \\ \hline 500 \\ -20 \\ -3 \\ \hline 477 \end{array}$$

Here the hundreds 800 − 300 is 500; the tens 50 − 70 is −20; and the ones 2 − 5 is −3. This adds up to 477.

**EXPLANATIONS:**

Check numbers are optional in the solutions.

There are at least eight different ways to subtract multi-digit numbers. Even though a person has learned one method, it is good to explore other methods to enhance understanding.

| ACTIVITIES FOR TEACHING CONTINUED: | EXPLANATIONS CONTINUED: |
|---|---|

Repeat for the third example:

$$\begin{array}{r} 6592 \\ -\ 3718 \\ \hline 3000 \\ -200 \\ 80 \\ -6 \\ \hline 2874 \end{array}$$

Here the hundreds and ones are negative numbers while the thousands and tens are not. It is easier to add in groups: 3000 − 200 is 2800 and 80 − 6 is 74. Combining them gives 2874.

**Worksheet 14.** Tell the child to complete the worksheet. The solutions are below.

| 62 | 910 | 859 | 6076 | 3843 | 7083 | 6005 |
|---|---|---|---|---|---|---|
| − 35 | − 112 | − 379 | − 4059 | − 3386 | − 3259 | − 1009 |
| 30 | 800 | 500 | 2000 | 500 | 4000 | 5000 |
| −3 | −2 | −20 | 20 | −40 | −200 | −4 |
| 27 | 798 | 480 | −3 | −3 | 30 | 4996 |
|  |  |  | 2017 | 457 | −6 |  |
|  |  |  |  |  | 3824 |  |

**On the Number Negative Five game.** Play the On the Number Negative Five game found in *Math Card Games* book, S28.

**In conclusion.** Ask: Which of Terry's two ways of subtraction is easier to understand? [Answers will vary.] Which of Terry's ways do you like better? [Answers will vary.]

# LESSON 28: REVIEW AND GAMES 2

## OBJECTIVES:
1. To review recent topics
2. To develop skills through playing math card games

## MATERIALS:
1. Worksheet 15-A or 15-B, Review 2
2. *Math Card Games* book, P34
3. Short Multiplication Table, Appendix p.1, if needed

---

## ACTIVITIES FOR TEACHING:

***Worksheet 15-A.*** Give the child the worksheet. Tell her to listen to the problems and write the answers. Read each problem twice.

$43 \times 10$ $\qquad$ $149 + 37$ $\qquad$ $70 \times 8$

Tell her to complete the worksheet. Solutions are below.

Write only the answers.
**430**
**186**
**560**

Write the answers.
$582 + 69 =$ **651**
$87 +$ **113** $= 200$
$(6 \div 3) + (6 \div 2) =$ **5**

Add or subtract. Use check numbers.

| 9575 (8) | 4763 (2) | 9515 (2) | 4012 (7) |
|---|---|---|---|
| + 5592 (3) | + 5251 (4) | − 5592 (3) | − 1802 (2) |
| **15,167 (2)** | **10,014 (6)** | **3923 (8)** | **2210 (5)** |

Utah's population is two <u>million</u> nine hundred <u>thousand</u> eight hundred seventy-two.
Underline the period names. Write the number using digits and commas. **2,900,872**

Fill in the blanks.
$3 \times$ **8** $= 24$
$8 \times$ **8** $= 64$
$7 \times$ **2** $= 14$
**4** $\times 11 = 44$
**6** $\times 9 = 54$
$6 \times$ **4** $= 24$
$2 \times$ **7** $= 14$

Solve the problem.
Kendra wants to walk her dog for an hour. She has 25 minutes left to walk. How long has she walked so far?

***w* = walked so far**
***w* + 25 = 60**
***w* = 35 minutes**

Draw lines to match the expressions.
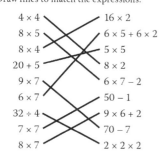

Complete the magic square.

| 7 | 4 | 1 | 15 |
|---|---|---|---|
| 8 | 7 | 8 | 4 |
| **6** | **4** | **8** | **9** |
| 6 | 12 | **10** | −1 |

## EXPLANATIONS:

The Review worksheets each have two versions. The second version can be used in various ways: as a quiz, as a test, as a check after tutoring, and so forth.

Ask the child to correct any errors during the lesson.

See page iii, number 17 of "Some General Thoughts on Teaching Mathematics," for additional information.

## ACTIVITIES FOR TEACHING CONTINUED:

**Multiply and Add game.** Play the Multiply and Add game found in the *Math Card Games* book, P34. Tell her to use the short multiplication table if she needs it.

**Worksheet 15-B.** Give the child the worksheet. Tell her to listen to the problems and write the answers. Read each problem twice.

$38 \times 10$ $\qquad$ $167 + 85$ $\qquad$ $80 \times 7$

Tell her to complete the worksheet. Solutions are below.

---

Write only the answers.

**380**

**252**

**560**

Write the answers.

$674 + 86 =$ **760**

$41 +$ **159** $= 200$

$(8 \div 4) + (8 \div 2) =$ **6**

Add or subtract. Use check numbers.

| $7864$ (**7**) | $9813$ (**3**) | $4603$ (**4**) | $7390$ (**1**) |
|---|---|---|---|
| $+ 3894$ (**6**) | $+ 9267$ (**6**) | $- 1597$ (**4**) | $- 3503$ (**2**) |
| **11,758 (4)** | **19,080 (0)** | **3006 (0)** | **3887 (8)** |

Hawaii's population is one <u>million</u> four hundred four <u>thousand</u> fifty-four. Underline the period names. Write the number using digits and commas. __**1,404,054**__

Fill in the blanks.

$2 \times$ **8** $= 16$

$6 \times$ **6** $= 36$

$7 \times$ **8** $= 56$

$11 \times$ **6** $= 66$

**4** $\times 4 = 16$

$8 \times$ **7** $= 56$

**4** $\times 9 = 36$

Solve the problem.

Kevin is playing hockey for an hour. He has 35 minutes left to play. How long has he played already?

**h = played hockey**

**h + 35 = 60**

**h = 25 minutes**

Draw lines to match the expressions.

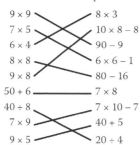

| | |
|---|---|
| $9 \times 9$ | $8 \times 3$ |
| $7 \times 5$ | $10 \times 8 - 8$ |
| $6 \times 4$ | $90 - 9$ |
| $8 \times 8$ | $6 \times 6 - 1$ |
| $9 \times 8$ | $80 - 16$ |
| $50 + 6$ | $7 \times 8$ |
| $40 \div 8$ | $7 \times 10 - 7$ |
| $7 \times 9$ | $40 + 5$ |
| $9 \times 5$ | $20 \div 4$ |

Complete the magic square.

| 5 | 2 | 6 | 8 |
|---|---|---|---|
| 7 | **3** | −1 | **12** |
| **-2** | 3 | 16 | 4 |
| 11 | **13** | **0** | −3 |

---

# LESSON 29: ADDITION AND SUBTRACTION PROBLEMS

## OBJECTIVES:

1. To solve two-step addition and subtraction problems

## MATERIALS:

1. Worksheet 16, Addition and Subtraction Problems

| ACTIVITIES FOR TEACHING: | EXPLANATIONS: |
|---|---|
| **Warm-up.** Ask: Is there more than one way to add 539 + 287? [yes, from the right and from the left] Is there more than one way to subtract? [yes, from the right, the left, and Terry's way] | |
| Ask: What is 2 – 3? [–1] What is 4 – 6? [–2] What is 43 rounded to the nearest ten? [40] What is 562 rounded to the nearest hundred? [600] What is 651 rounded to the nearest hundred? [700] What is 649 rounded to the nearest hundred? [600] | |
| **Worksheet 16.** Give the child the worksheet. Tell her to read the first problem: | See page iii, number 24 of "Some General Thoughts on Teaching Mathematics," for additional information. |

1. The populations of some states are: California, 38,332,521; New York, 19,651,127; and Florida, 19,552,860. Does California have more people than New York and Florida together?

Tell her: When you read a problem with several large numbers, first read it using simpler numbers. For example, you might think:

The populations of some states are: California, 38 million; New York, 19 million; and Florida, 19 million. Does California have more people than New York and Florida together?

Ask: Does that make it easier to understand using simpler numbers?

Tell her to solve the problem. One solution is shown below.

| New York | 19,651,127 (5) |
|---|---|
| Florida | 19,552,860 (0) |
| | 39,203,987 (5) |

No, California does not have more people.

Another solution is to round to millions place.

| ACTIVITIES FOR TEACHING CONTINUED: | EXPLANATIONS CONTINUED: |
|---|---|

**Problem 2.** Tell her to solve the second problem.

> Peyton has $30.00 and is buying three food items costing $9.49, $7.97, and $11.53. Does Peyton have enough money?

Then tell her to explain it. One solution is to add the three items. A better solution is to round each item to the next highest dollar:

> $10 + $8 + $12 = $30.
>
> Yes, Peyton has enough.

**Problem 3.** Tell the child to solve the third problem.

> When Skylar awoke in the morning, the temperature was −2°. By 3:00 p.m. the temperature is 10 degrees warmer. What is the temperature?

Then tell her to explain it. The temperature will be −2 + 10 = 8°. Ask: Does the 3:00 time have anything to do with solving the problem? [no]

**Problem 4.** Tell her to solve the fourth problem.

> Avery is thinking of even numbers less than 50 that when divided by 7 have a remainder of 1. What are the numbers?

Then tell her to explain it. Any number divided by 7 with a remainder of 1 will be 1 more than multiple of 7: 8, 15, 22, 29, 36, 43. The even numbers are: 8, 22, and 36.

**Problem 5.** Tell the child to solve the fifth problem.

> Tony and his family are traveling to visit relatives. The trip takes 2 hours and 40 minutes. If they leave at 9:10 and make two stops of 15 minutes each, what time will they arrive?

Then tell her to explain it. The total amount of travel time is:

> 2 hr 40 min + 15 min × 2 = 2 hr 70 min
>
> = 3 hr 10 min

Then 3 hr 10 min after 9:10 is 12:20, their arrival time.

**In conclusion.** Ask: Some people think you can solve problems by looking for key words like "altogether" or "difference"? Would that help for today's problems? [no] Does reading the problem several times and thinking about it help? [yes]

If there is additional time following this lesson, have the child choose a game to play.

# Lesson 30: Number Puzzles & Comparing Expressions

## OBJECTIVES:
1. To introduce "number puzzles"
2. To use number sense to compare expressions

## MATERIALS:
1. Worksheet 17, Number Puzzles & Comparing Expressions

## ACTIVITIES FOR TEACHING:

***Warm-up.*** Give the child the worksheet. Tell her to do just the warm-up equations. Solutions are:

$$638\ (8)$$
$$-\ 429\ (6)$$
$$200$$
$$10$$
$$-1$$
$$209\ (2)$$

$$742\ (4)$$
$$-\ 289\ (1)$$
$$500$$
$$-40$$
$$-7$$
$$453\ (3)$$

***Number puzzles.*** Tell the child that you have a "number puzzle" for her. Write the following four numbers with spaces between them as follows:

$$3\ \ 4\ \ 2\ \ 5$$

Explain that she is to make an equation with these numbers, using mathematical symbols such as "=, +, −, ×, ÷." The numbers must stay in the same order.

Write an equals sign between 4 and 2 as shown below.

$$3\ \ 4 = 2\ \ 5$$

Ask: What other symbols do you need to make this expression an equation? [plus signs, $3 + 4 = 2 + 5$] Are the two sides equal now: does $3 + 4$ equal $2 + 5$? [yes]

Next, rewrite the same numbers, but put the equal sign before the 5 as shown.

$$3\ \ 4\ \ 2 = 5$$

Ask: What other symbols do you need to make this an equation? [plus and minus signs, $3 + 4 − 2 = 5$] Are the two sides equal: does $3 + 4 − 2 = 5$? [yes]

***Worksheet 17, Puzzle 1.*** Tell her to find two solutions for the first number puzzle on the worksheet:

$$1\ \ 4\ \ 2\ \ 2$$

Solutions are: $\quad 1 \times 4 = 2 + 2 \quad 1 \times 4 = 2 \times 2$

***Puzzle 2.*** Tell her to find solutions for the second number puzzle on the worksheet:

$$2\ \ 3\ \ 1\ \ 6$$

## EXPLANATIONS:

Subtraction method will vary in the solutions.

Number puzzles are an introduction to algebra in that they emphasize the equality of the two sides of an equation. Finding solutions requires guessing and checking as well as persistence.

See page ii, numbers 3 and 7 of "Some General Thoughts on Teaching Mathematics," for additional information.

There is another solution: $3 = 4 \times 2 − 5$.

| ACTIVITIES FOR TEACHING CONTINUED: | EXPLANATIONS CONTINUED: |

Some solutions are:

$$2 + 3 + 1 = 6 \qquad 2 \times 3 \times 1 = 6 \qquad 2 \times 3 = 1 \times 6$$

**Puzzle 3.** Tell her: You can also use parentheses for number puzzles. Find some solutions for the third number puzzle on the worksheet: 6 2 1 2.

Some solutions are: $6 \times 2 = 12$

$$6 = (2 + 1) \times 2 \qquad 6 = 2 \times (1 + 2) \qquad 6 \div 2 = 1 + 2$$

Calculations inside parentheses are performed first.

**Worksheet 17.** Tell the child to do Problems a-j. Then ask her to explain her reasoning.

a. $384 + 197 + 802 \;\boxed{>}\; 381 + 196 + 799$ **Left side is greater because 384 > 381, 197 > 196, and 802 > 799.**

b. $363 - 236 + 220 \;\boxed{<}\; 363 - 236 + 234$ **Right side is greater because the first two numbers are the same and 220 < 234.**

c. $4765 - 2280 \;\boxed{>}\; 4765 - 2995$ **First number are equal, but 2280 < 2995 and subtracting less on the left side makes the left side greater.**

d. $994 + 994 + 994 \;\boxed{<}\; 994 \times 4$ **Left side is 994 × 3, which is less than 994 × 4.**

e. $45 \times 10 \;\boxed{=}\; 45 \times 5 \times 2$ **Since 10 = 5 × 2, they are equal.**

f. $79 + 81 \;\boxed{=}\; 80 \times 2$ **Since 79 is 1 less than 80 and 81 is 1 more than 80, they total 80 + 80, which is 80 × 2.**

g. $170 \div 2 \;\boxed{>}\; 170 \div 5$ **The left side is larger because dividing by a smaller number gives a larger answer.**

h. $682 \div 3 \;\boxed{<}\; 696 \div 3.$ **When two numbers are divided by 3, the larger number will give greater answer.**

i. $491 - 493 \;\boxed{<}\; 0$ **The left side is −2, which < 0.**

j. $37 \times 80 \times 923 \;\boxed{=}\; 923 \times 80 \times 37$ **They are equal because of the associative property: order does not matter.**

Tell her to complete the worksheet. Solutions are below.

k. $14 \times 68 \;\boxed{>}\; 2 \times 4 \times 68$ **Left side is 14 × 68; right side is 8 × 68, so the left side is greater.**

l. $5716 - 378 \;\boxed{=}\; 5720 - 382$ **Two numbers on the right are 4 more than those on the left. So difference is the same.**

m. $6472 - 2959 \;\boxed{<}\; 6472 - 2859$ **Subtraction on both sides is from 6472. The left side subtracts a larger number, which gives a smaller difference.**

n. $819 \times 3 + 819 \;\boxed{=}\; 819 \times 4$ **Left side is multiplying 819 three times and one more, same as right.**

o. $712 \div 9 \;\boxed{<}\; 712 \div 8$ **Dividing 712 by a larger number, 9, gives a smaller answer compared to dividing by 8.**

**In conclusion.** Ask: Do you always need to do the arithmetic to get the solution? [no]

# LESSON 31: PARTIAL PRODUCTS ON SIDE 2 OF THE ABACUS

## OBJECTIVES:

1. To review (or learn) multiplying on side 2 of the AL Abacus using partial products

## MATERIALS:

1. Worksheet 18, Partial Products on Side 2 of the Abacus
2. AL Abacus

## ACTIVITIES FOR TEACHING:

***Warm-up.*** Give the child the worksheet. Tell her to do just the warm-up equations. Possible solutions are:

| | |
|---|---|
| 1 − 2 = 3 − 4 | 5 = 11 − 6 |
| 12 = 3 × 4 | 5 − 11 = −6 |
| −1 + 2 = −3 + 4 | 5 + 1 = 1 × 6 |
| | 5 × 1 + 1 = 6 |

***Number of days problem.*** Give the child the abacus. Ask: If your brother or sister turned nine years old today, how many days old would they be? What do you need to know to find out? [number the days in a year] Tell the child to write the equation. [*d* = 365 × 9]

Tell the child that you will show her how to do this multiplication on side 2 of the abacus. Say: First write the equation vertically:

$$\begin{array}{r} 365 \\ \times\,9 \\ \hline \end{array}$$

Say: First, we move the beads halfway up on the abacus. Next, enter 365 at the bottom. See the left figure below. Say: Start by multiplying 5 × 9. [45] Remove the 5 by sliding them toward the center and then enter 45. See the right figure below. Write the *partial product* of 45.

## EXPLANATIONS:

Number puzzles are an introduction to algebra in that they emphasize the equality of the two sides of an equation. Finding solutions requires guessing and checking as well as persistence.

There may be additional solutions.

This method of multiplication was taught in the RightStart™ Mathematics Level D.

Having the child write out all the steps for multi-digit multiplication helps her understand the process in preparation for the traditional algorithm.

This process shows the partial products being combined vertically, unlike "lattice multiplication" or Montessori's "checkerboard" multiplication that combine the partial products diagonally.

Only the multiplicand, the quantity that is multiplied by another, is entered; the multiplier is not.

If the multiplicand is not removed, there may not be enough beads to enter the partial product.

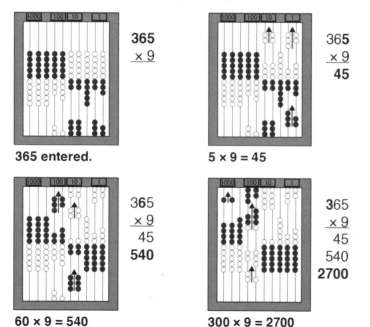

| | |
|---|---|
| 365 entered. | 5 × 9 = 45 |
| 60 × 9 = 540 | 300 × 9 = 2700 |

| ACTIVITIES FOR TEACHING CONTINUED: | EXPLANATIONS CONTINUED: |
|---|---|

Say: Now multiply 60 × 9. [540] Remove the 60 and enter 540. See the left figure at the bottom of the previous page. Write it below the other partial product 45 as shown.

Ask: What do we multiply next? [300 × 9] What is the partial product? [2700] Say: Remove the 3 hundred and enter 2700. Write it below the other partial product. See the last figure on the previous page.

Ask: What do you do to get the final product? [add the partial products] See the figures below. The left figure shows the trading and the right figure shows the solution.

See page ii, number 1 of "Some General Thoughts on Teaching Mathematics," for additional information.

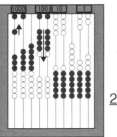

$$
\begin{array}{r}
365 \\
\times 9 \\
\hline
45 \\
540 \\
\underline{2700}
\end{array}
$$

**Trading.**

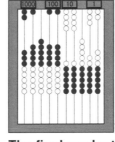

$$
\begin{array}{r}
365 \\
\times 9 \\
\hline
45 \\
540 \\
\underline{2700} \\
\mathbf{3285}
\end{array}
$$

**The final product.**

Ask: What does the answer mean? [the number of days a person has lived when they turn 9 years old]

*If desired, discuss that leap years will actually add 2 (or 3) days to the total.*

**Worksheet 18.** Tell the child to do the same problem on her abacus and to write it on the worksheet.

Tell her to complete the worksheet. The problems and solutions are below.

| 365 | 894 | 1468 | 1376 |
|---|---|---|---|
| × 9 | × 8 | × 5 | × 6 |
| 45 | 32 | 40 | 36 |
| 540 | 720 | 300 | 420 |
| 2700 | 6400 | 2000 | 1800 |
| 3285 | 7152 | 5000 | 6000 |
| | | 7340 | 8256 |

| 5608 | 9876 | 3579 | $51.86 |
|---|---|---|---|
| × 8 | × 9 | × 4 | × 7 |
| 64 | 54 | 36 | 42 |
| 4800 | 630 | 280 | 560 |
| 40000 | 7200 | 2000 | 700 |
| 44,864 | 81000 | 12000 | 35000 |
| | 88,884 | 14,316 | $363.02 |

***In conclusion.*** Ask: If you are multiplying a 3-digit number by 5, how many partial products will you have? [3] If you are multiplying a 7-digit number by 5, how many partial products will you have? [7]

*If there is additional time following this lesson, play the Multiplication Old Main game, found in* Math Card Games *book, P14.*

# LESSON 32: TRADITIONAL MULTIPLYING ON THE ABACUS

**OBJECTIVES:**

1. To learn to multiply traditionally on side 2 of the AL Abacus

**MATERIALS:**

1. Worksheet 19, Traditional Multiplying on the Abacus
2. AL Abacus

**ACTIVITIES FOR TEACHING:**

*Warm-up.* Give the child the worksheet and abacus. Tell her to do just the warm-up equations. Solutions are:

```
  382        639
  × 3        × 2
    6         18
  240         60
  900       1200
 1146       1278
```

*Traditional multiplying.* Explain to the child: Writing down all the partial products like you did in the warm up is a lot of writing. Today you will learn how to just write down the answer, the product. Write:

```
2736
×  3
```

Tell her to watch while you perform the multiplication. Tell her the multiplication is the same, but what is written down is different. Involve the child as much as possible.

Move all the beads to the middle of the abacus and enter 2736 at the bottom. See the left figure below.

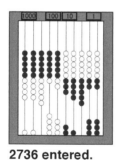

**2736 entered.**

```
2736
×  3
```

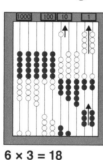

**6 × 3 = 18**

```
2736
×  3
```

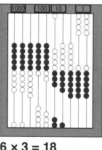

**6 × 3 = 18**

```
   1
2736
×  3
   8
```

Now multiply 6 × 3 by removing the 6 and entering 18 at the top. See the second figure above. Ask: How many ones do we have? [8] Write 8 below the line. Ask: What else do we have? [1 ten] Write 1 above the tens in 2736 as shown under the third figure.

**EXPLANATIONS:**

| ACTIVITIES FOR TEACHING CONTINUED: | EXPLANATIONS CONTINUED: |
|---|---|

Say: Let's multiply the tens next. Remove the 30 from the bottom and multiply 30 × 3. [90] See the left figure below. Ask: How many tens are there altogether? [10] What do we need to do? [trade] Trade and write the 0 tens and the extra hundred as shown under the second figure.

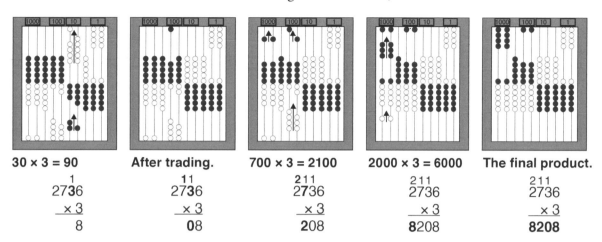

| 30 × 3 = 90 | After trading. | 700 × 3 = 2100 | 2000 × 3 = 6000 | The final product. |
|---|---|---|---|---|
| 1<br>2736<br>× 3<br>8 | 11<br>2736<br>× 3<br>08 | 211<br>2736<br>× 3<br>208 | 211<br>2736<br>× 3<br>8208 | 211<br>2736<br>× 3<br>8208 |

Ask: What do we multiply next? [700] Remove the 700 and multiply 700 × 3. [2100] See the third figure above. Ask: How many hundreds are there altogether? [2] Write the 2 hundred. Ask: What else do we have? [2 thousands] Write the extra 2 above the thousands as shown.

Ask: What do we multiply next? [2000] Remove the 2000 and multiply 2000 × 3. [6000] See the fourth figure above. Ask: How many thousands are there altogether. [8] Write the 8 thousands. The final product, 8208, is shown in the last figure.

***Worksheet 19.*** Tell the child to do the first problem on the worksheet. Then ask her to discuss the answer. Then tell her to complete the worksheet. The solutions are below.

| 11<br>2862<br>× 2<br>5724 | 234<br>1457<br>× 6<br>8742 |
|---|---|
| 322<br>2865<br>× 4<br>11,460 | 2 7<br>1309<br>× 8<br>10,472 |
| 64<br>987<br>× 7<br>6909 | 443<br>2897<br>× 5<br>14,485 |

***In conclusion.*** Ask: Which method do you like better, partial products or the abacus? Why? [Answers will vary.]

If there is additional time following this lesson, play the Multiplication Old Main game, found in *Math Card Games* book, P14.

# LESSON 33: TRADITIONAL MULTIPLYING ON PAPER

**OBJECTIVES:**

1. To multiply 4-digit numbers by a single digit
2. To use check numbers to check multiplication

**MATERIALS:**

1. Worksheet 20, Traditional Multiplying on Paper
2. AL Abacus

| ACTIVITIES FOR TEACHING: | EXPLANATIONS: |
|---|---|
| **Warm-up.** Ask: What is $9 \times 4$? [36] What is $9 \times 4 + 3$? [39] What is $6 \times 7$? [42] What is $6 \times 7 + 3$? [45] What is $8 \times 7$? [56] What is $8 \times 7 + 6$? [62] | |

Ask: What is $3 \times 7 + 2$? [23] What is $2 \times 8 + 4$? [20] What is $5 \times 9 + 5$? [50]

**Comparing different methods.** Give the child the worksheet and abacus. Tell the child to do the three problems in rectangle A on the worksheet. The solutions are below.

| | | |
|---|---|---|
| 3213 | 3213 | 3213 |
| × 3 | 3213 | × 3 |
| 9 | + 3213 | 9639 |
| 30 | 9639 | |
| 600 | | |
| 9000 | | |
| 9639 | | |

For the second problem, encourage the child to use multiplication facts, not skip counting.

The traditional multiplication was taught in the previous lesson on the abacus. Some children may want to use the abacus for the third problem.

Ask: What do you notice about the three problems? [different ways to get the same answer] Ask the child to explain how she did the third problem.

Now tell her to do the problems in rectangle B. The solutions are below.

| | 212 | 212 |
|---|---|---|
| 3849 | 3849 | 3849 |
| × 3 | 3849 | × 3 |
| 27 | + 3849 | 11,547 |
| 120 | 11,547 | |
| 2400 | | |
| 9000 | | |
| 11,547 | | |

Ask: How are these problems different from the first group? [They have trading.] Ask the child to explain how she did the second problem. [First, multiply 9 by 3; then write 7 in the ones place and 2 above the tens.]

It is important that the child understands this addition procedure because it explains why the trade number is added *after* the multiplying. A common multiplication error is adding the trade before multiplying.

| ACTIVITIES FOR TEACHING CONTINUED: | EXPLANATIONS CONTINUED: |
|---|---|

Next, multiply 4 by 3 and then add the 2, getting 14; write 4 in the tens place and 1 above the hundreds. Then, $8 \times 3 + 1$ is 25; write 5 in hundreds place and 2 above the thousands. Lastly, $3 \times 3 + 2$ is 11, which is written in the thousands place.

Ask the child to explain how she did the third problem. It is similar to the addition problem.

**Check numbers for multiplication.** Tell her to do the two problems in rectangle C. Solutions are shown below.

315
4519 (1)
4519 (1)
4519 (1)
4519 (1)
4519 (1)
4519 (1)
 4519 (1)
27,114 (6)

315
4519 (1)
 × 6 (6)
27,114 (6)

Ask: What do you notice about the check numbers for multiplying? [Check numbers of numbers being multiplied equal the check number of the answer.]

**Worksheet 20.** Tell her to complete the worksheet. The solutions are below.

| 1 | 414 | 441 |
|---|---|---|
| 1320 (**6**) | 3829 (**4**) | 4672 (**1**) |
| × 4 (**4**) | × 5 (**5**) | × 6 (**6**) |
| **5280** (**6**) | **19,145** (**2**) | **28,032** (**6**) |

| 13 | 364 | 677 |
|---|---|---|
| 7015 (**4**) | 3375 (**0**) | 5678 (**8**) |
| × 7 (**7**) | × 8 (**8**) | × 9 (**0**) |
| **49,105** (**1**) | **27,000** (**0**) | **51,102** (**0**) |

Answers will vary for the final question.

**In conclusion.** Ask: Which method do you like better— adding the same number or multiplying? Why? [Answers will vary.]

If there is additional time following this lesson, play What's on Top game, found in *Math Card Games* book, P12.

68

# LESSON 34: MULTIPLICATION COMPARISONS

## OBJECTIVES:
1. To understand the difference between addition and multiplication comparisons
2. To solve multiplication comparison problems

## MATERIALS:
1. Worksheet 21, Multiplication Comparisons
2. AL Abacus

## ACTIVITIES FOR TEACHING:

**Warm-up.** Give the child the worksheet. Tell her to do just the warm-up equations. Solutions are:

| 6 | −2 | 9 | 7 |
|----|----|----|----|
| **4** | 8 | **3** | 5 |
| 10 | **10** | **−1** | 1 |
| 0 | 4 | 9 | 7 |

$1 \times 2 \times 2 = 4$

$1 \times 2 + 2 = 4$

$1 \div 2 = 2 \div 4$

**Addition comparisons.** Say: In earlier levels, you solved comparing problems, for example:

Jack had two pails of water and Jill had three more pails than Jack. How many pails of water did Jill have? [5]

Ask: What are the equations? Write it as shown:

$$2 + 3 = 5$$

Tell her these types of problems are called *addition comparison* problems because they use addition.

**Multiplication comparisons.** Say: Today you will solve problems comparing how many times something is compared to something else. For example:

Zoey plays two sports. Zach plays three times as many sports. How many sports does Zach play? [6]

Ask: What is the equation? Write it as shown:

$$2 \times 3 = 6$$

Say: These types of problems are called *multiplication comparison* problems because they use multiplication.

**Comparisons on the abacus.** Give the child the abacus. Tell her to enter 2 and then add 3 more. Ask: What is the equation? [2 + 3 = 5] See the left figure below.

## EXPLANATIONS:

See page ii, number 9 of "Some General Thoughts on Teaching Mathematics," for additional information.

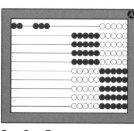

2 + 3 = 5

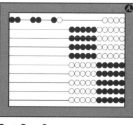

2 × 3 = 6

| ACTIVITIES FOR TEACHING CONTINUED: | EXPLANATIONS CONTINUED: |
|---|---|

Then tell her to clear the abacus and enter 2 three times. Ask: What is the equation? [2 × 3 = 6] See the right figure on the previous page.

Repeat for 1 and four more [5] and 1 that is four times greater. [4] Tell her to write the equations:

$$1 + 4 = 5$$

$$1 × 4 = 4$$

Some students think that two numbers multiplied together is always greater than the same two numbers added together. It is not true in this example.

**Worksheet 21.** Tell her to read the first problem:

1. Sherry is 11 years old. Her grandfather is 7 times older than she is. How old is her grandfather? How much younger is Sherry than her grandfather?

Then tell her to explain it.

$$g = 11 × 7 = 77 \text{ years old}$$

$$77 – 11 = 66 \text{ years younger}$$

**Problem 2.** Tell her to solve the second problem.

2. The Confederation Bridge in Canada is 8 miles long. Lake Pontchartrain Causeway in Louisiana is 24 miles long. How many times longer is the causeway than the bridge? How much longer is the causeway than the bridge?

$$8 × t = 24; t = 3 \text{ times longer}$$

$$24 – 8 = 16 \text{ miles longer}$$

**Problem 3.** Tell her to solve the third problem.

3. At birth an elephant weighs about 100 kg. When it is grown, it weighs 35 times as much. How much is that? How much weight did the baby gain growing up?

$$e = 100 × 35 = 3500 \text{ kg}$$

$$\text{gained: } 3500 – 100 = 3400 \text{ kg}$$

**Problem 4.** Tell her to solve the fourth problem.

4. Harry is 4 ft tall. A foot is 12 times longer than an inch. How tall is Harry in inches?

$$h = 4 × 12 = 48 \text{ in.}$$

**In conclusion.** Ask: When something is so many times greater than something else, do you add or multiply to find the answer? [multiply]

If there is additional time following this lesson, have the child choose a game to play.

# LESSON 35: ASSESSMENT REVIEW 1

## OBJECTIVES:
1. To review concepts learned in previous lessons

## MATERIALS:
1. Worksheet 22, Assessment Review 1
2. AL Abacus, if needed

## ACTIVITIES FOR TEACHING:

**Worksheet 22.** Give the child the worksheet. Tell her that today will be a review for the upcoming assessment. She will complete the two-page worksheet, then discuss the solutions.

Tell her to listen to the problems and write the answers. Read each problem twice.

$43 - 39$  $12 \times 2$  $70 \times 7 + 7$

Tell her to complete the worksheet. Solutions are below and on the next page.

Write only the answers.

  **4**

  **24**

  **497**

Write the answers.

$641 + 273 =$ **914**

$49 +$ **551** $= 600$

$(12 \div 3) + (12 \div 2) =$ **10**

Do the arithmetic. Use check numbers.

| 8374 (**4**) | 7000 (**7**) | 629 (**8**) | 4172 (**5**) |
| + 3558 (**3**) | − 2001 (**3**) | × 4 (**4**) | × 5 (**5**) |
| **11,932 (7)** | **4999 (4)** | **2516 (5)** | **20,860 (7)** |

Multiply and add.
$1 \times 9 + 2 =$ **11**  $12 \times 9 + 3 =$ **111**  $123 \times 9 + 4 =$ **1111**  $1234 \times 9 + 5 =$ **11,111**

Solve the problems.

Sam earned $7.75 on Tuesday and $7.25 on Thursday. Then Sam bought some items. They cost 99¢, $11.05, and $2.15. How much money does Sam have left?

**Sam earned $7.75 + 7.25 = $15.00**
**Spent $.99 + $11.05 + $2.15 = $14.19**
**Sam has: $15.00 − $14.19 = $0.81**

Steel is 8 times heavier than ice. If a cube of ice weighs 23 g, what would the cube weigh if it were made of steel?

**Steel is 8 × ice = 8 × 23**
**= 184 g**

The sun is one hundred forty-nine billion five hundred ninety-seven million eight hundred seventy thousand seven hundred meters from the earth. Write this number with numerals.

**149,597,870,700**

## EXPLANATIONS:

This lesson is a review of concepts learned so far. It is designed to prepare the child for the upcoming assessment lesson.

See page iii, number 17 of "Some General Thoughts on Teaching Mathematics," for additional information.

Space is given to write out the calculations. Some children can do them mentally; others will prefer writing them out.

## ACTIVITIES FOR TEACHING CONTINUED:

Round the populations of the three largest cities in England.

| City in England | Population | Round to nearest thousand. |
|---|---|---|
| London | 9,787,426 | **9,787,000** |
| Manchester | 2,553,379 | **2,553,000** |
| Birmingham | 2,440,986 | **2,441,000** |

Fill in the table.

| | Quotient | Remainder |
|---|---|---|
| 41 ÷ 5 | **8** | **1** |
| 41 ÷ 6 | **6** | **5** |
| 41 ÷ 7 | **5** | **6** |
| 41 ÷ 8 | **5** | **1** |
| 41 ÷ 9 | **4** | **5** |
| 41 ÷ 10 | **4** | **1** |

Complete the magic squares.

| 6 | 4 | **−1** |
|---|---|---|
| − 4 | 3 | 10 |
| **7** | **2** | 0 |

| 1 | 3 | 2 | 6 |
|---|---|---|---|
| 5 | **5** | 3 | −1 |
| **0** | −3 | 7 | **8** |
| 6 | 7 | 0 | **−1** |

Solve the number puzzle two ways using the symbols, =, +, −, ×, ÷.

2 **+** 3 **=** 5 **×** 1

2 **×** 3 **=** 5 **+** 1

Other solutions are possible.

**Worksheet solutions.** Check the answers to the review worksheet with the child. Discuss the various methods for the solutions.

The next lesson will be a day of games. Games review and practice facts and skills in an enjoyable environment.

# LESSON 36: REVIEW GAMES

**OBJECTIVES:**

1. To review recent topics by playing math card games

**MATERIALS:**

1. Math Card Games book, P32, P29, D7, and A60
2. AL Abacus, if needed
3. Short Multiplication Table, Appendix p.1, if needed

---

**ACTIVITIES FOR TEACHING:**

***Warm-up.*** Ask: Is there more than one way to add four-digit numbers? [yes, from the right and from the left] Is there more than one way to subtract four-digit numbers? [yes, from the right, the left, and Terry's way] When something is so many times greater than something else, do you add or multiply to find the answer? [multiply]

Ask: What is 3 − 4? [−1] What is 2 − 4? [−2] What is 44 rounded to the nearest ten? [40] What is 873 rounded to the nearest hundred? [900] What is 561 rounded to the nearest hundred? [600] What is 749 rounded to the nearest hundred? [700]

Ask: What is 9 × 3? [27] What is 9 × 3 + 2? [29] What is 6 × 8? [48] What is 6 × 8 + 3? [51] What is 8 × 5? [40] What is 8 × 5 + 6? [46] What is 3 × 8 + 2? [26] What is 2 × 4 + 3? [11] What is 7 × 9 + 1? [64]

***Ring around the Products game.*** Play the Ring around the Products game found in the *Math Card Games* book, P32. Tell her to use the short multiplication table if she needs it.

***Find the Two Factors game.*** Play the Find the Two Factors game found in Math Card Games book, P29. Players take five basic number cards and replace a card played after a turn.

**EXPLANATIONS:**

This lesson is a review of concepts learned so far by playing games. It is designed to prepare the child for the assessment in the next lesson.

See page iii, number 23 of "Some General Thoughts on Teaching Mathematics," for additional information.

| ACTIVITIES FOR TEACHING CONTINUED: | EXPLANATIONS CONTINUED: |
|---|---|

**Quotient and Remainder game.** Play this variation of Quotient and Remainder game from Math Card Games book, D7. The variation is the card layout. Place the dividend card, the multiplication card, first in the row as shown below.

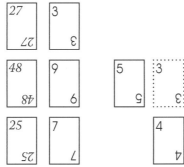

**The completed row is
48 ÷ 9 = 5 r3.**

**Magic Squares Memory.** Play the Magic Squares Memory game, found in Math Card Games book, A60, if there is still time. It may not be necessary to use blank cards for place holders.

**In conclusion.** Ask: What is opposite of addition? [subtraction] What is opposite of subtraction? [addition] What is opposite of multiplication? [division] What is opposite of division? [multiplication]

# LESSON 37: ASSESSMENT 1

## OBJECTIVES:
1. To assess concepts learned in previous lessons

## MATERIALS:
1. Worksheet 23, Assessment 1
2. AL Abacus, if needed

## ACTIVITIES FOR TEACHING:

**Worksheet 23.** Give the child the worksheet.

Tell her to listen to the problems and write the answers. Read each problem twice.

$73 - 68$        $13 \times 2$        $60 \times 6 + 6$

Tell her to complete the worksheet. Solutions are below and on the next page.

## EXPLANATIONS:

---

Write only the answers.

| |
|---|
| **5** |
| **26** |
| **366** |

Write the answers.

$783 + 156 =$ **939**

$51 +$ **649** $= 700$

$(16 \div 8) + (16 \div 4) =$ **6**

Do the arithmetic. Use check numbers.

| 7946 (**8**) | 8000 (**8**) | 847 (**1**) | 5286 (**3**) |
|---|---|---|---|
| + 4565 (**2**) | − 3002 (**5**) | × 4 (**4**) | × 5 (**5**) |
| **12,511 (1)** | **4998 (3)** | **3388 (4)** | **26,430 (6)** |

Multiply and add.

$1 \times 8 + 1 =$ **9**        $12 \times 8 + 2 =$ **98**        $123 \times 8 + 3 =$ **987**        $1234 \times 8 + 4 =$ **9876**

Solve the problems.

Micky earned $5.35 on Tuesday, $6.50 on Wednesday, and $7.65 on Thursday. Then Micky bought 2 items. They cost $5.99 and $12.15. How much money does Micky have left?

**Micky earned**
**$5.35+$6.50+$7.65 = $19.50.**
**Spent $5.99 + $12.15 = $18.14**
**Micky has: $19.50−$18.14=$1.36**

Gold is about 19 times heavier than ice. If a block of ice weighs 8 g, what would the block weigh if it were gold?

**Gold is 19 × ice =**
**19 × 8 = 152 g**

The sun is two billion seven hundred ninety-five million eighty-four thousand eight hundred miles from Neptune. Write this number with numerals.
**2,795,084,800 miles**

## ACTIVITIES FOR TEACHING CONTINUED:

## EXPLANATIONS CONTINUED:

Round the populations of the three largest cities in Scotland.

| City in Scotland | Population | Round to nearest thousand. |
|---|---|---|
| Glasgow | 599,650 | **600,000** |
| Edinburgh | 492,680 | **493,000** |
| Aberdeen | 217,120 | **217,000** |

Fill in the table.

|  | Quotient | Remainder |
|---|---|---|
| 51 ÷ 5 | **10** | **1** |
| 51 ÷ 6 | **8** | **3** |
| 51 ÷ 7 | **7** | **2** |
| 51 ÷ 8 | **6** | **3** |
| 51 ÷ 9 | **5** | **6** |
| 51 ÷ 10 | **5** | **1** |

Complete the magic squares.

| **1** | 0 | 8 |
|---|---|---|
| 10 | 3 | − 4 |
| **−2** | 6 | **5** |

| 1 | 4 | 6 | − 1 |
|---|---|---|---|
| 4 | 0 | **3** | 3 |
| **5** | 8 | **−1** | −2 |
| 0 | **−2** | 2 | 10 |

Solve the number puzzle two ways
using the symbols, =, +, −, ×, ÷.

6 **×** 1 **=** 2 **×** 3

6 **=** 1 **+** 2 **+** 3

Other solutions are possible.

*skipped 9/19*

# REVIEW LESSON 38: DRAWING HORIZONTAL LINES

## OBJECTIVES:

1. To learn to use the T-square
2. To learn to draw horizontal lines with a T-square
3. To review horizontal and diagonal
4. To review polygons

## MATERIALS:

1. Worksheet 24, Drawing Horizontal Lines
2. Drawing board*
3. T-square
4. **Tape**\*\*
5. **Sharp pencil (preferably mechanical) and eraser**

## ACTIVITIES FOR TEACHING:

***Warm-up.*** Ask: What is $4 \times 3$? [12] What is $40 \times 3$? [120] What is $3 \times 4$? [12] What is $30 \times 4$? [120] What is $9 \times 7$? [63] What is $90 \times 7$? [630] What is $7 \times 9$? [63] What is $70 \times 9$? [630]

Ask: What is a horizontal line? [a straight line that goes from side to side] What is a vertical line? [a line that goes straight up and down]

***Worksheet 24 and drawing tools.*** Give the child the worksheet, dry erase board, and T-square. Tell her the dry erase board is now a drawing board. Next show her the T-square and tell her it is called a *T-square.* Ask: Why do you think it is called a T-square? [looks like the letter T] Is this the same reason a certain shirt is called a T-shirt? [yes]

**T-square.**

***Taping the worksheet.*** Demonstrate taping the worksheet to the drawing board as follows: Place the T-square along a side of the board. Then look for a horizontal line on the worksheet. One possibility is the upper edge of the second octagon. Then position the worksheet so this horizontal line aligns with the top edge of the T-square. See the figure below.

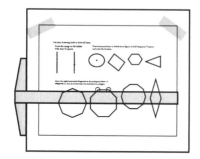

**Aligning and taping the worksheet to the drawing board.**

Hold the paper in place while taping the top two corners.

***T-square position.*** For a right-handed user, the T-square is placed along the left side of the board. For a left-handed user, the T-square is placed along the right side. See the figures on the next page.

## EXPLANATIONS:

This review lesson is designed for children with no experience using the drawing tools.

\* The dry erase board is also the drawing board.

\*\* The best tape is 3M's Removable Tape, which can be reused several times and doesn't tear the corners of the paper.

Teaching geometry with a drawing board, T-square, and triangles helps the child learn the informal, practical side of geometry. It also helps develop coordination, which improves with practice.

If this worksheet is bound in the child's worksheets, it needs to be removed.

The little white dots shown here indicate where to align the T-square, however they do not appear on the worksheet.

Tape is not used at the bottom corners because it interferes with moving the T-square.

| ACTIVITIES FOR TEACHING CONTINUED: | EXPLANATIONS CONTINUED: |
|---|---|

**T-square position for right-handed user.**

**T-square position for left-handed user.**

***Drawing horizontal lines.*** Say: Use the T-square to draw horizontal lines. It slides up and down the side of the board. Hold it tight against the board with one hand while you draw the line with your dominant (writing) hand along the top of the T-square.

Tell the child to check every time before drawing a line to be sure the T-square is hugging the board.

Say: Look at the first figure on the worksheet. Draw horizontal lines to make the rungs on a ladder. The little white dots tell you where to align your T-square. All lines must be drawn with the T-square.

***Polygons and diagonals.*** After she has drawn the rungs on the ladder, say: There are eight figures on your worksheet; seven of them are *polygons*. A polygon is a flat closed figure made with straight lines. Ask: Which figure is not a polygon? [the first figure, an ellipse] Do you notice anything special about the first two polygons in the second row? [same figure, but oriented differently]

Tell her to read and follow the instructions on the worksheet. Stress that she must use her T-square to draw all the lines, which will be horizontal.

Solutions are shown below.

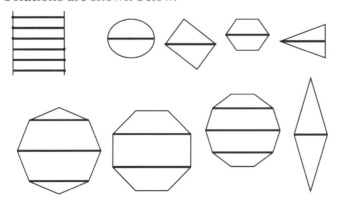

***In conclusion.*** Ask: What do you have to check before drawing a horizontal line? [that the T-square is touching the edge of the board] What is a diagonal line? [a line between any two vertices in a polygon]

See page ii, number 6 of "Some General Thoughts on Teaching Mathematics," for additional information.

If there is additional time following this lesson, play the Ring Around the Products game, found in *Math Card Games* book, P32.

# REVIEW LESSON 39: DRAWING LINES WITH THE TRIANGLES

## OBJECTIVES:

1. To learn to use the 45 triangle and the 30-60 triangle with the T-square
2. To review vertical
3. To draw the diagonals in a hexagon

## MATERIALS:

1. Worksheet 25, Drawing Lines with the Triangles
2. Drawing board, T-square, 45 triangle and 30-60 triangle
3. **Tape**

| ACTIVITIES FOR TEACHING: | EXPLANATIONS: |
|---|---|

**ACTIVITIES FOR TEACHING:**

***Warm-up.*** Ask: What is a horizontal line? [a straight line that goes from side to side] What is a vertical line? [a line that goes straight up and down] What is a polygon? [a closed figure with straight lines] What is a diagonal line? [a line between any two vertices in a polygon]

***Drawing vertical lines.*** Give the child the worksheet, drawing board, T-square, and triangles. Tell the child to tape her worksheet to the board.

Say: Today you will draw vertical and other lines using a T-square and both triangles. To draw these lines, the triangle needs to hug the T-square while the T-square hugs the board.

Demonstrate how to hold the tools in place use the following procedure (for right-handers) with the 45 triangle as shown on the right:

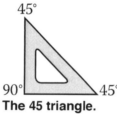

45°

90°          45°

**The 45 triangle.**

1. The left hand puts the T-square below the starting point and holds it in place. See the left figure below.

2. The right hand moves the 45 triangle toward the correct place on the T-square. See right figure below.

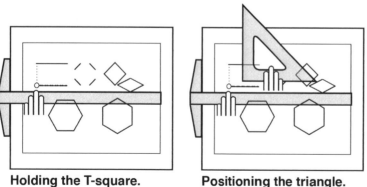

**Holding the T-square.**          **Positioning the triangle.**

3. Both hands hold the tools momentarily. See the left figure on the next page.

4. The left hand takes over holding both tools, see the right figure on the next page.

**EXPLANATIONS:**

This review lesson is designed for children with no experience using the drawing tools.

If this worksheet is bound in the child's worksheets, it needs to be removed.

The T-square must be below the starting point in order to draw a precise line.

The little white dot indicates where to align the triangle.

When appropriate, demonstrate this procedure for the child who is left-handed with the T-square on the right.

**ACTIVITIES FOR TEACHING CONTINUED:**　　　　**EXPLANATIONS CONTINUED:**

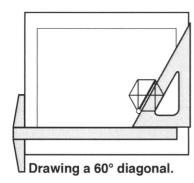

**Each hand holds a tool.**

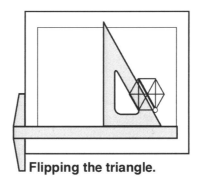

**One hand holds both tools.**

**Worksheet 25.** For the first problem on the worksheet, tell the child to draw vertical lines to make the slats for the fence. Say: The little white dots tell you where to align your triangle. All lines must be made with your T-square and the 45 triangle. You will need to flip your triangle to draw some of the lines in the octagon. An example of flipping a triangle is shown in the two left figures below. Tell her to do the Problems 1 to 4 on the worksheet. Solutions are shown at the right.

Some children find it helpful to place their triangle on the small figure to determine its correct orientation.

**Drawing the 60° lines.** Holding the 30-60 triangle, point to the 60° angle and tell her to look at Problem 5 on her worksheet. Ask: Do you see any diagonals that you could draw with this angle? [yes] See the left figure below. To draw the second diagonal, the triangle needs to be flipped as shown in the second figure below.

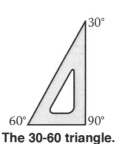

30°

60°　　90°

**The 30-60 triangle.**

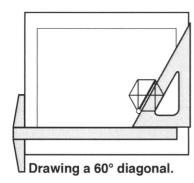
**Drawing a 60° diagonal.**

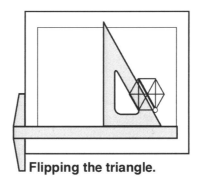
**Flipping the triangle.**

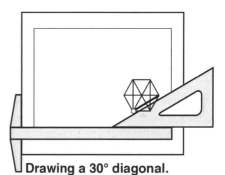
**Drawing a 30° diagonal.**

**Drawing the 30° lines.** Point to the 30° on the triangle. Ask: Do you see any diagonals that you could draw with this edge? [yes] See the right figure above.

**Worksheet 25.** Tell her to complete the worksheet. The solution to Problem 5 is shown at the right.

**In conclusion.** Ask: What do you have to check before drawing a line with a triangle? [that the T-square is hugging the edge of the board and the triangle is hugging the T-square]

# REVIEW LESSON 40: BASIC FRACTIONS

## OBJECTIVES:

1. To review basic fractions
2. To review that fractions can be equal to, or greater than 1

## MATERIALS:

1. Fraction chart
2. Fraction pieces
3. *Math Card Games* book, F3

---

| ACTIVITIES FOR TEACHING: | EXPLANATIONS: |
|---|---|

***Warm-up.*** Ask: Where is the T-square when using a triangle? [below the starting point] What do you have to check before drawing a line with a triangle? [that the T-square is hugging the edge of the board and the triangle is hugging the T-square]

***Reviewing the fraction chart.*** Give the child the fraction chart and fraction chart pieces. Tell her to use her pieces to build the fraction chart alongside, but not on top of, the chart. See the figure below.

See page ii, number 9 of "Some General Thoughts on Teaching Mathematics," for additional information.

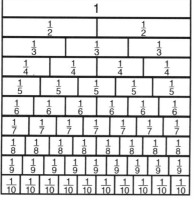

**The fraction chart.**

With the exception of one-half, the fraction names are the same as the ordinal numbers: third, fourth, fifth, sixth, and so on.

Ask: When you divide the 1 into two equal parts, what do you have? [one half] Write $\frac{1}{2}$ and point to the parts of the fraction while saying "one, divided by, two." See the figure at the right.

$$\frac{1}{2} \begin{cases} \text{one} \\ \text{divided by} \\ \text{two} \end{cases}$$

Ask: What do you have when you divide the 1 into three equal parts? [one third] Write $\frac{1}{3}$, point to the parts, and ask what they mean. [one, divided by, three]

The concept of fractions as division is fundamental to algebra.

Repeat for dividing the 1 into four parts. [one fourth; one, divided by, four]

---

## ACTIVITIES FOR TEACHING CONTINUED:

**The stairs.** Tell her to find and set aside ten fraction pieces, one piece of each size. Then tell her to build the stairs by setting the 1 at the bottom, the $\frac{1}{2}$ above it, keeping the left edges even. See the figure on the right. Continue with $\frac{1}{3}$ all the way to $\frac{1}{10}$.

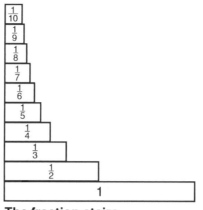

**The fraction stairs.**

With the stairs completed, ask if she could climb such stairs. Ask: Why not? [The top steps are too small to stand on.] Tell her: This curve is called a *hyperbola*.

Ask: Which is more, 2 or 3? [3] Tell her to look at her fraction stairs and ask: Which is more, $\frac{1}{2}$ or $\frac{1}{3}$? [$\frac{1}{2}$] Which is more, 4 or 5? [5] But which is more, $\frac{1}{4}$ or $\frac{1}{5}$? [$\frac{1}{4}$] Which is more, 6 or 8? [8] But which is more, $\frac{1}{6}$ or $\frac{1}{8}$? [$\frac{1}{6}$] Ask: Why is this true? [When something is divided into more pieces, the pieces are smaller.]

Tell her to look at her fraction chart. Then ask: How many thirds do you need to make a whole? [3] How many fourths do you need to make one? [4] How many fifths do you need to make a whole? [5]

**Non-unit fractions.** Say: Suppose you have a granola bar that you want to split among three children. Ask: How much will each one get? [one third] What is 1 divided by 3? [one third]

Say: Suppose you have two granola bars that you want to split among three children. Ask: How much will each one get? [two thirds] What is 2 divided by 3? [two thirds] Say: two thirds and write:

$$\text{two } \tfrac{1}{3}\text{s is } \tfrac{2}{3}$$

Tell the child to look at her fraction chart. Ask: If you have $\frac{2}{5}$, how many more fifths do you need to equal 1? [$\frac{3}{5}$] If you have $\frac{5}{8}$, how many more eighths do you need to equal 1? [$\frac{3}{8}$] What do you need with $\frac{1}{7}$ to make a whole? [$\frac{6}{7}$]

**Concentrating on One game.** Play the Concentrating on One game, found in the *Math Card Games* book, F3.

**In conclusion.** Ask: What is another name for one divided by two? [one-half] What is another name for two divided by five? [two-fifths] What is three divided by four? [three fourths]

## EXPLANATIONS CONTINUED:

The child is not expected to learn the term *hyperbola* at this point. She will meet it again when she studies algebra.

If there is additional time following this lesson, play the Quotient and Remainder game, found in *Math Card Games* book, D7.

# LESSON 41: EQUIVALENT FRACTIONS

## OBJECTIVES:

1. To find equivalent fractions using drawing tools
2. To learn the word *terms* as related to fractions

## MATERIALS:

1. Worksheet 26, Equivalent Fractions
2. Drawing board, T-square, and 30-60 triangle
3. **Tape***

## ACTIVITIES FOR TEACHING:

***Warm-up.*** Ask: When you divide one into two equal parts, what do you have? [one half] What is another name for one divided by two? [one half] What is another name for one divided by four? [one fourth] What is another name for three divided by four? [three fourths] What is another name for two divided by three? [two-thirds]

***Worksheet 26.*** Give the child the worksheet. Ask: What does the top half of the sheet show? [two fraction charts] What pattern do you notice about the size of the pieces? [the greater the number, the smaller the piece] Which is largest and which is smallest? [1 is largest and $\frac{1}{10}$ is smallest] Why is $\frac{1}{10}$ less than $\frac{1}{9}$? [Dividing something into 10 pieces means each piece must be smaller than if it was divided into 9 pieces.]

Write:                    $\frac{2}{5}$

and ask the child to read it. [two fifths] Ask: What does it mean? [two $\frac{1}{5}$s or 2 divided into 5 pieces]

***Equivalent fractions.*** Give the child the drawing board, T-square, and triangle. Tell the child to align the worksheet with the T-square, and then tape the upper corners to the drawing board. See the left figure below.

Ask: How many fourths equal one half? [2] How many sixths equal one half? [3] How could you use the triangle to find all the halves? See the left figure below.

## EXPLANATIONS:

*The best tape is 3M's Removable Tape, which can be reused several times and doesn't tear the corners of the paper.

If this worksheet is bound in the child's worksheets, it needs to be removed.

Tape is not used at the bottom corners because it interferes with moving the T-square.

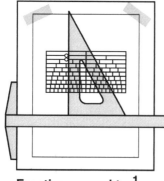

Fractions equal to $\frac{1}{2}$.

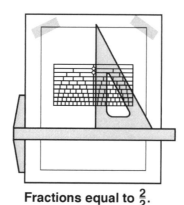

Fractions equal to $\frac{2}{2}$.

| **ACTIVITIES FOR TEACHING CONTINUED:** | **EXPLANATIONS CONTINUED:** |
|---|---|

Write the fractions as the child names them:

$$\frac{1}{2} \quad \frac{2}{4} \quad \frac{3}{6} \quad \frac{4}{8} \quad \frac{5}{10}$$

What pattern do you see? [The upper number is half of the lower number.] Tell her the two numbers in a fraction are called *terms*. Ask: Which of these fractions has the lowest numbers, called the *lowest terms*? $[\frac{1}{2}]$

See page iii, number 18 of "Some General Thoughts on Teaching Mathematics," for additional information.

Tell the child to move her triangle to show two halves. See the right figure on the previous page. Ask: What other fractions equal two halves?

$$\frac{2}{2} \quad \frac{3}{3} \quad \frac{4}{4} \quad \frac{5}{5} \quad \frac{6}{6} \quad \frac{7}{7} \quad \frac{8}{8} \quad \frac{9}{9} \quad \frac{10}{10}$$

Ask: What other fractions are equal to $\frac{3}{9}$? Write them:

$$\frac{3}{9} \quad \frac{1}{3} \quad \frac{2}{6}$$

Ask: Which of these fractions has the lowest terms? $[\frac{1}{3}]$ What other fractions are equal to $\frac{9}{6}$?

$$\frac{9}{6} \quad \frac{3}{2} \quad \frac{6}{4} \quad \frac{12}{8} \quad \frac{15}{10}$$

Ask: Which fraction has the lowest terms? $[\frac{3}{2}]$

***Fraction number line.*** Draw a horizontal line and label it with a 0 and 1 as shown below.

Ask: Where would you put a mark for 2? Ask the child to make the mark and write the number. Continue for $\frac{1}{2}$, $\frac{1}{4}$, $\frac{3}{4}$, $1\frac{1}{2}$, and $\frac{5}{4}$. See below.

***Worksheet 26.*** Tell the child to do the worksheet. The solutions are below.

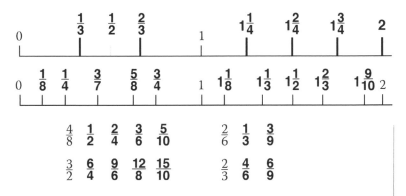

***In conclusion.*** Ask: Which fraction is in lowest terms, one half or four eighths? [one-half] Which is more, three halves or one and a half? [same]

If there is additional time following this lesson, play the Magic Squares Memory game, found in *Math Card Games* book, A60.

# LESSON 42: HALVES OF HALVES

## OBJECTIVES:

1. To find halves of a line
2. To find halves of geometric figures

## MATERIALS:

1. Worksheet 27, Halves of Halves
2. Drawing board, T-square, 30-60 triangle, and 45 triangle
3. **Tape**

---

| ACTIVITIES FOR TEACHING: | EXPLANATIONS: |
|---|---|
| **Warm-up.** Ask: What is another name for one divided into two equal parts? [one half] How many one fourths equal one half? [2] Which fraction, one half or two fourths, is in the lowest terms? [one half] Which fraction, one fourth or two eighths, is in the lowest terms? [one fourth] | |
| **Finding one-half.** Give the child the worksheet, drawing board, and drawing tools. Tell the child to tape the worksheet to the drawing board. Demonstrate the procedure for finding half of the line as follows. First align the triangle at the right end of the line as shown in the first figure below. Draw a small line near the estimated halfway point. Tell her that small line is called a *tick mark*. See the first figure below. | If this worksheet is bound in the child's workbook, it needs to be removed. |
| Next the triangle is flipped over and the procedure is repeated from the left end of the line. See the second figure. Then the one-half mark is drawn from the intersection of the tick marks. See the third figure. | The little white dots shown here indicate where to align the triangle. |

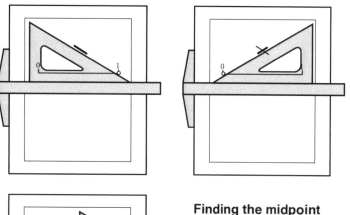

**Finding the midpoint of a line using drawing tools.**

| ACTIVITIES FOR TEACHING CONTINUED: | EXPLANATIONS CONTINUED: |
|---|---|

**Worksheet 27.** Tell the child to do the first problem on the worksheet. The solutions are below.

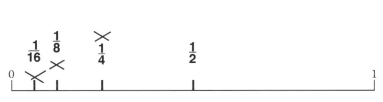

Ask: What is half of one half? [one fourth] What is half of one fourth? [one eighth] What is half of one eighth? [one sixteenth]

**Problem 2.** Tell the child to read the second problem. Ask: Which triangle do you need to use? [45 triangle] Tell her to think how she could draw the divisions using diagonals. Tell her to do it on the worksheet. The solutions are below.

Some children might need to sketch what they think the solutions might look like.

Other solutions are possible.

**Problem 3.** Tell her to read the third problem. Ask: Which triangle do you need to use this time? [30-60 triangle] Remind her to look at the little figures that have hints. Say: For the triangle divided into fourths, you need to find the midpoint of the base line. Ask: How could you draw the tick mark? [pretend to divide the triangle in half with a vertical line]

Tell her to think how she could divide the triangles. Tell her to finish the worksheet. The solutions are below.

Some children might need to sketch what they think the solutions might look like.

There are other solutions for the halves and eighths may be rotated.

**In conclusion.** Ask: What is one half of one eighth? [one sixteenth] What is one fourth of one fourth? [one sixteenth]

If there is additional time following this lesson, play the Double the Fraction Memory game, found in *Math Card Games* book, F5.

# LESSON 43: FRACTIONS CLOSEST TO

### OBJECTIVES:

1. To become more familiar with the fraction chart
2. To find fractions closest to zero, one half, or one

### MATERIALS:

1. Fraction chart
2. 30-60 triangle
3. Fraction cards (without the percent cards and the 1s)

---

### ACTIVITIES FOR TEACHING:

***Warm-up.*** Ask: What is another name for one divided into two equal parts? [one half] What is one half of one half? [one fourth] How many one fourths equal one half? [2]

Ask: What is another name for one divided into three equal parts? [one third] What is one half of one third? [one sixth] How many one sixths equal one third? [2]

***Naming fractions closest to zero.*** Give the child the fraction chart and the 30-60 triangle. Tell the child to use the triangle as shown with the fraction chart and find the five fractions that are closest to zero. [$\frac{1}{10}, \frac{1}{9}, \frac{1}{8}, \frac{1}{7}, \frac{1}{6}$] See the left figure below.

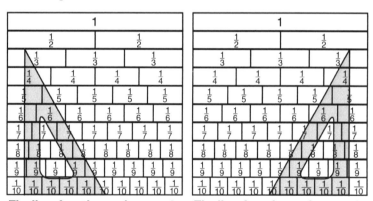

Finding fractions close to 0.     Finding fractions close to 1.

***Naming fractions closest to one.*** Now tell her to find the five fractions closest to one. [$\frac{9}{10}, \frac{8}{9}, \frac{7}{8}, \frac{6}{7}, \frac{5}{6}$] See the right figure above.

***Naming fractions closest to one half.*** Tell her to find and name the five fractions that are half of a whole, or one. [$\frac{1}{2}, \frac{2}{4}, \frac{3}{6}, \frac{4}{8}, \frac{5}{10}$] See the left figure on the next page.

Next, tell her to name fractions pairs that are closest to, but not equal to, one half. [$\frac{5}{9}$ and $\frac{4}{9}$, $\frac{4}{7}$ and $\frac{3}{7}$, $\frac{3}{5}$ and $\frac{2}{5}$, $\frac{6}{10}$ and $\frac{4}{10}$, $\frac{5}{8}$ and $\frac{3}{8}$, $\frac{2}{6}$ and $\frac{4}{6}$] See the right figure on the next page.

### EXPLANATIONS:

See page ii, number 9, and page iii, number 43, of "Some General Thoughts on Teaching Mathematics," for additional information.

---

**ACTIVITIES FOR TEACHING CONTINUED:**

**EXPLANATIONS CONTINUED:**

| | 1 | |
|---|---|---|

Fractions equal to one half.

Fractions close to one half.

***Fraction Closest To game.*** Demonstrate how to play the Fraction Closest To game. Use a set of fraction cards but no 1s or percents. To start, each player takes four cards. After each turn, players pick up enough cards to again have four.

The first player decides which of the three possibilities to call: Closest to Zero, Closest to One Half, or Closest to One. All players then play their card having the fraction closest to what is called. The player laying down the card with the closest fraction collects all the cards. In the event of a tie, everyone plays another card closest to what was called. The player playing the closest card this time takes all the cards.

For example, if the player calls Closest to One Half, players lay down their cards closest to one half. See the figure below.

**The $\frac{3}{5}$ card is closest to $\frac{1}{2}$.**

Then the player to the left takes a turn. She will call one of the three possibilities: Closest to Zero, Closest to One Half, or Closest to One. The players will then play their closest card to what is called.

Play continues until the cards are gone. The winner is the player with the most cards, which can be determined by comparing the heights of the stacks of collected cards.

***In conclusion.*** Ask: Which fraction is closer to one, five sixths or three fourths? [five sixths] Which fraction is closer to one half, two fifths or three fifths? [the same] Which fraction is closer to zero, one fifth or one sixth? [one sixth]

Rather than removing the cards with 1s beforehand, they can be set aside during play.

# LESSON 44: SKETCHING FRACTIONS

## OBJECTIVES:
1. To sketch and shade fractions freehand
2. To find some equivalent fractions

## MATERIALS:
1. Worksheet 28, Sketching Fractions

---

| ACTIVITIES FOR TEACHING: | EXPLANATIONS: |
|---|---|

**Warm-up.** Give the child the worksheet. Tell her to do just the warm-up equations. Solutions are:

| 2 | 4 | 2 | 14 |
|---|---|---|---|
| 27 **(0)** | 46 **(1)** | 94 **(4)** | 129 **(3)** |
| × 3 **(3)** | × 8 **(8)** | × 6 **(6)** | × 5 **(5)** |
| 81 **(0)** | 368 **(8)** | 564 **(6)** | 645 **(6)** |

**Sketching fractions.** Draw a rectangle as shown below. Ask: How could we divide this rectangle into fourths, using vertical lines? [first divide it into halves and divide those halves into half again]

Explain the procedure as follows: First make tick marks at the estimated halfway mark. Next make tick marks at the halfway marks again. Then draw the lines. See the process below.

| | |
|---|---|
| **A tick mark at the half.** | **Tick marks at the fourths.** |
| **The fourths drawn.** | **One fourth crosshatched.** |

If an adjustment needs to be made, tick marks are easier to erase than an entire line.

Ask: How much is one fourth? [one of the four sections] Tell her we will show it by crosshatching. Explain that crosshatching means drawing parallel lines at 45°. Draw them from the lower left to the upper right.

**Finding one third.** Tell the child that estimating one third is a little trickier than estimating one half. Draw another rectangle. Say: We want to put the tick mark so one space is twice the other space. See below.

Those who are left-handed will find crosshatching easier by drawing from the lower right to the upper left.

**To estimate one third,**
**b needs to be twice a.**

| **ACTIVITIES FOR TEACHING CONTINUED:** | **EXPLANATIONS CONTINUED:** |
|---|---|

Tell her to make the tick marks and adjust if necessary. Then draw the lines. Ask: How much is one third? [one of the three section] Say: Crosshatch one third.

***Worksheet 28.*** Tell the child to do the first three problems. Solutions are below.

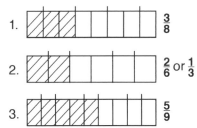

1. $\frac{3}{8}$

2. $\frac{2}{6}$ or $\frac{1}{3}$

3. $\frac{5}{9}$

Then tell her to complete the worksheet. The solutions are below.

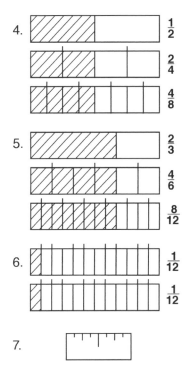

4. $\frac{1}{2}$

   $\frac{2}{4}$

   $\frac{4}{8}$

5. $\frac{2}{3}$

   $\frac{4}{6}$

   $\frac{8}{12}$

6. $\frac{1}{12}$

   $\frac{1}{12}$

7.

Problem 7 results in constructing a one-inch ruler. You might want the child to compare it to a ruler.

***In conclusion.*** Ask: How many fourths do you need to make one half? [2] How many sixths do you need to make one half? [3] What fraction do you get if you divide something in half, then divide it in half two more times? [one eighth]

Some children are amazed that this procedure results in 1 inch on a ruler.

If there is additional time following this lesson, play the Fraction Closest To game from Lesson 43.

# LESSON 45: FRACTIONS TOTALING ONE

## OBJECTIVES:

1. To become more familiar with the size of fractions
2. To become more familiar with adding fractions to total 1

## MATERIALS:

1. Fraction chart
2. *Math Card Games* book, F6

## ACTIVITIES FOR TEACHING:

***Warm-up.*** Ask: How many one fourths do you need to make 1? [4] How many one fourths do you need to make one half? [2] How many one eighths do you need to make 1? [8] How many one eighths do you need to make one half? [4] How many one eighths do you need to make one fourth? [2] What fraction do you get if divide something in half, then divide it in half two more times? [one eighth]

***Fractions equaling one.*** Give the child the fraction chart shown below.

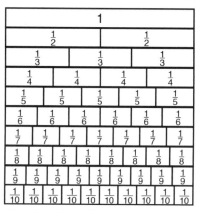

**The fraction chart.**

Write: $$1 = \frac{2}{3} + \underline{\quad}$$

Tell the child to look at her fractions chart and ask: What fraction do you need with $\frac{2}{3}$ to make 1? [$\frac{1}{3}$] Remind the child to refer to her fraction chart.

## EXPLANATIONS:

| ACTIVITIES FOR TEACHING CONTINUED: | EXPLANATIONS CONTINUED: |

Write another equation:

$$1 = \frac{1}{4} + \frac{1}{2} + \underline{\quad}$$

Ask: What fraction do you need to complete this equation? [$\frac{1}{4}$] How do you know? [Two fourths make one half, so another fourth is needed.]

Write: $\qquad 1 = \frac{1}{10} + \frac{1}{2} + \frac{1}{10} + \underline{\quad}$

Ask: What fraction do you need to complete this equation? [$\frac{3}{10}$] How do you know? [The two one tenths make two tenths, but five tenths is needed for the other half, so three tenths more is needed.]

**The One game.** Play the game of One, found in *Math Card Games* book, F6.

**In conclusion.** Ask: If you have three fourths, how many eighths do you need to make one? [2] If you have two thirds, how many sixths do you need to make one? [2] If you have seven eighths, how many eighths do you need to make one? [1]

# LESSON 46: WHOLE NUMBER PLUS A FRACTION

**OBJECTIVES:**
1. To work with mixed numbers
2. To add fractions informally

**MATERIALS:**
1. Worksheet 29, Whole Number Plus a Fraction
2. Fraction chart

| ACTIVITIES FOR TEACHING: | EXPLANATIONS: |
|---|---|

**Warm-up.** Give the child the worksheet. Tell her to do just the warm-up equations. Solutions are:

| | | | |
|---|---|---|---|
| 4982 **(5)** | 4982 **(5)** | 498 **(3)** | 2894 **(5)** |
| + 2894 **(5)** | − 2894 **(5)** | × 4 **(4)** | × 7 **(7)** |
| **7876 (1)** | **2088 (0)** | **1992 (3)** | **20,258 (8)** |

**Drawing a rectangle 2 times longer.** Draw the rectangle as shown below. Explain that this rectangle represents one.

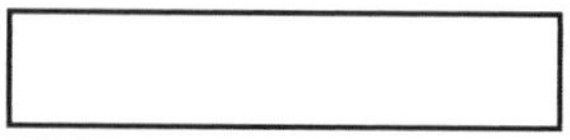

**This rectangle represents 1.**

Ask the child to draw and crosshatch a rectangle two times longer. [Draw a second rectangle the same size next to the first.] See the figure below.

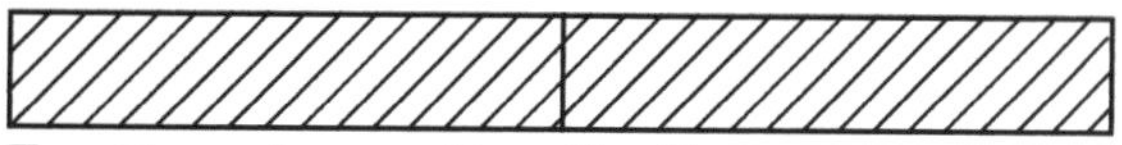

**Two times longer than the first rectangle.**

**Drawing a rectangle $1\frac{1}{2}$ times longer.** Draw another double rectangle. Ask the child to show one and a half by crosshatching. See the figure below.

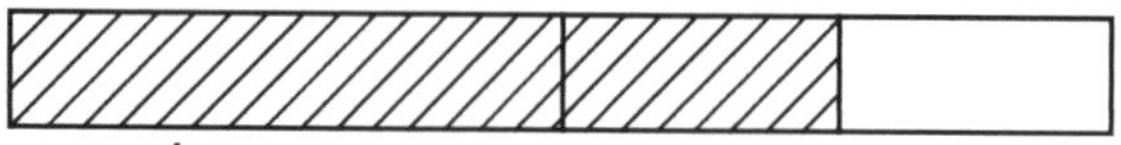

**1 and $\frac{1}{2}$ crosshatched.**

**Drawing a rectangle $1\frac{3}{4}$ times longer.** Draw a third double rectangle. Ask the child to crosshatch one and three fourths. See the figure below.

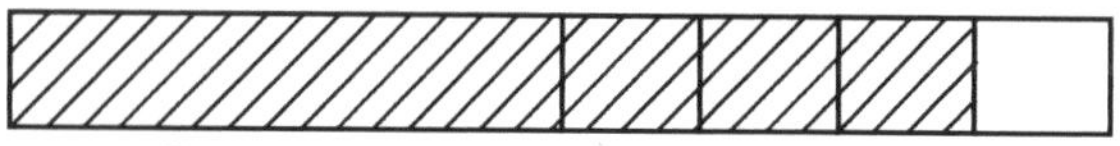

**1 and $\frac{3}{4}$ crosshatched.**

**ACTIVITIES FOR TEACHING CONTINUED:**

**EXPLANATIONS CONTINUED:**

**Worksheet 29.** Give the child the fraction chart. Tell the child to do the worksheet. Solutions are below.

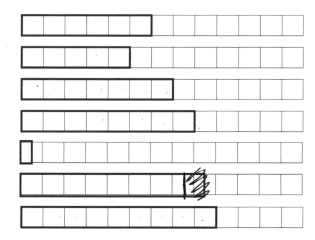

8. $\dfrac{1}{8}$    9. $\dfrac{1}{4}$    10. $\dfrac{2}{5}$

11. $\dfrac{1}{2}$    12. $\dfrac{1}{2}$

13. $\dfrac{7}{10}$    14. $\dfrac{3}{8}$

15. $\dfrac{1}{8}$    16. $\dfrac{1}{3}$

**In conclusion.** Ask: If a whole is 3 squares, how many squares do you need to make two wholes? [6] If a whole is 3 squares, how many squares do you need to make two thirds? [2] If a whole is 3 squares, how many squares do you need to make one and two thirds? [5]

If there is additional time following this lesson, play the One game, found in *Math Card Games* book, F6.

# LESSON 47: A FRACTION OF TWELVE

**OBJECTIVES:**

1. To learn the terms *numerator* and *denominator*
2. To practice finding a fraction of 12

**MATERIALS:**

1. Decks of basic number cards
2. *Math Card Games* book, F10

| ACTIVITIES FOR TEACHING: | EXPLANATIONS: |
|---|---|
| **Warm-up.** Ask: If a whole is 4 squares, how many squares do you need to make one half? [2] If a whole is 4 squares, how many squares do you need to make two wholes? [8] If a whole is 4 squares, how many squares do you need to make three wholes? [12] | |

Ask: If a whole is 6 squares, how many squares do you need to make one half? [3] If a whole is 6 squares, how many squares do you need to make two wholes? [12]

**The terms numerator and denominator.** Write:

$$\frac{1}{3}$$

Say: The two terms in a fraction have names. The bottom term, which tells us what to divide by, is called the *denominator*. It starts with a "d" just like "divide."

Say: The top term tells the number of parts and is called the *numerator*. The word "numerator" is related to the word "number."

Write the following as a reference and to help the child who thinks visually.

$$\underline{numerator} \atop denominator$$

**A fraction of 12.** Give the child the decks of basic number cards. Tell her to lay out 12 cards face down in a row as shown below.

**Twelve cards laid out.**

Cards are used here because they will be used later in a game.

Write: $\frac{1}{3}$

and ask her to find that fraction of the cards. [4] See the figure below.

**12 cards grouped in thirds, showing $\frac{1}{3}$ of 12 is 4.**

Guide the child to make three equal groups using the 12 cards and note how many cards are in each group.

**ACTIVITIES FOR TEACHING CONTINUED:**   |   **EXPLANATIONS CONTINUED:**

Ask: How much is one-third of 12? [4] Write:

$$\tfrac{1}{3} \text{ of } 12 = 4$$

Say: Change the numerator to 2, and now find two-thirds of 12. [8] Ask for an explanation. [two thirds is twice one third, or $4 \times 2 = 8$] See the figure below.

**12 cards grouped in thirds, showing $\frac{2}{3}$ of 12 is 8.**

Write:                          $\tfrac{2}{3}$ of 12 = 8

Repeat the process for $\tfrac{3}{4}$. See the figures below.

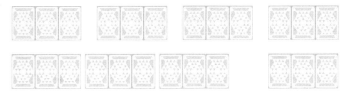

**Finding $\frac{3}{4}$ of 12, which is 9**

Repeat for $\tfrac{5}{6}$. See the figures below.

**Finding $\frac{5}{6}$ of 12, which is 10.**

***Fraction of Twelve game.*** Play the Fraction of Twelve game found in *Math Card Games* book, F10, twice. For the first game, lay the cards out in a row as done in the first part of the lesson. For the second game, lay the cards in a 4 by 3 array or a 6 by 2 array. See below.

**The 4 by 3 array.**

**The 6 by 2 array.**

***In conclusion.*** Ask: In the fraction one half, what is the denominator? [2] In the fraction one half, what number is the numerator? [1] If the denominator and numerator are the same, what does the fraction equal? [1]

# LESSON 48: REVIEW AND GAMES 3

## OBJECTIVES:

1. To review recent topics
2. To develop skills through playing math card games

## MATERIALS:

1. Worksheet 30-A or 30-B, Review 4
2. *Math Card Games* book, F6

---

| **ACTIVITIES FOR TEACHING:** | **EXPLANATIONS:** |
|---|---|

***Worksheet 30-A.*** Give the child the worksheet. Tell her to listen to the problems and write the answers. Read each problem twice.

$56 \times 100$ $\qquad$ $199 + 38$ $\qquad$ $80 \times 8$

Tell her to complete the worksheet. Solutions are below.

Ask the child to correct any errors during the lesson.

Write only the answers.

 **5600**

**237**

**640**

Write the answers.

 $746 + 84 =$ **830**

$45 +$ **955** $= 1000$

$2\frac{2}{5} + 1\frac{3}{5} =$ **4**

Do the arithmetic. Use check numbers.

$\begin{array}{r} 24{,}479\ (\mathbf{8}) \\ +\ 37{,}548\ (\mathbf{0}) \\ \hline 62{,}027\ (\mathbf{8}) \end{array}$  $\begin{array}{r} 9047\ (\mathbf{2}) \\ -\ 3567\ (\mathbf{3}) \\ \hline 5480\ (\mathbf{8}) \end{array}$  $\begin{array}{r} 8529\ (\mathbf{6}) \\ \times\ 7\ (\mathbf{7}) \\ \hline 59{,}703\ (\mathbf{6}) \end{array}$  $\begin{array}{r} 4172\ (\mathbf{5}) \\ \times\ 5\ (\mathbf{5}) \\ \hline 20{,}860\ (\mathbf{7}) \end{array}$

The population of Red Deer and the nearby area is 100,807. Write this number in words.

**one hundred thousand eight hundred seven**

Write >, <, or = on the lines.

$\frac{1}{2}$ of 4 $\mathbf{>}$ $\frac{1}{2}$ of 2

$\frac{2}{4}$ **=** $\frac{1}{2}$

$1 + \frac{1}{2}$ **=** $1\frac{1}{2}$

$\frac{2}{3}$ **>** $\frac{2}{4}$

$\frac{3}{3}$ **=** $\frac{4}{4}$

$\frac{1}{6}$ **<** $\frac{5}{6}$

Solve the problem.

Aidan earned $16 on Tuesday and three times as much on Saturday. How much did Aidan earn on Saturday? How much did Aidan earn on both days?

**s = amount on Saturday**

**s = 16 × 3 = $48**

**total = 16 + 48 = $64**

Draw lines to match the expressions.

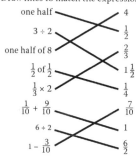

Crosshatch $\frac{2}{3}$ of the hexagon.

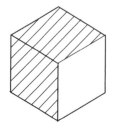

There are other ways to crosshatch the hexagon, such as the one shown below.

---

| ACTIVITIES FOR TEACHING CONTINUED: | EXPLANATIONS CONTINUED: |

**The One game.** Play the game of One, found in *Math Card Games* book, F6.

**Worksheet 30-B.** Give the child the worksheet. Tell her to listen to the problems and write the answers. Read each problem twice.

$79 \times 100$ $\qquad$ $199 + 85$ $\qquad$ $70 \times 9$

Tell her to complete the worksheet. Solutions are below.

---

Write only the answers.

**7900**

**284**

**630**

Write the answers.

$657 + 94 =$ **751**

$63 +$ **937** $= 1000$

$1\frac{5}{6} + 2\frac{1}{6} =$ **4**

Do the arithmetic. Use check numbers.

$\begin{array}{r} 42,974\ (\textbf{8}) \\ +\ 38,845\ (\textbf{1}) \\ \hline \textbf{81,819}\ (0) \end{array}$ $\qquad$ $\begin{array}{r} 8703\ (\textbf{0}) \\ -\ 4596\ (\textbf{6}) \\ \hline \textbf{4107}\ (3) \end{array}$ $\qquad$ $\begin{array}{r} 2958\ (\textbf{6}) \\ \times\ 8\ (\textbf{8}) \\ \hline \textbf{23,664}\ (3) \end{array}$ $\qquad$ $\begin{array}{r} 7251\ (\textbf{6}) \\ \times\ 6\ (\textbf{6}) \\ \hline \textbf{43,506}\ (0) \end{array}$

The population of Markham, Ontario, is 301,709. Write this number in words.

**three hundred one thousand seven hundred nine**

Write >, <, or = on the lines.

$\frac{1}{2}$ of 3 **<** $\frac{1}{2}$ of 4

$\frac{1}{2}$ **=** $\frac{3}{6}$

$\frac{1}{2} + 1$ **=** $1\frac{1}{2}$

$\frac{3}{4}$ **>** $\frac{3}{6}$

$\frac{2}{2}$ **=** $\frac{8}{8}$

$\frac{1}{8}$ **<** $\frac{5}{8}$

Solve the problem.

James and his friends earned $24 on Friday and three times as much on Saturday. How much did they earn on Saturday? How much did they earn on both days?

**s = amount on Saturday**

**s = 24 × 3 = $72**

**total = 24 + 72 = $96**

Draw lines to match the expressions.

one third
5 ÷ 2
one half of 6
$\frac{1}{2}$ of $\frac{1}{3}$
$\frac{1}{5} \times 2$
$\frac{3}{10} + \frac{7}{10}$
7 ÷ 2
$1 - \frac{1}{10}$

3
$\frac{1}{3}$
$\frac{2}{5}$
$2\frac{1}{2}$
$\frac{1}{6}$
$\frac{9}{10}$
1
$\frac{7}{2}$

Crosshatch $\frac{3}{4}$ of the octagon.

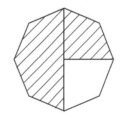

---

There are other ways to crosshatch the octagon.

# LESSON 49: ADDING FRACTIONS INFORMALLY

**OBJECTIVES:**

1. To work with whole numbers and fractions

2. To become more familiar with adding several fractions to total 1 or 2

**MATERIALS:**

1. Worksheet 31, Adding Fractions Informally

2. Fraction chart

3. *Math Card Games* book, F18

| ACTIVITIES FOR TEACHING: | EXPLANATIONS: |
|---|---|

**ACTIVITIES FOR TEACHING:**

***Warm-up.*** Give the child the worksheet. Tell her to do just the warm-up equations. Solutions are:

| 7268 **(5)** | 7268 **(5)** | 726 **(6)** | 2687 **(5)** |
|---|---|---|---|
| + 2687 **(5)** | − 2687 **(5)** | × 8 **(8)** | × 3 **(3)** |
| **9955 (1)** | **4581 (0)** | **5808 (3)** | **8061 (6)** |

***Worksheet 31.*** Give the child the fraction chart. Tell the child to read the first problem on the worksheet and to solve it.

Which rectangle has the greater perimeter? [A, perimeter of A is $11\frac{3}{4}$ and perimeter of B is 11.]

$3\frac{3}{4}$          $2\frac{3}{4}$

A    $2\frac{1}{8}$          B    $2\frac{3}{4}$

Ask the child to explain how she solved the problem. One way to find the perimeter of A is to double each side and add them together:

$$3\frac{3}{4} \times 2 = 7\frac{1}{2}$$
$$2\frac{1}{8} \times 2 = 4\frac{1}{4}$$
$$7\frac{1}{2} + 4\frac{1}{4} = 11\frac{3}{4}$$

One way is to find the perimeter of B is to multiply the whole numbers and fractions separately:

$$2\frac{3}{4} \times 4 = 2 \times 4 + \frac{3}{4} \times 4 = 8 + 3 = 11$$

***One or Two game.*** Play the One or Two game, found in *Math Card Games* book, F18.

***In conclusion.*** Ask: How many fourths do you need to make one? [4] How many fourths do you need to make two? [8] How many thirds do you need to make one? [3] How many thirds do you need to make two? [6]

**EXPLANATIONS:**

The child is not to use an algorithm. She is to find the solutions in a way that makes sense to her.

There is no need to teach the terms *proper* and *improper* at this time.

The second problem on this worksheet will be completed in the next lesson.

# LESSON 50: ADDING AND SUBTRACTING FRACTIONS INFORMALLY

**OBJECTIVES:**

1. To become more familiar with the fraction sizes
2. To become more familiar with adding and subtracting fractions to total $\frac{1}{2}$

**MATERIALS:**

1. Worksheet 31, Adding Fractions Informally
2. Fraction chart
3. *Math Card Games* book, F8

| ACTIVITIES FOR TEACHING: | EXPLANATIONS: |
|---|---|
| ***Warm-up.*** Ask: In the fraction one third, what is the denominator? [3] In the fraction one third, what number is the numerator? [1] If the denominator and numerator are the same, what does the fraction equal? [1] | |
| Ask: How many fourths do you need to make one? [4] How many fourths do you need to make two? [8] How many eighths do you need to make one? [8] How many eighths do you need to make two? [16] | |
| ***Worksheet 31.*** Give the child the fraction chart. Tell the child to read the second problem on the worksheet and to solve it. Emphasize she must explain her work so anyone, even grandparents, could understand what she did to get the answer. | The first problem was done in the previous lesson. |
|     Sammy is making a craft project and has one foot of very expensive ribbon. Sammy cuts pieces $1\frac{1}{4}$, $1\frac{3}{4}$, $2\frac{5}{8}$, $2\frac{3}{4}$, $\frac{7}{8}$, and $1\frac{1}{2}$ inches long. How much is left? [$1\frac{1}{4}$] | |
| Ask her to explain how she solved the problem. | |
| One way is to add the whole numbers, which is 7. Then adding $\frac{1}{4}$ and $\frac{3}{4}$ gives 1. Also, adding $\frac{5}{8}$, $\frac{7}{8}$, and $\frac{1}{2}$ gives 2. The total is $10\frac{3}{4}$, which leaves $1\frac{1}{4}$ inches of ribbon remaining. | The child needs to find the solutions in a way that she understands, not to plug into an algorithm. |
| ***The One Half game.*** Play the One Half game, found in *Math Card Games* book, F8. | |
| ***In conclusion.*** Ask: Three fourths minus what equals one half? [one fourth] Five eighths minus what equals one half? [one eighth] One third plus what equals one half? [one sixth] | |

# LESSON 51: COMPARING FRACTIONS

**OBJECTIVES:**
1. To solve a fraction problem
2. To compare fractions

**MATERIALS:**
1. Worksheet 32, Comparing Fractions
2. Fraction chart
3. *Math Card Games* book, F7

---

**ACTIVITIES FOR TEACHING:**

***Warm-up.*** Give the child the worksheet. Tell her to do just the warm-up equations. Solutions are:

| | | | |
|---|---|---|---|
| 5854 **(4)** | 5854 **(4)** | 585 **(0)** | 4585 **(4)** |
| + 4585 **(4)** | − 4585 **(4)** | × 6 **(6)** | × 7 **(7)** |
| 10,439 **(8)** | 1269 **(0)** | 3510 **(0)** | 32,095 **(1)** |

***Worksheet 32.*** Give the child the fraction chart. Tell her to read the first problem on the worksheet.

The perimeter of each regular figure below is 13 cm. What is the length of the sides of each figure?

Remind the child that a *regular* figure has equal sides and equal angles. Tell her to solve it and then to explain how she solved the problem.

To find the length of a side of the triangle, 13 divided by 3 is 4 with 1 left. That 1 divided by 3 is $\frac{1}{3}$. Adding 4 and $\frac{1}{3}$ gives $4\frac{1}{3}$ as the length of one side of the triangle.

The solutions are summarized below.

Triangle: $13 \div 3 = 4\frac{1}{3}$ cm

Square: $13 \div 4 = 3\frac{1}{4}$ cm

Hexagon: $13 \div 6 = 2\frac{1}{6}$ cm

***Fraction Peace game.*** Play Fraction Peace game, a new variation Fraction War game found in *Math Card Games* book, F7. Now the player with the lower fraction collects the cards. Remind her to use her fraction chart.

***In conclusion.*** Ask: Which is less, three fourths or one half? [one half] Which is less, an eighth or a fourth? [an eighth] Which is less, seven eighths or three fourths? [three fourths]

**EXPLANATIONS:**

The child is to find the solutions in a way that makes sense to her, not to use an algorithm.

The second problem on this worksheet will be completed in the next lesson.

If this game seems too easy, make it more challenging by telling each player to take two cards and add them together before comparing.

# LESSON 52: COMPARING HARDER FRACTIONS

**OBJECTIVES:**
1. To solve a fraction problem
2. To practice comparing fractions

**MATERIALS:**
1. Worksheet 32, Comparing Fractions
2. Fraction chart
3. *Math Card Games* book, F9

| ACTIVITIES FOR TEACHING: | EXPLANATIONS: |
|---|---|
| **Warm-up.** Ask: In the fraction one sixth, what is the denominator? [6] In the fraction one sixth, what number is the numerator? [1] If the denominator and numerator are the same, what does the fraction equal? [1] | |

Ask: How many fourths do you need to make one? [4] How many fourths do you need to make two? [8] How many fourths do you need to make one and one half? [6] One half minus what equals one fourth? [one fourth]

**Worksheet 32.** Give the child the fraction chart. Tell her to read the second problem on the worksheet and to solve it.

*The first problem was done in the previous lesson.*

Find of the perimeter of the square and the regular octagon. Which has the greater perimeter?

 $3\frac{1}{2}$    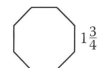 $1\frac{3}{4}$

One way is to find the perimeter of the square is to multiply the 3 and the $\frac{1}{2}$ separately:

$$3\frac{1}{2} \times 4 = (3 \times 4) + (\frac{1}{2} \times 4) = 12 + 2 = 14 \text{ cm}$$

Likewise, the perimeter of the octagon is:

$$1\frac{3}{4} \times 8 = (1 \times 8) + (\frac{3}{4} \times 8) = 8 + 3 \times (\frac{1}{4} \times 8)$$
$$= 8 + 3 \times 2 = 14 \text{ cm}$$

Therefore, the perimeters are the same.

**Harder Fraction War game.** Play Harder Fraction War game, found in *Math Card Games* book, F9. Remind the child to use her fraction chart.

**In conclusion.** Ask: Three fourths minus what equals one fourth? [one half] Seven eighths minus what equals one half? [three eighth] One sixth plus what equals one half? [one third]

# LESSON 53: FRACTION OF SIXTEEN

**OBJECTIVES:**

1. To experience relationships between fractions
2. To compare fractions

**MATERIALS:**

1. Worksheet 33, Sixteenths and Eighths
2. *Math Card Games* book, F12

---

**ACTIVITIES FOR TEACHING:**

**EXPLANATIONS:**

***Warm-up.*** Give the child the worksheet. Tell her to do just the warm-up equations. Solutions are:

$$
\begin{array}{r}
7642\ \textbf{(1)} \\
+\ 2467\ \textbf{(1)} \\
\hline
\textbf{10,109}\ \textbf{(2)}
\end{array}
\qquad
\begin{array}{r}
7642\ \textbf{(1)} \\
-\ 2467\ \textbf{(1)} \\
\hline
\textbf{5175}\ \textbf{(0)}
\end{array}
\qquad
\begin{array}{r}
764\ \textbf{(8)} \\
\times 8\ \textbf{(8)} \\
\hline
\textbf{6112}\ \textbf{(1)}
\end{array}
\qquad
\begin{array}{r}
2467\ \textbf{(1)} \\
\times 4\ \textbf{(4)} \\
\hline
\textbf{9868}\ \textbf{(4)}
\end{array}
$$

***Worksheet 33.*** Tell the child to do first problem on the worksheet. The solutions are shown below.

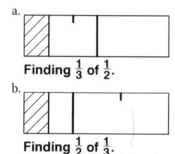

a. Finding $\frac{1}{3}$ of $\frac{1}{2}$.

b. Finding $\frac{1}{2}$ of $\frac{1}{3}$.

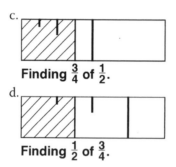

c. Finding $\frac{3}{4}$ of $\frac{1}{2}$.

d. Finding $\frac{1}{2}$ of $\frac{3}{4}$.

Ask the child to explain how she did it. For the figure A, first divide the rectangle in half and then divide one half into thirds. For the rectangle B, first divide the rectangle into thirds and then divide a third in half.

For the figure C, first divide the rectangle in half and then divide it into fourths. Then crosshatch three of those fourths. For figure D, first divide the rectangle in fourths. Then crosshatch half of three fourths.

Ask: What pattern did you observe? [One third of one half is the same as one half of one third and three fourths of one half is the same as one half of three fourths.] Does that remind you of the commutative property? [yes]

The second problem on this worksheet will be completed in the next lesson.

***Fraction of Sixteen game.*** Play the Fraction of Sixteen game found in the *Math Card Games* book, F12.

***In conclusion.*** Ask: What is one eighth of 16? [2] What is two eighths of 16? [4] What is one fourth of 16? [4]

---

# LESSON 54: ADDING EIGHTHS

## OBJECTIVES:

1. To become more familiar with the size of fractions
2. To add and subtract fractions

## MATERIALS:

1. Worksheet 33, Sixteenths and Eighths
2. *Math Card Games* book, F20

| ACTIVITIES FOR TEACHING: | EXPLANATIONS: |
|---|---|
| **Warm-up.** Ask: Which is less, one half or three fourths? [one half] Which is less, a third or a fourth? [a fourth] Which is less, two thirds or three fourths? [two thirds] What is three fourths minus one half? [one fourth] | |
| **Worksheet 33.** Tell the child to read the second problem on the worksheet and to solve both parts independently. | The first problem was done in the previous lesson. |

Then tell her to share her process. The solutions are below.

For the first part of the problem, finding $\frac{2}{3}$ of 6 is 4. Since there are three thirds in each rectangle, the total number of thirds is $4 \times 3 = 12$.

For the second part of the problem, $\frac{2}{3} \times 6$, $\frac{2}{3}$s are needed 6 times, giving 12 thirds. The two answers are the same.

**Concentrating on Eighths game.** Play the Concentrating on Eighths game found in *Math Card Games* book, F20, twice. For the first game, both players start by collecting a $\frac{1}{2}$ card. For the next card, one player collects $\frac{1}{8}$ and the other player collects $\frac{7}{8}$. Subsequent cards are the sum of the two preceding fractions, but ignoring the whole numbers.

For the second game, both players start by collecting a $\frac{1}{2}$ card again. For the next card, one player collects $\frac{3}{8}$ and the other player collects $\frac{5}{8}$. Play continues like the first game.

**In conclusion.** Ask: What is three fourths plus one eighth? [$\frac{7}{8}$] What is three fourths plus two eighths? [1] What is three fourths plus three eighths? [$1\frac{1}{8}$]

# LESSON 55: READING RULERS TO EIGHTHS

**OBJECTIVES:**

1. To practice reading rulers to eighths
2. To measure various objects to eighths of an inch

**MATERIALS:**

1. Worksheet 34, Reading Rulers to Eighths
2. 4-in-1 ruler
3. **Objects for the child to measure, such as books or boxes**
4. Math journal

---

**ACTIVITIES FOR TEACHING:**

***Warm-up.*** Give the child the worksheet. Tell her to do just the warm-up equations. Solutions are:

| 6374 (2) | 6374 (2) | 637 (7) | 4736 (2) |
|---|---|---|---|
| + 4736 (2) | − 4736 (2) | × 4 (4) | × 8 (8) |
| **11,110 (4)** | **1638 (0)** | **2548 (1)** | **37,888 (7)** |

***Worksheet 34.*** Give the child the 4-in-1 ruler. Tell her to find the scale that says 1/16 inch.

Ask: What marks each inch? [a number] Tell her to point to the longest line on the scale between the 1 and the 2 and ask: What does the line show? [halves] What does the next longest line show? [fourths] What does the next longest line show? [eighths] Ask: What does the shortest line show? [sixteenths]

***Problem 1.*** Tell her to look at the first figure of an inch on the worksheet. Tell her to do the crosshatching for the three problems. The solutions are below.

What fraction are these inches divided into? **sixteenths**

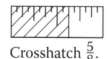

Crosshatch $\frac{3}{4}$.   Crosshatch $\frac{3}{8}$.   Crosshatch $\frac{5}{8}$.

***Problem 2.*** Tell her to do the next problem on the worksheet. The solutions are given below.

After she has finished, ask: Where did you start? [at the left end] How did you know where to end? [counted the whole inches and found the fraction of the inch]

**EXPLANATIONS:**

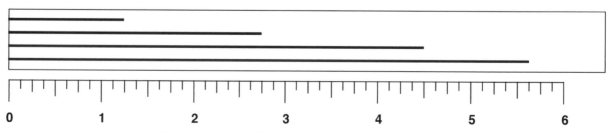

Showing lines that are $1\frac{1}{4}$, $2\frac{3}{4}$, $4\frac{1}{2}$, and $5\frac{5}{8}$ inches long (actual size).

| ACTIVITIES FOR TEACHING CONTINUED: | EXPLANATIONS CONTINUED: |
|---|---|

**Measuring other objects.** Show the child the objects to measure. Tell her to measure them to the nearest eighth of an inch, then write down the name of the object and its measurements in her math journal.

**Problem 3.** Tell the child to complete the worksheet. The solutions are below.

She should use informal processes to find the perimeters, NOT an algorithm.

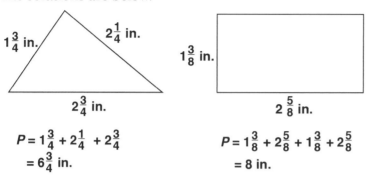

$$P = 1\frac{3}{4} + 2\frac{1}{4} + 2\frac{3}{4}$$
$$= 6\frac{3}{4} \text{ in.}$$

$$P = 1\frac{3}{8} + 2\frac{5}{8} + 1\frac{3}{8} + 2\frac{5}{8}$$
$$= 8 \text{ in.}$$

Ask her to explain her solution.

**In conclusion.** Ask: Why are there numbers on a ruler? [so you don't have count the inches] If a ruler is 12 inches long, how many half inches does it have? [24]

If there is additional time following this lesson, play the Concentrating on Eights game, found in *Math Card Games* book, F20.

# LESSON 56: ADDING MIXED NUMBERS WITH EIGHTHS

## OBJECTIVES:

1. To learn the terms *proper fraction* and *improper fraction*
2. To practice adding fractions with eighths
3. To convert improper eighths to proper eighths

## MATERIALS:

1. Fraction chart and fraction pieces
2. *Math Card Games* book, F22.1
3. Math journal

## ACTIVITIES FOR TEACHING:

***Warm-up.*** Ask: In the fraction one fifth, what is the denominator? [5] In the fraction one fifth, what number is the numerator? [1] If the denominator and numerator are the same, what does the fraction equal? [1]

***Improper fractions.*** Give the child the fraction chart and fraction pieces.

Write: $\dfrac{9}{8}$

and ask the child to show it with her fraction chart and fraction pieces. [8 eighths plus 1 more eighth] See figure below.

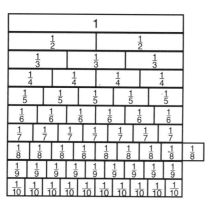

**Showing $\dfrac{9}{8}$ with the fraction chart and pieces.**

Write: $\dfrac{5}{3}$

and tell her to show it with the fraction materials. See figure below.

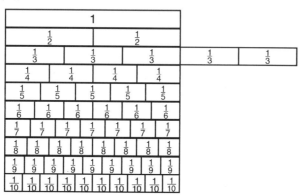

**Showing $\dfrac{5}{3}$ with the fraction chart and pieces.**

## EXPLANATIONS:

| ACTIVITIES FOR TEACHING CONTINUED: | EXPLANATIONS CONTINUED: |
|---|---|

Write: $\quad\quad \frac{9}{8} \quad \frac{5}{3} \quad \frac{3}{4}$

Ask: Which of these three fractions is less than one? [$\frac{3}{4}$] How can you tell by looking only at the numerators and denominators? [The numerator is less than the denominator.]

Say: When the numerator is less than the denominator, the fraction is called a *proper fraction*. This name results from hundreds of years ago when people thought a "real" fraction had to be less than one. The word "fraction" comes from the Latin word "frangere" meaning "to break." Two other words from this root word are fracture and fragment. Mathematicians realized fractions were division and often were not less than one. They called fractions equal to or greater than one *improper fractions*.

Write: $\quad\quad \frac{4}{8} \quad \frac{7}{4} \quad \frac{4}{3} \quad \frac{8}{8} \quad \frac{12}{8} \quad \frac{1}{6}$

Ask: Which of these are proper fractions? [only the first and last fractions, $\frac{4}{8}$ and $\frac{1}{6}$]

Ask: How can we rewrite the improper fractions using a whole number plus a fraction? [$1\frac{3}{4}$, $1\frac{1}{3}$, 1, $1\frac{4}{8}$]

This can be done by referring to the fraction chart. No algorithm is necessary.

**Preparation for Corners™ with Eighths game.**
Explain that the game for the day will be a Corners™ Three game variation. Now each number on the cards will be *eighths*. For example, 3 is $\frac{3}{8}$ and 9 is $\frac{9}{8}$.

Write: $\quad\quad 1\frac{3}{8} + \frac{9}{8} =$

and ask the child to add it. Ask the child to explain her work.

One way is: $\quad 1\frac{3}{8} + \frac{9}{8} = 1\frac{12}{8} = 2\frac{4}{8}$

The answers need not be in lowest terms.

Another way is: $\quad\quad 1\frac{1}{8}$
$$1\frac{3}{8} + \frac{\cancel{9}}{\cancel{8}} = 2\frac{4}{8}$$

Give her another example: $\quad\quad 2\frac{2}{8}$
$$2\frac{5}{8} + \frac{18}{8} = [2\frac{23}{8} = 4\frac{7}{8} \text{ or } 2\frac{5}{8} + \frac{\cancel{18}}{\cancel{8}} = 4\frac{7}{8}]$$

**Corners™ with Eighths game.** Play Corners™ with Eighths game, found in *Math Card Games* book, F22.1. Stress that the fractions in the scoring sums must be proper fractions. Tell her to write the scoring in her math journal.

**In conclusion.** Ask: What do we call a fraction when the numerator is greater than the denominator? [improper] What is a fraction called when the denominator is greater than the numerator? [proper]

# LESSON 57: REVIEW AND GAMES 4

## OBJECTIVES:

1. To review recent topics
2. To develop skills through playing math card games

## MATERIALS:

1. Worksheet 35-A or 35-B, Review 4
2. *Math Card Games* book, F22.1

---

## ACTIVITIES FOR TEACHING:

**Worksheet 35-A.** Give the child the worksheet. Tell her to listen to the problems and write the answers. Read each problem twice.

$$74 \times 100 \qquad 299 + 18 \qquad 90 \times 9$$

Tell her to complete the worksheet. Solutions are below.

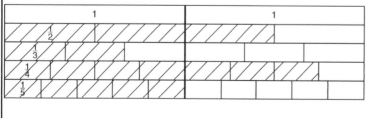

Write only the answers.

**7400**

**317**

**810**

Write the answers.

$389 + 78 =$ **467**

$61 +$ **939** $= 1000$

$2 - 1\frac{1}{3} =$ **$\frac{2}{3}$**

Do the arithmetic. Use check numbers.

| | | | Add 387 + 10,793. |
|---|---|---|---|
| 7432 (**7**) | 7685 (**8**) | 6369 (**6**) | **10,793 (2)** |
| − 888 (**6**) | × 6 (**6**) | × 7 (**7**) | **+ 387 (0)** |
| **6544 (1)** | **46,110 (3)** | **44,583 (6)** | **11,180 (2)** |

Write >, <, or = on the lines.    Solve the problem.

$\frac{1}{2}$ of 4 **=** $\frac{1}{2} \times 4$

$\frac{2}{5}$ **<** $\frac{4}{5}$

$1 + \frac{4}{7}$ **=** $1\frac{4}{7}$

$\frac{5}{6}$ **>** $\frac{4}{5}$

$\frac{7}{10}$ **<** $\frac{7}{8}$

$\frac{11}{8}$ **=** $1\frac{3}{8}$

Willie walked around a rectangular block. The north side of the block was 486 ft. The west side was twice this distance. How far did Willie walk?

486 ft

**west = 486 × 2 = 972**

**P = (486 + 972) × 2**

**P = 2916 ft**

Circle the improper fractions.

(9/8) (7/1) 2/3 (6/6) 12/13 5/6

Put these fractions in order from least to greatest.

$\frac{5}{4} \quad \frac{7}{8} \quad \frac{3}{5} \quad \frac{1}{3} \quad \frac{17}{8} \quad \frac{1}{4}$

$\frac{1}{4} \quad \frac{1}{3} \quad \frac{3}{5} \quad \frac{7}{8} \quad \frac{5}{4} \quad \frac{17}{8}$

On the fraction charts below, crosshatch $1\frac{1}{2}$, $\frac{2}{3}$, $\frac{7}{4}$, and $\frac{5}{5}$.

## EXPLANATIONS:

Ask the child to correct any errors during the lesson.

This problem could also be solved by multiplying 486 × 6.

---

## ACTIVITIES FOR TEACHING CONTINUED:

**EXPLANATIONS CONTINUED:**

***Corners with Eighths game.*** Play Corners with Eighths game, found in *Math Card Games* book, F22.1.

***Worksheet 35-B.*** Give the child the worksheet. Tell her to listen to the problems and write the answers. Read each problem twice.

$38 \times 100$      $198 + 73$      $80 \times 9$

Tell her to complete the worksheet. Solutions are below.

---

Write only the answers.

**3800**

**271**

**720**

Write the answers.

$576 + 85 =$ **661**

$73 +$ **927** $= 1000$

$2 - 1\frac{1}{4} = \frac{\textbf{3}}{\textbf{4}}$

Do the arithmetic. Use check numbers.

$6345$ (**0**)    $5867$ (**8**)    $7849$ (**1**)

$- 548$ (**8**)    $\times 7$ (**7**)    $\times 6$ (**6**)

$5797$ (**1**)   $41{,}069$ (**2**)   $47{,}094$ (**6**)

Add 268 + 23,564.

$23{,}564$ **(2)**

$+ 268$ **(7)**

$23{,}832$ **(0)**

Write >, <, or = on the lines.     Solve the problem.

$\frac{1}{3} \times 6$ **=** $\frac{1}{3}$ of 6

$\frac{5}{8}$ **>** $\frac{3}{8}$

$2 + \frac{5}{7}$ **=** $2\frac{5}{7}$

$\frac{7}{8}$ **<** $\frac{8}{9}$

$\frac{3}{10}$ **<** $\frac{3}{8}$

$\frac{13}{8}$ **=** $1\frac{5}{8}$

Matt's dog, Barky, ran around her pen. The east side of the pen was 57 ft. The south side was three times this distance. How far did Barky run?

*57 ft*

**south** = 57 × 3 = 171

**P** = (57 + 171) × 2

**P** = 456 ft

Circle the improper fractions.

$\frac{7}{8}$   ($\frac{7}{3}$)   ($\frac{2}{1}$)   ($\frac{6}{6}$)   $\frac{1}{5}$   ($\frac{7}{6}$)

Put these fractions in order from least to greatest.

$\frac{4}{4}$   $\frac{1}{8}$   $\frac{4}{7}$   $\frac{2}{5}$   $\frac{15}{8}$   $\frac{1}{6}$

$\frac{\textbf{1}}{\textbf{8}}$   $\frac{\textbf{1}}{\textbf{6}}$   $\frac{\textbf{2}}{\textbf{5}}$   $\frac{\textbf{4}}{\textbf{7}}$   $\frac{\textbf{4}}{\textbf{4}}$   $\frac{\textbf{15}}{\textbf{8}}$

On the fraction charts below, crosshatch $\frac{2}{2}$, $\frac{4}{3}$, $\frac{3}{4}$, and $\frac{7}{5}$.

---

© Activities for Learning, Inc. 2016

# LESSON 58: MULTIPLYING BY TENS

**OBJECTIVES:**

1. To learn the term *annex*
2. To understand multiplying by several tens

**MATERIALS:**

1. Worksheet 36, Multiplying by Tens

---

**ACTIVITIES FOR TEACHING:**

*Warm-up.* Give the child the worksheet. Tell her to do just the warm-up equations. Solutions are:

$$
\begin{array}{cccc}
6532\ (7) & 6532\ (7) & 653\ (5) & 2356\ (7) \\
+\,2356\ (7) & -\,2356\ (7) & \times 3\ (3) & \times 4\ (4) \\
\hline
8888\ (5) & 4176\ (0) & 1959\ (6) & 9424\ (1)
\end{array}
$$

*Multiplying by 10.* Write:

$$532 \times 10$$

and ask the child to find the product and to be able to explain it. When she is ready, ask her to explain her thinking.

One way is to use the distributive property as follows:

$$532 \times 10 = (500 \times 10) + (30 \times 10) + (2 \times 10)$$
$$= 5000 + 300 + 20 = 5320$$

Ask: How does the answer compare to the problem? [The 532 has a zero after it.] Say: Putting a zero after a number is called *annexing* a zero.

Write: $\qquad 8305 \times 10$

and ask for the answer. [83,050]

*Multiplying by several 10s.* Write:

$$222 \times 40$$

and ask the child to find the product and to be able to explain it. When she is ready, ask her to explain her thinking.

Continuing with the distributive property gives the following:

$$222 \times 40 = 222 \times 4 \times 10 = 888 \times 10 = 8880$$

or

$$222 \times 40 = 222 \times 10 \times 4 = 2220 \times 4 = 8880$$

Ask: How does the answer compare to the problem? [It is $222 \times 4$ with a zero annexed.]

Repeat for: $\qquad 312 \times 30 = [9360]$

**EXPLANATIONS:**

The solution could be shown concretely on side 2 of the abacus or by adding a column of the 10 numbers. This more abstract explanation requires deeper thinking needed for algebra.

To multiply by 10, we do not add a zero, rather we annex a zero. Adding zero to a number does not change the number; for example, adding 0 to 18 is still 18.

We need to keep in mind that annexing only works for whole numbers. While it is valid for $54 \times 10$, it is not valid for $0.54 \times 10$.

---

| ACTIVITIES FOR TEACHING CONTINUED: | EXPLANATIONS CONTINUED: |
|---|---|

Summarize by saying: To multiply a number by several 10s, first multiply by 10 and then multiply by the number of 10s.

***Multiplying vertically.*** Say: Now we will multiply vertically. First we will start with a single digit. Write $143 \times 2$ and ask the child to multiply. See below.

$$\begin{array}{r} 143 \\ \times 2 \\ \hline 286 \end{array}$$

Next write:

$$\begin{array}{r} 143 \\ \times 20 \\ \hline \end{array}$$

Ask: How does this compare to $143 \times 2$? [ten times more] Say: We can show multiplying times 10 by writing the zero before multiplying $143 \times 2$. See left figure below.

$$\begin{array}{r} 143 \\ \times 20 \\ \hline 0 \end{array} \qquad \begin{array}{r} 143 \\ \times 20 \\ \hline 2860 \end{array}$$

Now multiply as usual. See the right figure above.

Ask: When you multiplied $3 \times 2$, you wrote the 6 in the ones place; where did you write the 6 when you multiplied $3 \times 20$? [tens place] When you multiplied $40 \times 2$, you wrote the 8 in the tens place; where did you write the 8 when you multiplied $40 \times 20$? [hundreds place]

Repeat for $452 \times 60$.

$$\begin{array}{r} 31 \phantom{0} \\ 452 \\ \times 60 \\ \hline 27{,}120 \end{array}$$

***Worksheet 36.*** Tell her to do the worksheet. The solutions are below.

$412 \times 10 = \mathbf{4120}$ $\quad 720 \times 10 = \mathbf{7200}$ $\quad 8397 \times 10 = \mathbf{83{,}970}$

$86 \times 2 = \mathbf{172}$ $\quad 346 \times 2 = \mathbf{692}$ $\quad 5976 \times 2 = \mathbf{11{,}952}$
$86 \times 20 = \mathbf{1720}$ $\quad 346 \times 20 = \mathbf{6920}$ $\quad 5976 \times 20 = \mathbf{119{,}520}$

$217 \times 4 = \mathbf{868}$ $\quad 706 \times 5 = \mathbf{3530}$ $\quad 4231 \times 3 = \mathbf{12{,}693}$
$217 \times 40 = \mathbf{8680}$ $\quad 706 \times 50 = \mathbf{35{,}300}$ $\quad 4231 \times 30 = \mathbf{126{,}930}$

| $\begin{array}{r}212\\ \times 2\\ \hline \mathbf{424}\end{array}$ | $\begin{array}{r}212\\ \times 20\\ \hline \mathbf{4240}\end{array}$ | $\begin{array}{r}143\\ \times 3\\ \hline \mathbf{429}\end{array}$ | $\begin{array}{r}143\\ \times 30\\ \hline \mathbf{4290}\end{array}$ | $\begin{array}{r}3502\\ \times 4\\ \hline \mathbf{14{,}008}\end{array}$ | $\begin{array}{r}3502\\ \times 40\\ \hline \mathbf{140{,}080}\end{array}$ |
|---|---|---|---|---|---|

| $\begin{array}{r}365\\ \times 5\\ \hline \mathbf{1825}\end{array}$ | $\begin{array}{r}365\\ \times 50\\ \hline \mathbf{18{,}250}\end{array}$ | $\begin{array}{r}4321\\ \times 6\\ \hline \mathbf{25{,}926}\end{array}$ | $\begin{array}{r}4321\\ \times 60\\ \hline \mathbf{259{,}260}\end{array}$ | $\begin{array}{r}2432\\ \times 7\\ \hline \mathbf{17{,}024}\end{array}$ | $\begin{array}{r}2432\\ \times 70\\ \hline \mathbf{170{,}240}\end{array}$ |
|---|---|---|---|---|---|

***In conclusion.*** Ask: What is $44 \times 2$? [88] What is $44 \times 20$? [880] What is $44 \times 200$? [8800]

If there is additional time following this lesson, play the Lowest in the Corners game, found in *Math Card Games* book, P18.

# LESSON 59: MULTIPLYING BY TWO DIGITS

## OBJECTIVES:

1. To develop a procedure for multiplying by two digits

## MATERIALS:

1. Worksheet 37, Multiplying by Two Digits

| ACTIVITIES FOR TEACHING: | EXPLANATIONS: |
|---|---|
| **Warm-up.** Ask: What is $31 \times 2$? [62] What is $31 \times 20$? [620] What is $31 \times 200$? [6200] | |

Ask: What is $23 \times 3$? [69] What is $23 \times 30$? [690] What is $23 \times 300$? [6900]

**Multiplying by two digits.** Write these three problems:

$$
\begin{array}{r} 312 \\ \times 2 \\ \hline 624 \end{array} \qquad
\begin{array}{r} 312 \\ \times 30 \\ \hline 9360 \end{array} \qquad
\begin{array}{r} 312 \\ \times 32 \\ \hline \end{array}
$$

Say: You have been multiplying problems like the first one for several months now. In yesterday's lesson you multiplied numbers with tens like the second problem. Today you will multiply numbers with two digits like the third problem.

Ask: How do you think you could do it? Tell the child to share her thoughts. Two solutions are below.

$$
\begin{array}{r} 312 \\ \times 32 \\ \hline 624 \\ 9360 \\ \hline 9984 \end{array} \qquad
\begin{array}{r} 312 \\ \times 32 \\ \hline 9360 \\ 624 \\ \hline 9984 \end{array}
$$

It is acceptable to multiply the leftmost digit first.

**Worksheet 37.** Give the child the worksheet and tell her to do the first two rows in the left box. The solutions are below.

Then tell her to discuss her answer.

$$
\begin{array}{r} 63 \\ \times 5 \\ \hline 315 \end{array} \quad
\begin{array}{r} 63 \\ \times 30 \\ \hline 1890 \end{array} \quad
\begin{array}{r} 63 \\ \times 35 \\ \hline 315 \\ 1890 \\ \hline 2205 \end{array} \quad
\begin{array}{r} 825 \\ \times 6 \\ \hline 4950 \end{array} \quad
\begin{array}{r} 825 \\ \times 50 \\ \hline 41{,}250 \end{array} \quad
\begin{array}{r} 825 \\ \times 56 \\ \hline 4950 \\ 41250 \\ \hline 46{,}200 \end{array}
$$

Repeat for the last two rows in the left box. The solutions are below.

|  |  |  |  |  |  |
|---|---|---|---|---|---|
| 3674 | 3674 | 3674 | 9062 | 9062 | 9062 |
| × 1 | × 80 | × 81 | × 7 | × 20 | × 27 |
| 3674 | 293,920 | 3674 | 63,434 | 181,240 | 63434 |
|  |  | 293920 |  |  | 181240 |
|  |  | 297,594 |  |  | 244,674 |

**Writing the 'carries.'** Write:

$$\begin{array}{r} 28 \\ \times\,43 \end{array}$$

and multiply the 28 × 3 part. See below.

$$\begin{array}{r} 2 \\ 28 \\ \times\,43 \\ \hline 84 \end{array}$$

Continue with multiplying the 28 × 40.

$$\begin{array}{r} 3 \\ 2 \\ 28 \\ \times\,43 \\ \hline 84 \\ 1120 \\ \hline 1204 \end{array}$$

Explain that the carries, the little numbers, can be written in rows above the problem, but many people do not write them at all; they do it mentally.

**Worksheet 37.** Tell the child to complete the worksheet. The solutions are below.

|  |  |  |  |
|---|---|---|---|
| 81 | 143 | 572 | 2927 |
| × 52 | × 33 | × 64 | × 81 |
| 162 | 429 | 2288 | 2927 |
| 4050 | 4290 | 34320 | 234160 |
| 4212 | 4719 | 36,608 | 237,087 |

|  |  |  |  |  |
|---|---|---|---|---|
| 365 | 365 | 365 | 365 | 365 |
| × 2 | × 9 | × 10 | × 55 | × 26 |
| 730 | 3285 | 3650 | 1825 | 2190 |
|  |  |  | 18250 | 7300 |
|  |  |  | 20,075 | 9490 |

**In conclusion.** Ask: If you multiply 2 by 50 and then 2 by 3 and add them together, what is the answer? [106, 2 × 53] If you multiply any number by 50 and then by 3 and add them together, what is the answer? [number × 53]

Do not insist that the child write the little ones. Some can do it mentally.

Technically, it is not necessary to write the 0 in the right column of the second line. However, it helps children in their understanding that they are multiplying by 3 tens and not by 3 ones.

Unfortunately, some children have been taught to write an "x" as the placeholder. This nonstandard use of x has caused those children considerable confusion when they studied algebra.

If there is additional time following this lesson, play the Multiples Solitaire game, found in *Math Card Games* book, P19.

# LESSON 60: FACTOR PAIRS

**OBJECTIVES:**

1. To review factors
2. To find all the factors and factor pairs for a given number

**MATERIALS:**

1. Math Balance
2. Worksheet 38, Factor Pairs

---

## ACTIVITIES FOR TEACHING:

***Warm-up.*** Give the child the worksheet. Tell her to do just the warm-up equations. Solutions are:

$$\begin{array}{r} 43 \ (7) \\ \times\,27 \ (0) \\ \hline 301 \\ \underline{860} \\ 1161 \ (0) \end{array} \qquad \begin{array}{r} 287 \ (8) \\ \times\,45 \ (0) \\ \hline 1435 \\ \underline{11480} \\ 12{,}915 \ (0) \end{array} \qquad \begin{array}{r} 8263 \ (1) \\ \times\,58 \ (4) \\ \hline 66104 \\ \underline{413150} \\ 479{,}254 \ (4) \end{array}$$

***Finding factor pairs for 24.*** Write:

$$24 = 4 \times \underline{\ \ }$$

and ask: What is the missing factor in this equation? [6] Say: A factor must be a whole number. Ask: Can one half be a factor? [No, a factor must be a whole number.] What are two other factors when multiplied together equal 24?

$$24 = 3 \times 8$$

$$24 = 12 \times 2$$

$$24 = 24 \times 1$$

Ask: What are factor pairs for 24? [1 & 24, 2 & 12, 3 & 8, 4 & 6] Write them in order from least to greatest:

$$1, 2, 3, 4, 6, 8, 12, 24$$

***Verifying factors on the math balance.*** Distribute the math balance to the child. Say: To check if 2 is a factor of 24, put 24 on the left side of the balance. Ask: How many weights do you need to put on the right 2-peg? [12] More weights can be put on the back and on top of the hanging weights. See the figure below.

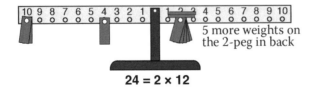

5 more weights on the 2-peg in back

**24 = 2 × 12**

Now tell her to check if 3 is a factor of 24? [yes] See the figure on the next page.

## EXPLANATIONS:

Since the warm-up may take longer, this lesson is shorter.

Although using check numbers with 2-digit multiplication has not specifically been taught, it is similar to previous lessons.

Factors are important for adding and subtracting fractions with different denominators.

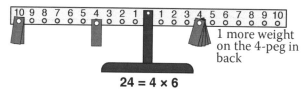

3 more weights on the 3-peg in back

**24 = 3 × 8**

Then tell her to check if 4 is a factor of 24? [yes] See the figure below.

1 more weight on the 4-peg in back

**24 = 4 × 6**

***Finding factor pairs for 36.*** Write:

36

and ask: What are factor pairs for 36? [1 & 36, 2 & 18, 3 & 12, 4 & 9, 6 & 6]

Ask: How can you tell by looking at a number if 2 is a factor? [if the number is even] Is 2 a factor of 36? [yes]

Say: You can tell by looking at a number if 3 is a factor when the check number is 3, 6, or 0. Ask: Is 3 a factor of 12? [yes] Is 3 a factor of 14? [no] Is 3 a factor of 36? [yes]

Ask: How can you tell by looking if 5 is a factor? [if the number ends in 0 or 5] Is 5 a factor of 36? [no]

Ask: How can you tell by looking at a number if 9 is a factor? [if the check number is 0] Is 9 a factor of 36? [yes]

Ask: How can you tell by looking at a number if 10 is a factor? [if the number ends in 0] Is 10 a factor of 36? [no]

***Worksheet 38.*** Tell her to complete the worksheet. The solutions are below.

The child may use the math balance to do the worksheet.

Factor pairs for 12: **1 & 12, 2 & 6, 3 & 4**
Factors of 12: **1, 2, 3, 4, 6, 12**

Factor pairs for 10: **1 & 10, 2 & 5**
Factors of 10: **1, 2, 5, 10**

Factor pairs for 11: **1 & 11**
Factors of 11: **1, 11**

Factor pairs for 18: **1 & 18, 2 & 9, 3 & 6**
Factors of 18: **1, 2, 3, 6, 9, 18**

Factor pairs for 25: **1 & 25, 5 & 5**
Factors of 25: **1, 5, 25**

Factor pairs for 56: **1 & 56, 2 & 28, 4 & 14, 7 & 8**
Factors of 56: **1, 2, 4, 7, 8, 14, 28, 56**

Factor pairs for 48: **1 & 48, 2 & 24, 3 & 16, 4 & 12, 6 & 8**
Factors of 48: **1, 2, 3, 4, 6, 8, 12, 16, 24, 48**

Factor pairs for 100: **1 & 100, 2 & 50, 4 & 25, 5 & 20, 10 & 10**
Factors of 100: **1, 2, 4, 5, 10, 20, 25, 50, 100**

***In conclusion.*** Ask: If $n$ is any number, what are two factors? [1 and $n$] If $n$ is 51, is 2 a factor? [no] How do you know? [not even]

If there is additional time following this lesson, play the Find the Two Factors game, found in *Math Card Games* book, P29,

# Lesson 61: Prime Numbers

## OBJECTIVES:

1. To learn the terms *prime number* and *composite number*
2. To find prime numbers

## MATERIALS:

1. Worksheet 39, Prime Numbers
2. Casio SL-450S calculator

| ACTIVITIES FOR TEACHING: | EXPLANATIONS: |
|---|---|

**Warm-up.** Give the child the worksheet. Tell her to do just the warm-up equations. Solutions are:

$$823 \ (4)$$
$$\underline{\times 67} \ (4)$$
$$5761$$
$$\underline{49380}$$
$$55{,}141 \ (7)$$

$$4539 \ (3)$$
$$\underline{\times 83} \ (2)$$
$$13617$$
$$\underline{363120}$$
$$376{,}737 \ (6)$$

**Worksheet 39.** Tell the child to read and answer the questions down to the first dotted line on the worksheet. Questions and answers are below.

What are the factors of 7? **1, 7** of 6? **1, 2, 3, 6** of 2? **1, 2**

A number having only two factors is called a *prime number*.

Is 7 a prime number? **yes** Is 6 a prime number? **no** Is 2 a prime number? **yes**

The number 1 has only one factor, so 1 is not a prime number.

A number having more than two factors is called a *composite number*. "Composite" means composed of parts.

Is 7 a composite number? **no** Is 6 a composite number? **yes**

Discuss the answers. Then ask the child to do the true and false questions. Questions and answers are below.

**true** A prime number has only two factors.

**false** A composite number always has an even number of factors.

**true** Two is the only even prime number.

**true** The number one is neither a prime number nor a composite number.

**Determining primes.** Write:

$$8 \quad 10$$

and ask: How can you tell that these two numbers are not prime? [They are even numbers, so they are multiples of 2.]

Write: $$10 \quad 15 \quad 20$$

and ask: How can you tell that these three numbers are not prime? [They are multiples of 5.]

Write: $$6 \quad 9 \quad 12$$

and ask: How can you tell by looking at the check

Mathematicians have not considered 1 to be a prime number for over 100 years. Excluding 1 as a prime number has more advantages than disadvantages, especially in advanced math.

An artistic child might like to draw a cartoon showing 1 not fitting in with either the prime or the composite numbers. (Please send us copies of good examples to info@RightStartMath.com.)

If a number has more than one factor pair, it is not prime.

| ACTIVITIES FOR TEACHING CONTINUED: | EXPLANATIONS CONTINUED: |
|---|---|

numbers of these three numbers that they are not prime? [Check numbers of multiples of 3 are 0, 3, 6.]

Write:         22   33   44

and ask: How can you tell that these three numbers are not prime? [ -- multiples of 11.]

Tell her to do the next section of the worksheet. The questions and answers are below.

How do you know that 8, 10, 16, and 98 are not primes? **even numbers**

How do you know that 15, 30, and 85 are not primes? **multiples of 5**

How do you know that 12, 51, and 84 are not primes? **multiples of 3**

How do you know that 14, 28, and 63 are not primes? **multiples of 7**

***Using a calculator to find prime numbers.*** Give the child the calculator. Write:

89

Say: We want to find out if 89 is a prime number. Ask: Is it a multiple of 2? [no] Is it a multiple of 3? [no] Is it a multiple of 5? [no]

To check for harder multiples, we only need to see if any prime numbers are a factor and we can use a calculator. Ask: What is the next prime? [7] Say: Divide 89 by 7. [12.714285] The digits after the dot mean that there is a remainder, so 7 is not a multiple.

Ask: What is the next prime? [11] Say: Divide 89 by 11. [8.090909] Ask: Is 11 a multiple? [no] Do we need to continue? [no] Why not? [Any further quotients will be less than 11.]

Write:         399

Say: Rather than entering 399 every time on the calculator, put 399 into memory. First, clear memory by pressing (MRC)(MRC). To put 399 into memory, enter 399 and press (M+). Divide by the next prime, 13. To divide 399 by another number, press (MRC) to get 399 again and continue to divide. Check if 399 is a prime. [no, 19 and 21 are factors]

Tell her to complete the worksheet. See below.

Is 97 a prime number? **yes**

Is 307 a prime number? **yes**

Is 667 a prime number? **no, (factors are 23 and 29)**

***In conclusion.*** Ask: What number is neither prime nor composite? [1] What is the smallest prime number? [2] Is 100 prime or composite? [composite]

The word "dot" is used here because the term "decimal point" has not yet been introduced.

When checking for factor pairs, 89 ÷ 7 is close to 12 and 89 ÷ 11 is close to 8, then checking 89 ÷ 13 would be even less than 8, so there's no need to check further.

By performing these repetitive calculations, the child may come to appreciate the Sieve of Eratosthenes in the next lesson.

Finding prime numbers on a supercomputer tests its speed and accuracy.

Prime numbers are a very important part of computer security.

# LESSON 62: SIEVE OF ERATOSTHENES

### OBJECTIVES:
1. To find prime numbers using the Sieve of Eratosthenes
2. To introduce the Goldbach conjecture

### MATERIALS:
1. Worksheet 40, Sieve of Eratosthenes
2. Casio SL-450S calculator

| ACTIVITIES FOR TEACHING: | EXPLANATIONS: |
|---|---|

**Warm-up.** Give the child the worksheet. Tell her to do just the warm-up equations. Solutions are:

$$
\begin{array}{r}
382\ \textbf{(4)} \\
\times\,49\ \textbf{(4)} \\
\hline
3438 \\
\underline{15280} \\
\textbf{18,718}\ \textbf{(7)}
\end{array}
\qquad
\begin{array}{r}
1786\ \textbf{(4)} \\
\times\,25\ \textbf{(7)} \\
\hline
8930 \\
\underline{35720} \\
\textbf{44,650}\ \textbf{(1)}
\end{array}
$$

Ask: What is a prime number? [a number having only two factors, 1 and itself] What are the first five prime numbers? [2, 3, 5, 7, and 11]

**Sieve of Eratosthenes.** Tell the child about Eratosthenes (air-uh-TOSS-the-knees). Say: Eratosthenes was a Greek mathematician, who lived from 276 to 194 B.C. He was interested in prime numbers and developed a method for finding them.

Say: His idea was to find and cross out all the composite numbers, leaving the prime numbers. Today we call this method the *Sieve of Eratosthenes*. A sieve is similar to a strainer used to remove water after cooking macaroni.

**Worksheet 40.** Give the child the calculator. Say: On the hundred chart on your worksheet, you will be finding primes like Eratosthenes did with his sieve method. He crossed out the multiples of primes, but not the primes themselves. Start with the first prime, 2; circle it. Ask: What are the multiples of 2? [4, 6, ... 100] Say: Cross them out.

Ask: What is the next prime number? [3] Say: Circle it. Use your calculator to find the multiples and cross them out. Enter 3, then press ⊕⊕⊜⊜. Keep pressing ⊜ until you have all the multiples. Ask: Did you need to cross out the even multiples of 3? [no]

Ask: What is the next prime number? [5] Say: Circle it. Ask: What do you cross out? [5, 10, . . ., 100] Do you need your calculator? [no]

| ACTIVITIES FOR TEACHING CONTINUED: | EXPLANATIONS CONTINUED: |
|---|---|

Say: Continue until you have found all the prime numbers. Be sure to circle all the primes, then write them on the lines on the worksheet.

The solution is shown below. Tell her to correct any errors.

| 1 | 2 | 3 | 4 | 5 | 6 | 7 | 8 | 9 | 10 |
|---|---|---|---|---|---|---|---|---|---|
| 11 | 12 | 13 | 14 | 15 | 16 | 17 | 18 | 19 | 20 |
| 21 | 22 | 23 | 24 | 25 | 26 | 27 | 28 | 29 | 30 |
| 31 | 32 | 33 | 34 | 35 | 36 | 37 | 38 | 39 | 40 |
| 41 | 42 | 43 | 44 | 45 | 46 | 47 | 48 | 49 | 50 |
| 51 | 52 | 53 | 54 | 55 | 56 | 57 | 58 | 59 | 60 |
| 61 | 62 | 63 | 64 | 65 | 66 | 67 | 68 | 69 | 70 |
| 71 | 72 | 73 | 74 | 75 | 76 | 77 | 78 | 79 | 80 |
| 81 | 82 | 83 | 84 | 85 | 86 | 87 | 88 | 89 | 90 |
| 91 | 92 | 93 | 94 | 95 | 96 | 97 | 98 | 99 | 100 |

**The Sieve of Eratosthenes with the prime numbers circled.**

List the prime numbers:
**2, 3, 5, 7, 11**
**13, 17, 19, 23, 29**
**31, 37, 41, 43, 47**
**53, 59, 61, 67, 71**
**73, 79, 83, 89, 97**

***Goldbach conjecture.*** Tell the child about the Goldbach conjecture. Say: In 1742, Christian Goldbach (GOLD-bahk), a German mathematician, wrote to his friend that he was quite sure that every even number greater than 2 could be the sum of two primes.

Goldbach's conjecture is called a "conjecture" because no one has been able to prove it beyond 4 quintillion digits, 4,000,000,000,000,000,000.

Write: $10 = \_\_ + \_\_$

and ask: Can you find two prime numbers that will add to 10? [3 + 7 or 5 + 5]

Write: $24 = \_\_ + \_\_$

and ask: Can you find more than one way that two primes will add to 24? [5 + 19, 7 + 17, 11 + 13]

Tell her to complete the worksheet. The solutions are below.

| | | | |
|---|---|---|---|
| 12 = **7 + 5** | | | |
| 18 = **13 + 5** | 18 = **11 + 7** | | |
| 32 = **29 + 3** | 32 = **19 + 13** | | |
| 40 = **37 + 3** | 40 = **29 + 11** | 40 = **23 + 17** | |
| 58 = **53 + 5** | 58 = **47 + 11** | 58 = **41 + 17** | 58 = **29 + 29** |

***In conclusion.*** Ask: What number is neither prime nor composite? [1] Is your birth date a prime number?

If there is additional time following this lesson, play the Find the Two Factors game, found in *Math Card Games* book, P29.

# ENRICHMENT LESSON 63: PRIME NUMBERS TO 1000

## OBJECTIVES:
1. To find prime numbers to 1000
2. To look for patterns in prime numbers

## MATERIALS:
1. Sieve of Eratosthenes, Appendix 2, 1 copy of each page
2. Casio SL-450S calculator
3. **Scissors**

| ACTIVITIES FOR TEACHING: | EXPLANATIONS: |
|---|---|
| ***Appendix pages.*** Show the child the 10 different charts from the appendix, emphasizing that one chart includes numbers from 1 to 100. Another chart has numbers from 101 to 200, another from 201 to 300, and so on to 1000. Give the child the charts. | This year's Math Project consists of finding the prime numbers to 1000. |
| Say: You will be finding the prime numbers from 1 to 1000 on these charts, using the Sieve of Eratosthenes algorithm, or procedure. | This enrichment lesson is designed to bring the world of math into everyday life. If necessary because of time restraints, the lesson may be omitted without loss of continuity. |
| ***Multiples of 2, 3, and 5.*** Say: On the first chart, circle 2 and cross out all the multiples of 2 on all the charts. Repeat for multiples of 3 and 5. | |
| ***Other multiples.*** Tell the child she can take turns being the caller, similar to a bingo game. The other person listens for the numbers that are on the chart and cross out any she hears. The caller should not say any numbers ending in an even number or a 5 or over 1000. | This is a great activity for the whole family. |
| Explain that for 7, the caller enters 7 on the calculator, then presses $+$ $+$ $=$. Continuing to press $=$ will give numbers 21, 28, 35, 42, 49, . . . , 987, 994, 1001. The caller will say 21, 49, . . . , 987 because the other numbers are even or end in 5 or are over 1000. | |
| Continue with the 11, 13, and other primes to 499. Then circle the remaining primes on the charts starting with 500 or higher. Solutions are on the next page | If each number is said in an average of 3 seconds, the total time to call all the numbers will be about 15 minutes. This assumes the unnecesary numbers are not spoken. |
| ***Displaying the prime numbers.*** Have the child cut out her charts. Attach them to a wall with the 1–100 chart on top and the 901–1000 at the bottom. With the charts touching, the column will be 64" (163 cm) high. | |
| ***Finding patterns.*** There are no repeating patterns. But note how often primes are separated by 10. | On January 20, 2016, in Missouri, the record was broken for finding the largest prime number. This number has 22,338,618 digits. |
| ***In conclusion.*** Ask: Except for the first row, which columns have no prime numbers? [the columns with even numbers and multiples of 5] In the last lesson, you checked to see if a number was prime by lots of dividing; how long would it take to do the divisions for numbers to 1000? [a really long time] Is the sieve algorithm easier? | The previous record was 17,425,170 digits, found on February 6, 2013. |

## EXPLANATIONS CONTINUED:

More patterns can be seen when the charts are arranged vertically as shown, rather than horizontally.

# LESSON 64: REMAINDER PROBLEMS

## OBJECTIVES:
1. To solve problems involving remainders

## MATERIALS:
1. Worksheet 41, Remainder Problems
2. *Math Card Games* book, D12

| ACTIVITIES FOR TEACHING: | EXPLANATIONS: |
|---|---|

**ACTIVITIES FOR TEACHING:**

***Warm-up.*** Give the child the worksheet. Tell her to do just the warm-up problems. Solutions are:

> In February, 2013, the largest known prime number had 17,425,170 digits. Then in January, 2016, a larger prime was found with 4,913,448 more digits. How many digits does the newest prime have? **22,338,618**

> With five thousand digits fitting on an ordinary sheet of paper, the prime would take about 4400 sheets of paper. How many books does this make if each book has 100 pages? **44 books**

***Worksheet 41, Problem 1.*** Tell the child to read and solve Problem 1 on the worksheet in two ways.

> Valerie has $23. She is buying books, which cost $5 each. How many books can she buy? What is her change?

After she has solved the problem, ask if she considered solving it using subtraction. Tell the child to explain it. It is done by subtracting 5 from 23.

$$23 - 5 - 5 - 5 - 5 = 3$$

Counting the number of 5s gives 4 books with $3 left over.

Ask if she can solve it using addition. Do it by adding 5s until the sum goes over 23,

$$5 + 5 + 5 + 5 = 20$$

Again, counting the number of 5s gives 4 books with $3 left over.

Ask if she can solve it using multiplication. Find the highest *n* that is less 23.

$$5 \times n = 23$$

The answer *n* is 4 with $3 change.

Now, have her solve it with division and explain it.

$$n = 23 \div 5$$

The answer *n* is 4 books with $3 change.

**EXPLANATIONS:**

It is interesting to note that any of the four operations can be used to solve this problem, although division is the most practical.

| ACTIVITIES FOR TEACHING CONTINUED: | EXPLANATIONS CONTINUED: |

**Problem 2.** Tell her to read and solve the second problem.

> Van is dividing 48 sheets of construction paper equally among 4 boys and 5 girls. How many will each child get? How many sheets of paper will be left?

One way to solve the problem is:

$$p = 48 \div (4 + 5)$$

$$p = 5 \text{ r}3$$

Each child gets 5 sheets of paper and 3 sheets will be left.

These problems can be solved in other ways.

**Problem 3.** Tell her to read and solve the third problem.

> Victor wants to buy 30 small items. They are sold 8 to a package. Each package costs $9. What will the items cost? How many extras will there be?

One way to solve the problem is:

$$p \times 8 = 30$$

$$p = 30 \div 8 = 3 \text{ r}6$$

To get 30 items, Victor needs to buy 4 packages.

$$4 \times 8 = 32$$

There will be 2 extra. The cost is $9 \times 4 = \$36$.

**Problem 4.** Tell her to read and solve the fourth problem.

> Violet is making a square pen for a pet rabbit. She has 14 m of fencing. What is the largest pen she can make? How much fencing will remain?

A square has 4 equal sides.

$$14 \div 4 = 3 \text{ r}2$$

Violet can make a square pen 3 m on a side. There will be 2 m of fencing left over.

**Division War game variation.** Play the following variation of Division War game from *Math Card Games* book, D12. Instead of the higher quotient, the player with the higher remainder takes the cards. The multiplication card can always be the dividend. It is not necessary to exclude cards greater than 11 times the divisor.

The best way to find a remainder is by "going up." For example, find the remainder for $40 \div 6$. Rather than thinking $40 - 36$, think going up from 36 to 40, which is 4.

**In conclusion.** Ask: What is the remainder when dividing 17 by 7? [3] What is the remainder when dividing 17 by 8? [1] What is the remainder when dividing 17 by 9? [8]

# LESSON 65: WORKING WITH REMAINDERS

**OBJECTIVES:**
1. To practice finding remainders
2. To discuss dividing by zero

**MATERIALS:**
1. Basic number cards

| ACTIVITIES FOR TEACHING: | EXPLANATIONS: |
|---|---|
| **Warm-up.** Ask: What is the smallest prime number? [2] Is 19 prime or composite? [prime] Is 180 prime or composite? [composite] What number is neither prime nor composite? [1] | |

**Warm-up.** Ask: What is the smallest prime number? [2] Is 19 prime or composite? [prime] Is 180 prime or composite? [composite] What number is neither prime nor composite? [1]

Ask: What is the remainder when dividing 16 by 5? [1] What is the remainder when dividing 16 by 6? [4] What is the remainder when dividing 16 by 7? [2]

**Problem.** Give the following problem to the child:

Jacob is dividing a bag of apples by putting them on 6 trays. Three apples fit on each tray. Two apples remain. How many apples does he have to divide?

Tell her to solve it. One way is the following:

$$n \div 6 = 3$$

and ask: How can you find $n$? [$6 \times 3 = 18$]

Write: $\qquad n \div 6 = 3\,r2$

and ask: Now how can you find $n$? [$6 \times 3 + 2 = 20$, 20 apples to divide]

**Preparation for Division Remainder War game.** Explain that for today's game, she will be forming division expressions with three numbers to make the greatest remainder. Write:

$$2 \qquad 5 \qquad 3$$

and say: Use these three digits to make an expression with a 2-digit number divided by a single digit.

$$25 \div 3 \qquad 52 \div 3 \qquad 23 \div 5 \qquad 53 \div 2 \qquad 32 \div 5 \qquad 35 \div 2$$

and ask: Are these all the expressions using the three numbers? [yes] What are the remainders for each expression? [1, 1, 3, 1, 2, 1] Which expression has the greatest remainder? [$23 \div 5$]

**Dividing by zero.** Say: Supposing the numbers were

$$2 \qquad 0 \qquad 2$$

and ask: Can you have $20 \div 2$? [yes]

| ACTIVITIES FOR TEACHING CONTINUED: | EXPLANATIONS CONTINUED: |
|---|---|

Write: $\quad\quad\quad\quad 20 \div 2 = 10$

because $\quad\quad\quad 2 \times 10 = 20$

Say: Let's see what happens when we divide by zero:

$$22 \div 0 = x$$

But $\quad\quad\quad\quad 0 \times x = 0, \text{ not } 22!$

Say: Dividing by 0 does not work. Another way to look at it is to think $20 \div 2 = 10$ means how many 2s are in 20. Ask: How many are there? [10] How many 0s are in 22, or any number? Say: Calculators cannot find the answer, either.

***Division Remainder War game.*** Play the Division Remainder War game. Use half a deck of basic number cards, from 0 to 10, for two players. Divide the deck between the players by comparing heights. The object of the game is to capture the most cards by having the greater remainder.

To start, each player takes three cards and combines two cards to form a number to be divided leaving the third card as the divisor. The "0" on a 10 card may be overlapped by another card.

Some possible arrangements for cards with numbers 2, 1, 6 are shown below.

| Remainder for 21 ÷ 6 is 3. | Remainder for 12 ÷ 6 is 0. | Remainder for 61 ÷ 2 is 1. |
|---|---|---|

Players state their remainder; the player with the greater remainder takes all six cards. Wars are resolved by players each taking another turn without laying any extra cards face down. The greater remainder takes all 12 cards in the war.

Players continue by taking three more cards. The game continues for a certain amount of time or until one player has collected all the cards. The winner is the player with the most cards.

***In conclusion.*** Ask: If you are dividing a number by 5, what is the largest possible remainder? [4] If you are dividing a number by 9, what is the largest possible remainder? [8] If you are dividing a number by $n$, what is the largest possible remainder? [$n - 1$]

# Lesson 66: Dividing 4-Digit Numbers on the Abacus

## OBJECTIVES:
1. To learn to divide by 2 on side 2 of the AL Abacus in preparation for short division

## MATERIALS:
1. AL Abacus
2. Worksheet 42, Dividing 4-Digit Numbers
3. Short Multiplication Table, Appendix p. 1, if needed

## ACTIVITIES FOR TEACHING:

***Warm-up.*** Ask: What is the remainder when dividing 9 by 6? [3] What is the remainder when dividing 9 by 3? [0]

Ask: How many ones are in 7? [7] How many ones are in 10? [10] How many ones are in 14? [14] Make certain the child understands that there are 14 ones in 14 as well as 1 ten and 4 ones. Ask: How many ones are in 27? [27]

***Division symbols.*** Tell the child there are several ways to write division. Ask: How many can you think of? Write the examples. Give the following hints as necessary: How would you write 12 divided by 4 in a division equation? How would you write 3 divided by 4 as a fraction? Say: Recipes and road signs use fractions. See below.

$$12 \div 4 \qquad \frac{3}{4} \qquad \frac{3}{4}$$

Tell her there is another way to write division problems that is a tool for short division or long division. Say: We write the dividend, the number to be divided, then put a "box" around it. The divisor, the number we are dividing by, goes in front and the quotient, the answer, goes on top. Demonstrate with the following number:

$$260 \qquad \overline{)260} \qquad 2\overline{)260} \qquad 2\overline{)260}^{130}$$

Ask: What happens when you multiply the two numbers on the outside of the box? [130 × 2 = 260]

***Dividing by 2 on the abacus.*** Give the child the abacus. Tell her to watch while you perform division on the abacus. Involve the child as much as possible.

Write: $2\overline{)8476}$

and say: We will divide 8476 by 2 on side 2 of the abacus. Move all the beads to the middle of the abacus as shown on the left figure on next page. Then enter 8476 at the top as shown in the second figure. Explain that the answer will appear at the bottom of the abacus.

Say: Let's divide 8 thousands by 2. We do this by removing the 8 thousands and entering the quotient,

## EXPLANATIONS:

There is no actual name for this symbol. It is sometimes referred to as the "division box" or "division house."

It works better for the child to watch the demonstration first rather than copying each step.

The little lines indicating the missing quotient helps the child keep track of place value.

## ACTIVITIES FOR TEACHING CONTINUED:    ## EXPLANATIONS CONTINUED:

4 thousand, at the bottom. Write the 4 in the thousands place. See the third figure below.

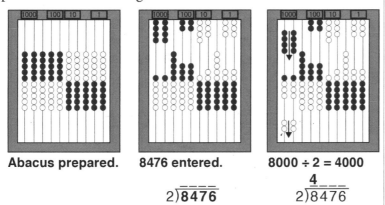

**Abacus prepared.**     **8476 entered.**     **8000 ÷ 2 = 4000**

$$2\overline{)8476}$$     $$\begin{array}{r} 4 \\[-3pt] 2\overline{)8476} \end{array}$$

Say: Next we divide 4 hundreds by 2. Remove 4 hundreds and enter 2 hundreds at the bottom. Ask: What do we write? [2 in the hundreds place] See the first figure below.

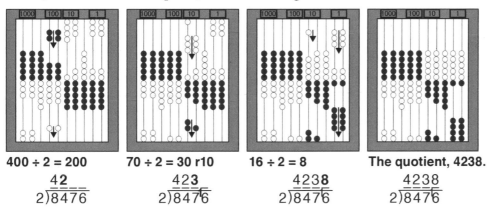

**400 ÷ 2 = 200**     **70 ÷ 2 = 30 r10**     **16 ÷ 2 = 8**     **The quotient, 4238.**

$$\begin{array}{r} 42 \\[-3pt] 2\overline{)8476} \end{array}$$     $$\begin{array}{r} 423 \\[-3pt] 2\overline{)8476} \end{array}$$     $$\begin{array}{r} 4238 \\[-3pt] 2\overline{)8476} \end{array}$$     $$\begin{array}{r} 4238 \\[-3pt] 2\overline{)8476} \end{array}$$

Ask: What do we divide next? [7 tens] What is 7 tens divided by 2? [3 tens and remainder 1] Remove 6 tens and enter 3 tens at the bottom. Ask: What do we write? [3 in the tens place] How many ones are there? [16] Say: To show 16 ones, we write a small 1 before the ones place. See second figure above.

Ask: What is 16 divided by 2? [8] Remove the 16 and enter at the bottom. Ask: What do we write? [8] See the last figures.

***Worksheet 42.*** Give the child the worksheet and tell her to do the first two problems. Tell her to only do the first two rows. The solutions are below.

Some children may need to use the short multiplication table.

$$\begin{array}{r} 4238 \\[-3pt] 2\overline{)8476} \end{array} \quad \begin{array}{r} 3120 \\[-3pt] 2\overline{)6240} \end{array} \quad \begin{array}{r} 1425 \\[-3pt] 2\overline{)2850} \end{array} \quad \begin{array}{r} 3364 \\[-3pt] 2\overline{)6728} \end{array}$$

$$\begin{array}{r} 1732 \\[-3pt] 2\overline{)3464} \end{array} \quad \begin{array}{r} 4573 \\[-3pt] 2\overline{)9146} \end{array} \quad \begin{array}{r} 3681 \\[-3pt] 2\overline{)7362} \end{array} \quad \begin{array}{r} 2277 \\[-3pt] 2\overline{)4554} \end{array}$$

The remaining problems on this worksheet will be completed in future lessons.

***In conclusion.*** Ask: What is 24 divided by 6? [4] What is 240 divided by 6? [40] What is 2400 divided by 6? [400]

If there is additional time following this lesson, play the Division Remainder War game from Lesson 65.

# LESSON 67: MORE DIVIDING 4-DIGIT NUMBERS ON THE ABACUS

### OBJECTIVES:

1. To practice dividing on side 2 of the AL Abacus in preparation for short division

### MATERIALS:

1. Worksheet 42, Dividing 4-Digit Numbers
2. AL Abacus
3. Short Multiplication Table, Appendix p.1, if needed

### ACTIVITIES FOR TEACHING:

***Warm-up.*** Ask: What is the remainder when dividing 12 by 5? [2] What is the remainder when dividing 12 by 6? [0] What is the remainder when dividing 12 by 7? [5]

Ask: How many ones are in 2? [2] How many ones are in 20? [20] How many tens are in 20? [2] How many tens are in 80? [8] How many tens are in 140? [14] How many tens are in 320? [32]

***Dividing by 3 on the abacus.*** Tell the child to watch while you divide a number by 3 on the abacus.

Write: 　　　　　　　3)6742 (with overline)

Enter 6742 on side 2 of the abacus as shown in the first figure below.

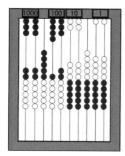 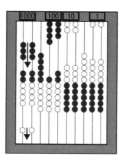 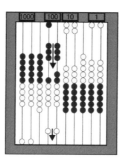

| **6742 entered.** | **6000 ÷ 3 = 2000** | **700 ÷ 3 = 200 r100** |
|---|---|---|
| 3)6742 | 2<br>3)6742 | 22<br>3)6742 |

Ask: What are we dividing by? [3] What is 6000 divided by 3? [2000] Remove the 6 thousand and enter 2000 at the bottom. Write the 2 in the thousands place. See the second figure above.

Ask: What is 7 hundreds divided by 3? [2 hundred leaving 1 hundred as the remainder] Remove 6 hundreds and enter 2 hundreds at the bottom. Ask: What do we write? [2 in the hundreds place] See the third figure.

Ask: What do we divide next? [tens] How many tens are there? [14 tens] Say: To show 14 tens, we write a small 1 before the 4. Ask: What is 14 tens divided by 3? [4 tens and remainder 2] Remove 12 tens and enter 4 tens at the bottom.

### EXPLANATIONS:

Short division, where nothing is written below the dividend, is taught in these lessons. Long division is unnecessary for single-digit divisors.

Using long division for single digits interferes with learning a more efficient method, and is not necessary for learning long division for double-digits.

Long division does not foster mathematical understanding and is rarely used in everyday life. Also, it is time-consuming and is very difficult for some children to learn.

| ACTIVITIES FOR TEACHING CONTINUED: | EXPLANATIONS CONTINUED: |
|---|---|

Ask: What do we write? [4 in the tens place] See the first figure below.

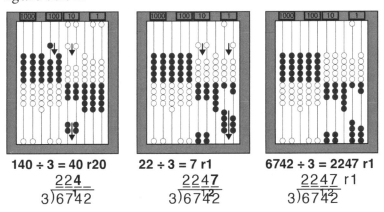

**140 ÷ 3 = 40 r20**

$$\frac{224}{3)67\overset{1}{4}2}$$

**22 ÷ 3 = 7 r1**

$$\frac{2247}{3)67\overset{1}{4}\overset{2}{2}}$$

**6742 ÷ 3 = 2247 r1**

$$\frac{2247}{3)67\overset{1}{4}\overset{2}{2}} \text{ r1}$$

Ask: How many ones are there? [22] Say: To show 22 ones, we write a small 2 before the 2 in the dividend. Ask: What is 22 divided by 3? [7 and remainder 1] Remove 21 and enter 7 at the bottom. Ask: What do we write? [7] Explain that we can write the remainder as r1. See the third figure.

Let the child discover for herself that the remainder after dividing a digit becomes the "little number" for the next digit.

**Worksheet 42.** Give the child the abacus. Tell her to do the first problem in the third row on the worksheet, which is the same problem as the one above.

Tell her to complete the three rows, down to the next dotted line. The solutions are below.

Some children may need to use the short multiplication table.

$$\frac{2247}{3)674\overset{1}{2}} \text{ r1} \qquad \frac{2346}{4)93\overset{1}{8}4} \qquad \frac{1198}{7)83\overset{1}{8}6} \qquad \frac{1219}{8)97\overset{5}{5}9} \text{ r7}$$

$$\frac{1104}{9)993\overset{3}{6}} \qquad \frac{1460}{5)73\overset{2}{0}4} \text{ r4} \qquad \frac{1091}{6)65\overset{5}{4}6} \qquad \frac{1540}{3)46\overset{1}{2}2} \text{ r2}$$

$$\frac{856}{5)42\overset{2}{8}0} \qquad \frac{456}{4)18\overset{2}{2}4} \qquad \frac{604}{3)18\overset{1}{2}} \qquad \frac{537}{7)37\overset{2}{6}0} \text{ r1}$$

**In conclusion.** Ask: What is 72 divided by 8? [9] What is 720 divided by 8? [90] What is 7200 divided by 8? [900] What is 72,000 divided by 8? [9000]

The second row introduces zeros in the quotient, which presents no problem on the abacus.

The third row introduces the case where the first digit is less than the divisor, which again is no problem on the abacus. Do not insist that the child write a leading 0 in the quotient nor an extra little number before the second digit.

If there is additional time following this lesson, have the child choose a game to play.

# LESSON 68: SHORT DIVISION

**OBJECTIVES:**

1. To learn to do short division, including remainders
2. To use check numbers for checking division

**MATERIALS:**

1. Worksheet 42, Dividing 4-Digit Numbers
2. AL Abacus

| **ACTIVITIES FOR TEACHING:** | **EXPLANATIONS:** |
|---|---|

**ACTIVITIES FOR TEACHING:**

***Warm-up.*** Ask: What is the remainder when dividing 40 by 6? [4] What is the remainder when dividing 40 by 7? [5] What is the remainder when dividing 40 by 8? [0]

Ask: What is 40 divided by 8? [5] What is 400 divided by 8? [50] What is 4000 divided by 8? [500] What is 40,000 divided by 8? [5000]

***Worksheet 42.*** Give the child the abacus. Tell her to do the first row of problems after the second dotted line on the worksheet. Say: Try to do them without your abacus, but use the abacus if you get stuck. The problems and solutions are below.

$$\begin{array}{r} 3423 \\ 2\overline{)6846} \end{array} \qquad \begin{array}{r} 4937 \\ 2\overline{)9874} \end{array} \qquad \begin{array}{r} 1517 \\ 5\overline{)7585} \end{array} \qquad \begin{array}{r} 1240 \\ 7\overline{)8680} \end{array}$$

Then tell the child to check the four problems and explain each of the problems. Then tell her: This algorithm, or procedure, you are using for doing division is called *short division.*

***Checking the quotient.*** Tell her to look at the first problem:

$$\begin{array}{r} 3423 \\ 2\overline{)6846} \end{array}$$

Ask: What do you get when you multiply the two numbers outside the division house? [number inside the division house, 6846] Write:

$$3423 \times 2 = 6846$$

Say: In mathematical language, we say the quotient multiplied by the divisor equals the dividend.

***Using check numbers.*** Ask: What are the check numbers for the multiplication equation? See below.

$$\begin{array}{ccc} (3) & (2) & (6) \\ 3423 \times 2 & = & 6846 \end{array}$$

Does it work? [yes, (3) × (2) = (6)]

**EXPLANATIONS:**

Short division, where nothing is written below the dividend, should always be used when dividing by one digit. The traditional long division algorithm — once considered the pinnacle of arithmetic — is a rote procedure that is disappearing into history alongside the square root algorithm.

Unfortunately, many adults in the U.S. did not learn short division in school. It was mistakenly felt that learning short division would make learning long division more difficult. This is not the case.

Long division will be taught in the next level. However, children with learning difficulties should not be expected to learn it. With calculators so readily available, they will never use long division. Their time is better spent in learning other mathematics.

| ACTIVITIES FOR TEACHING CONTINUED: | EXPLANATIONS CONTINUED: |
|---|---|

Show her where she can write the check numbers for the short division problem. See below.

$$\frac{3423}{2\overline{)6846}}\ \begin{matrix}(3)\\(6)\end{matrix}$$

Tell her to use check numbers for the rest of the completed row on the worksheet. Solutions are below.

$$\frac{3423}{2\overline{)6846}}\ \begin{matrix}(3)\\(6)\end{matrix} \qquad \frac{4937}{2\overline{)9874}}\ \begin{matrix}(5)\\(1)\end{matrix} \qquad \frac{1517}{5\overline{)7585}}\ \begin{matrix}(5)\\(7)\end{matrix} \qquad \frac{1240}{7\overline{)8680}}\ \begin{matrix}(7)\\(4)\end{matrix}$$

**Because the check number for 2 is 2, it does not need to be written, although some children may prefer to write it.**

*Using check numbers with remainders.* Say: Now let's see what happens when we have a remainder. Write 607 divided by 3 as shown in the left figure below. Ask: What is the quotient? [201 r1] See the second figure below.

$$\frac{\phantom{---}}{3\overline{)607}} \qquad\qquad \frac{202\ \text{r1}}{3\overline{)607}}$$

Ask: What is the multiplication equation?

$$202 \times 3 + 1 = 607$$

Ask: What are the check numbers for the multiplication equation? See below.

$$\begin{matrix}(4)\ \ (3)\ \ (1)\ \ \ (4)\\202 \times 3 + 1 = 607\end{matrix}$$

Does it work? [yes, (4) × (3) + (1) = (4)]

Say: Since there is no space beside 202 to write its check number, we will write the (4) above it.

$$\begin{matrix}(4)\\\frac{202\ \text{r1}}{3\overline{)607}}\ (4)\end{matrix}$$

**Because the check numbers for the divisor and remainder are 3 and 1, they do not need to be written, although some children may prefer to write them.**

Ask: Does it work? [yes, (4) × (3) + (1) = (4)]

*Worksheet 42.* Then tell the child to complete the last two rows on the page. The solutions are below.

$$\frac{1341}{3\overline{)4023}}\ \begin{matrix}(0)\\(0)\end{matrix} \qquad \begin{matrix}(0)\\\frac{1341\ \text{r1}}{3\overline{)4024}}\ (1)\end{matrix} \qquad \frac{856}{5\overline{)4280}}\ \begin{matrix}(1)\\(5)\end{matrix} \qquad \begin{matrix}(1)\\\frac{856\ \text{r3}}{5\overline{)4283}}\ (8)\end{matrix}$$

$$\begin{matrix}(5)\\\frac{320\ \text{r6}}{9\overline{)2886}}\ (6)\end{matrix} \qquad \begin{matrix}(1)\\\frac{991\ \text{r2}}{6\overline{)5948}}\ (8)\end{matrix} \qquad \begin{matrix}(4)\\\frac{1912\ \text{r2}}{5\overline{)9562}}\ (4)\end{matrix} \qquad \begin{matrix}(4)\\\frac{886\ \text{r7}}{8\overline{)7095}}\ (3)\end{matrix}$$

*In conclusion.* Ask: What operation do you use to check subtraction? [addition] What operation do you use to check division? [multiplication] How do you check a division problem with a remainder? [The quotient multiplied by the divisor plus the remainder must equal the dividend.]

**If there is additional time following this lesson, play the Short Division game, found in *Math Card Games* book, D10.**

# LESSON 69: MULTIVIDES

**OBJECTIVES:**

1. To practice multiplication and division with "multivides"

2. To realize more fully that the order of multiplying and dividing makes no difference

**MATERIALS:**

1. Worksheet 43, Multivides

---

**ACTIVITIES FOR TEACHING:**

***Warm-up.*** Give the child the worksheet. Tell her to do just the warm-up problems. Solutions are:

$$
\begin{array}{ccc}
(4) & (0) & (3) \\
3226\ \text{r1} & 2151 & 1290\ \text{r3} \\
2)\overline{6453}\ (0) & 3)\overline{6453}\ (0) & 5)\overline{6453}\ (0)
\end{array}
$$

***Worksheet 43.*** Tell the child she is going to do an activity that uses multiplication and division, so it's called a *multivide*.

***Multivide for 2.*** Say: Look at the first column on your worksheet. Multiply 2 by 2 and write the product and check number.

Now multiply that product by 3, that product by 4, and so on to 6. Use the check numbers to check your work. Instead of using commas, extra space is used to show the periods. See the left figure below.

$$
\begin{array}{cccc}
2 & 2 & 2 & 2 \\
\times 2 & \times 2 & \times 2 & \times 2 \\
\hline
4\ (4) & 4\ (4) & 4\ (4) & 4\ (4) \\
\times 3 & \times 3 & \times 3 & \times 3 \\
\hline
12\ (3) & 12\ (3) & 12\ (3) & 12\ (3) \\
\times 4 & \times 4 & \times 4 & \times 4 \\
\hline
48\ (3) & 48\ (3) & 48\ (3) & 48\ (3) \\
\times 5 & \times 5 & \times 5 & \times 5 \\
\hline
240\ (6) & 240\ (6) & 240\ (6) & 240\ (6) \\
\times 6 & \times 6 & \times 6 & \times 6 \\
\hline
1\ 440\ (0) & 2)\overline{1\ 440}\ (0) & 2)\overline{1\ 440}\ (0) & 2)\overline{1\ 440}\ (0) \\
 & 720\ (0) & 3)\overline{720}\ (0) & 3)\overline{720}\ (0) \\
 & & 240\ (6) & 4)\overline{240}\ (6) \\
 & & & 5)\overline{60}\ (6) \\
 & & & 6)\overline{12}\ (3) \\
 & & & 2
\end{array}
$$

Say: The next part of the multivide is to divide by the same numbers: 2, 3, 4, 5, and 6.

**EXPLANATIONS:**

Multivides are a great self-checking activity that uses multiplication and short division.

---

133

## ACTIVITIES FOR TEACHING CONTINUED:

Write:  2)1 440 (0)

and say: The division box is turned upside down and the quotient is written below the number. Write the quotient:

2)1 440 (0)
720 (0)

Tell the child to use check numbers to check her quotients. See the figure above.

Ask: Do the check numbers work? [yes, (2) × (0) = (0)] Say: Next divide by 3:

2)1 440 (0)
3)720 (0)
240 (0)

**Worksheet 43.** Tell her to complete the multivide for 2. See the right figure on the previous page. Say: You can never have a remainder when doing a multivide. If you get a remainder, it means you have made a mistake somewhere and you need to find it and correct it before going on.

Tell her to complete the worksheet. The solutions are below.

```
      3                    4
    × 2                  × 2
    6 (6)                8 (8)
    × 3                  × 3
   18 (0)               24 (6)
    × 4                  × 4
   72 (0)               96 (6)
    × 5                  × 5
  360 (0)              480 (3)
    × 6                  × 6
 2 160 (0)            2 880 (0)
    × 7                  × 7
2)15 120 (0)         20 160 (0)
3)7 560 (0)             × 8
4)2 520 (0)         2)161 280 (0)
5)630 (0)           3)80 640 (0)
6)126 (0)           4)26 880 (6)
7)21 (3)            5)6 720 (6)
   3                6)1 344 (3)
                    7)224 (8)
                    8)32 (5)
                       4
```

**161,280: one hundred sixty one thousand two hundred eighty**

***In conclusion.*** Ask: When you do a multivide, what will the last number be? [same as the starting number] What do you do if you have a remainder? [look for an error]

## EXPLANATIONS CONTINUED:

According to a U.S. textbook from the 1800s, the inverted division box, or division house, was used for single-digit divisors and the quotients were written *below* the dividend.

Let the child discover that the final quotient will be the same as the starting number.

A regular multivide starts with a number and multiplies it by 2 through 9, then divides by 2 through 9. The one on the right is an example. These "partial" multivides are preparation.

Use check numbers to check each step of the process. This will help catch errors along the way.

If there is additional time following this lesson, play the Short Division game, found in *Math Card Games* book, D10.

# LESSON 70: ASSESSMENT REVIEW 2

**OBJECTIVES:**

1. To assess mastery of concepts learned in previous lessons

**MATERIALS:**

1. Worksheet 44, Assessment Review 2
2. 4-in-1 ruler

**ACTIVITIES FOR TEACHING:**

***Worksheet 44.*** Give the child the worksheet and ruler. Tell her that today will be a review for the upcoming assessment. She will complete the two-page worksheet, then discuss the solutions.

Tell her to listen to the problems and write the answers. Read each problem twice.

$$70 - 39 \qquad 13 \times 2 \qquad 30 \times 3 + 3$$

Tell her to complete the worksheet. Solutions are below and on the next page.

**EXPLANATIONS:**

This lesson is a review of concepts learned so far. It is designed to prepare the child for the upcoming assessment lesson.

---

Write only the answers.

**31**

**26**

**93**

Write the answers.

$641 + 273 =$ **914**

$2\frac{2}{3} + 1\frac{1}{3} =$ **4**

$(42 \div 6) + (42 \div 42) =$ **8**

Do the arithmetic. Use check numbers.

Add: $467 + 14,829$.

$$\begin{array}{r} 467 \ (8) \\ + \ 14,829 \ (6) \\ \hline 15,296 \ (5) \end{array}$$

Subtract: $9037 - 288$.

$$\begin{array}{r} 9037 \ (1) \\ - \ 288 \ (0) \\ \hline 8749 \ (1) \end{array}$$

$$\begin{array}{r} 2676 \ \textbf{(3)} \\ \times 25 \ \textbf{(7)} \\ \hline 13\ 380 \\ 53\ 520 \\ \hline 66,900 \ (3) \end{array}$$

An astronomical unit is the distance of the Earth to the sun, which is 149,597,870,700 meters.

Round this number to billions and to millions.

**150,000,000,000** **149,598,000,000**

Solve the problems.

Which rectangle has the greater perimeter?

$1\frac{7}{8}$     $1\frac{3}{4}$

A   $1\frac{5}{8}$    B   $1\frac{3}{4}$

$P(A) = 2 \times (1\frac{7}{8} + 1\frac{5}{8})$
$= 2 \times (2\frac{12}{8}) = 2 \times (3\frac{1}{2}) = 7$

$P(B) = 2 \times (1\frac{7}{8} + 1\frac{5}{8})$
$= 2 \times (2\frac{12}{8}) = 2 \times (3\frac{1}{2}) = 7$

**Perimeter is the same.**

Use a ruler to measure the triangle below in centimeters. Then find the perimeter.

$2\frac{1}{2}$    **6**

$6\frac{1}{2}$

$P = 2\frac{1}{2} + 6 + 6\frac{1}{2} = 15$ cm

A baby giraffe at birth is 6 ft tall. A fully grown male giraffe is three times taller. How tall is a male giraffe? What is the difference in height between the baby and the adult?

$m = b \times 3 = 6 \times 3 = 18$ ft
**The difference in height is** $18 - 6 = 12$ ft

**ACTIVITIES FOR TEACHING CONTINUED:**  |  **EXPLANATIONS CONTINUED:**

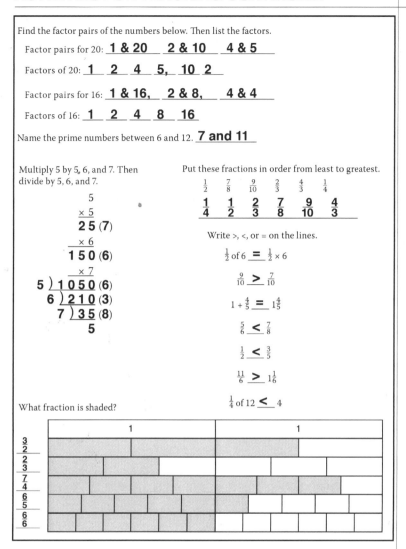

Find the factor pairs of the numbers below. Then list the factors.

Factor pairs for 20: **1 & 20    2 & 10    4 & 5**

Factors of 20: **1    2    4    5,  10  2**

Factor pairs for 16: **1 & 16,    2 & 8,    4 & 4**

Factors of 16: **1    2    4    8    16**

Name the prime numbers between 6 and 12. **7 and 11**

Multiply 5 by 5, 6, and 7. Then divide by 5, 6, and 7.

$$\begin{array}{r} 5 \\ \times\,5 \\ \hline \mathbf{2\,5}\,(7) \\ \times\,6 \\ \hline \mathbf{1\,5\,0}\,(6) \\ \times\,7 \\ \hline \end{array}$$

5 ) 1 0 5 0 (6)
6 ) 2 1 0 (3)
7 ) 3 5 (8)
  5

Put these fractions in order from least to greatest.

$\frac{1}{2}$    $\frac{7}{8}$    $\frac{9}{10}$    $\frac{2}{3}$    $\frac{4}{3}$    $\frac{1}{4}$

**$\frac{1}{4}$    $\frac{1}{2}$    $\frac{2}{3}$    $\frac{7}{8}$    $\frac{9}{10}$    $\frac{4}{3}$**

Write >, <, or = on the lines.

$\frac{1}{2}$ of 6 **=** $\frac{1}{2} \times 6$

$\frac{9}{10}$ **>** $\frac{7}{10}$

$1 + \frac{4}{5}$ **=** $1\frac{4}{5}$

$\frac{5}{6}$ **<** $\frac{7}{8}$

$\frac{1}{2}$ **<** $\frac{3}{5}$

$\frac{11}{6}$ **>** $1\frac{1}{6}$

$\frac{1}{4}$ of 12 **<** 4

What fraction is shaded?

**Worksheet solutions.** Check the answers to the review worksheet with the child. Discuss the various methods for the solutions.

The next lesson will be a day of games. Games review and practice facts and skills in an enjoyable environment.

# LESSON 71: REVIEW GAMES

| OBJECTIVES: | MATERIALS: |
|---|---|
| 1. To review recent topics by playing math card games | 1. *Math Card Games* book, P29, F8, and F22.1 |
| | 2. Basic number cards |
| | 3. AL Abacus or Short Multiplication Table, Appendix p.1, if needed |
| | 4. Fraction chart, if needed |
| | 5. Math journal |

| ACTIVITIES FOR TEACHING: | EXPLANATIONS: |
|---|---|
| ***Warm-up.*** Ask: What is 4 × 3? [12] What is 40 × 3? [120] What is 400 × 3? [1200] What is 4000 × 3? [12,000] What is 32 × 2? [64] What is 320 × 2? [640] What is 3200 × 2? [6400] | This lesson is a review of concepts learned so far by playing games. It is designed to prepare the child for the assessment in the next lesson. |
| Ask: What is the smallest prime number? [2] What are the first six prime numbers? [2, 3, 5, 7, 11, and 13] Is 23 prime or composite? [prime] Is 190 prime or composite? [composite] What number is neither prime nor composite? [1] | The first half of these RightStart™ Mathematics lessons referred to the child as a female and the second half refers to the child as a male. |
| Ask: What is the remainder when dividing 17 by 5? [2] What is the remainder when dividing 17 by 6? [5] What is the remainder when dividing 17 by 7? [3] | |
| Ask: When you divide one into two equal parts, what do you have? [one half] What is another name for one divided by two? [one half] What is another name for one divided by four? [one fourth] How many one fourths equal one half? [2] Which fraction, one half or two fourths, is in the lowest terms? [one half] Which fraction, one fourth or two eighths, is in the lowest terms? [one fourth] | |
| Ask: In the fraction two fifths, what is the denominator? [5] In the fraction two fifths, what number is the numerator? [2] If the denominator and numerator are the same, what does the fraction equal? [1] | |
| Ask: What do we call a fraction when the numerator is greater than the denominator? [improper] What is a fraction called when the denominator is greater than the numerator? [proper] | |
| ***Find the Two Factors game.*** Play Find the Two Factors game, found in *Math Card Games* book, P29. | |
| ***Division Remainder War game.*** Play the Division Remainder War game. Use half a deck of basic number cards, from 0 to 10, for two players. Divide the deck between the players by comparing heights. The object of the game is to capture the most cards by having the greater remainder. | |

| ACTIVITIES FOR TEACHING CONTINUED: | EXPLANATIONS CONTINUED: |
|---|---|

To start, each player takes three cards and combines two cards to form a number to be divided leaving the third card as the divisor. The "0" on a 10 card may be overlapped by another card.

Some possible arrangements for cards with numbers 2, 1, 6 are shown below.

**Remainder for 21 ÷ 6 is 3.**  **Remainder for 12 ÷ 6 is 0.**  **Remainder for 61 ÷ 2 is 1.**

Players state their remainder; the player with the greater remainder takes all six cards. Wars are resolved by players each taking another turn without laying any extra cards face down. The greater remainder takes all 12 cards in the war.

Players continue by taking three more cards. The game continues for a certain amount of time or until one player has collected all the cards. The winner is the player with the most cards.

**The One Half game.** Play the One Half game, found in *Math Card Games* book, F8.

**Corners™ with Eighths game.** Play Corners™ with Eighths game, found in *Math Card Games* book, F22.1. Stress that the fractions in the scoring sums must be proper fractions. Tell him to write the scoring in his math journal.

**In conclusion.** Ask: When you do a multivide, what will the last number be? [same as the starting number] What do you do if you have a remainder? [look for an error]

# LESSON 72: ASSESSMENT 2

## OBJECTIVES:
1. To assess mastery of concepts learned in previous lessons

## MATERIALS:
1. Worksheet 45, Assessment 2
2. 4-in-1 ruler

---

| ACTIVITIES FOR TEACHING: | EXPLANATIONS: |
|---|---|

**Worksheet 45.** Give the child the worksheet and ruler.

Tell him to listen to the problems and write the answers. Read each problem twice.

$90 - 19$ $\qquad$ $13 \times 3$ $\qquad$ $76 + 27$

Tell him to complete the worksheet. Solutions are below and on the next page.

---

Write only the answers.

**71**

**39**

**103**

Write the answers.

$726 + 184 =$ **910**

$4\frac{1}{5} + 1\frac{4}{5} =$ **6**

$(42 \div 7) + (42 \div 42) =$ **7**

Do the arithmetic. Use check numbers.

Add: $582 + 23{,}609$

$$\begin{array}{r} 582\ (6) \\ +\ 23{,}609\ (2) \\ \hline 24{,}191\ (8) \end{array}$$

Subtract: $8403 - 788$.

$$\begin{array}{r} 8403\ (6) \\ -\ 788\ (5) \\ \hline 7615\ (1) \end{array}$$

$$\begin{array}{r} 4628\ (\mathbf{2}) \\ \times\ 35\ (\mathbf{8}) \\ \hline 23\ 140 \\ 138\ 840 \\ \hline 161{,}980\ (7) \end{array}$$

The distance of around the Earth at the equator is 1,577,727,360 inches.

Round this number to millions and to thousands.

**1,578,000,000** $\qquad$ **1,577,727,000**

Solve the problems.

Which rectangle has the greater perimeter?

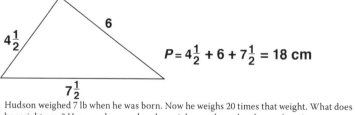

$P(A) = 2 \times (1\frac{3}{4} + 1\frac{1}{2})$

$= 2 \times (3\frac{1}{4}) = 6\frac{1}{2}$

$P(B) = 2 \times (2\frac{1}{8} + 1\frac{3}{8})$

$= 2 \times (3\frac{4}{8}) = 7$

**P(B) is greater.**

Use a ruler to measure the triangle below in centimeters. Then find the perimeter.

$P = 4\frac{1}{2} + 6 + 7\frac{1}{2} = 18$ cm

Hudson weighed 7 lb when he was born. Now he weighs 20 times that weight. What does he weight now? How much more does he weigh now than when he was born?

**$a = b \times 20 = 7 \times 20 = 140$ lb**

**The difference in weight is $140 - 7 = 133$ lb**

---

## ACTIVITIES FOR TEACHING CONTINUED:

## EXPLANATIONS CONTINUED:

Find the factor pairs of the numbers below. Then list the factors.

Factor pairs for 24:   **1 & 24**   **2 & 12**   **3 & 8**   **4 & 6**

Factors of 24:  **1   2   3   4   6   8   12  24**

Factor pairs for 18:  **1 & 18**   **2 & 9**   **3 & 6**

Factors of 18:  **1   2   3   6   9   18**

Name the prime numbers between 4 and 10.  **5 and 7**

Multiply 7 by 5, 6, and 7. Then divide by 5, 6, and 7.

$$\begin{array}{r} 7 \\ \times\ 5 \\ \hline \mathbf{3\,5}\ (8) \\ \times\ 6 \\ \hline \mathbf{2\,1\,0}\ (3) \\ \times\ 7 \\ \hline \end{array}$$

$$5\ \overline{)\,\mathbf{1\,4\,7\,0}}\ (3)$$
$$6\ \overline{)\,\mathbf{2\,9\,4}}\ (6)$$
$$7\ \overline{)\,\mathbf{4\,9}}\ (4)$$
$$7$$

Put these fractions in order from least to greatest.

$$\frac{2}{5} \qquad \frac{1}{8} \qquad \frac{9}{10} \qquad \frac{1}{2} \qquad \frac{3}{5} \qquad \frac{5}{4}$$

$$\mathbf{\frac{1}{8}} \qquad \mathbf{\frac{2}{5}} \qquad \mathbf{\frac{1}{2}} \qquad \mathbf{\frac{3}{5}} \qquad \mathbf{\frac{9}{10}} \qquad \mathbf{\frac{5}{4}}$$

Write >, <, or = on the lines.

$$\frac{1}{4} \text{ of } 4 \ \mathbf{=}\ \frac{1}{4} \times 4$$

$$\frac{9}{7} \ \mathbf{>}\ \frac{7}{7}$$

$$1\frac{5}{8} \ \mathbf{=}\ 1 + \frac{5}{8}$$

$$\frac{5}{8} \ \mathbf{<}\ \frac{5}{7}$$

$$\frac{1}{2} \ \mathbf{<}\ \frac{4}{7}$$

$$\frac{11}{6} \ \mathbf{=}\ 1\frac{5}{6}$$

$$\frac{1}{6} \text{ of } 12 \ \mathbf{=}\ 2$$

What fraction is shaded?

# LESSON 73: WORKING WITH TENTHS

## OBJECTIVES:
1. To practice reading rulers to tenths
2. To informally add and multiply fractions

## MATERIALS:
1. Warm-up Practice 1, found after the math journal in the child's worksheets
2. 4-in-1 ruler
3. Worksheet 46, Working with Tenths
4. *Math Card Games* book, F22.2
5. Math journal

## ACTIVITIES FOR TEACHING:

***Warm-up.*** Give the child the warm-up practice sheet. Tell him to do only the first multivide. Solutions are on the right.

***Tenths of an inch.*** Give the child the 4-in-1 ruler. Tell him to find the scale that says 1/10 inch.

Ask: How can you tell how long an inch is? [the space between numbers] Tell him to point to the longer line on the scale between the 1 and the 2 and ask: What does the line show? [halves]

Tell him to look at his ruler and to show with his hands how long 5 inches is. See the figure at the right. Repeat for 2 inches, 12 inches, and 10 inches.

Ask him to look at his ruler again and to find 9 tenths. Ask: Where is it? [the ninth little line after the 0] Tell him to find 12 tenths. Ask: Where is it? [2 tenths past 1 in.] Tell him to find 30 tenths. Ask: Where is it? [at the line for 3 in.] Tell him to find 24 tenths. Ask: Where is it? [4 tenths past 2]

***Worksheet 46, Problem 1.*** Give the child the worksheet and tell him to do the first problem. The solution is below.

$$P = 1\frac{3}{10} \times 4 = 4\frac{12}{10}$$
$$= 5\frac{2}{10} \text{ in.}$$

$1\frac{3}{10}$ in.

Tell him to discuss his answer. Ask: Could you also add the four sides? [yes] Would you get the same answer? [yes]

## EXPLANATIONS:

Remind the child to use check numbers with each step as he proceeds through the multivide.

The second multivide on the warm-up practice sheet will be completed in a future lesson.

This helps the child become more adept with various units of measurements.

```
        6
      × 2
       12 (3)
      × 3
       36 (0)
      × 4
      144 (0)
      × 5
      720 (0)
      × 6
     4 320 (0)
      × 7
  2) 30 240 (0)
  3) 15 120 (0)
  4) 5 040 (0)
  5) 1 260 (0)
  6) 252 (0)
  7) 42 (6)
        6
```

The child should use informal processes to find the perimeters, NOT any algorithms.

**ACTIVITIES FOR TEACHING CONTINUED:**

**EXPLANATIONS CONTINUED:**

**Problem 2.** Tell him to do the second problem on the worksheet. The solution is below.

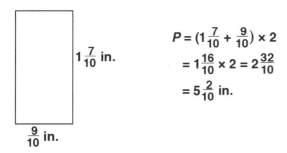

$$P = (1\tfrac{7}{10} + \tfrac{9}{10}) \times 2$$
$$= 1\tfrac{16}{10} \times 2 = 2\tfrac{32}{10}$$
$$= 5\tfrac{2}{10} \text{ in.}$$

There are more than one method to find this solution. Another method is shown here.

$$P = (1\tfrac{7}{10} \times 2) + (\tfrac{9}{10} \times 2)$$
$$= 2\tfrac{14}{10} + \tfrac{18}{10} = 3\tfrac{4}{10} + 1\tfrac{8}{10}$$
$$= 5\tfrac{2}{10} \text{ in.}$$

Then ask the child to explain his solution.

**Tenths of a centimeter.** Tell him to turn his ruler over and to find the centimeter scale with the 10 divisions. Ask: Between which two numbers is 2 and a half centimeters? [between 2 and 3] How can you tell where the half is? [a little longer line halfway between the 2 and 3]

**Problems 3 and 4.** Tell him to complete the worksheet and discuss his answer. The solutions are below.

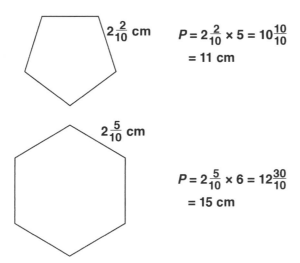

$$P = 2\tfrac{2}{10} \times 5 = 10\tfrac{10}{10}$$
$$= 11 \text{ cm}$$

$$P = 2\tfrac{5}{10} \times 6 = 12\tfrac{30}{10}$$
$$= 15 \text{ cm}$$

**Corners with Tenths game.** Play Corners with Tenths game, found in *Math Card Games* book, F22.2. In this game a score of 12 is considered to be $\tfrac{12}{10}$. Tell him to use his math journal for scoring.

**In conclusion.** Ask: How many tenths are in 4 inches? [40] How many tenths are in 4 centimeters? [40] Which is longer, 4 inches or 4 centimeters? [4 inches] Why? [Inches are longer than centimeters.]

# LESSON 74: INTRODUCING HUNDREDTHS

## OBJECTIVES:

1. To review or learn the term *meter*
2. To introduce the term *yard*
3. To learn the term *decimeter*
4. To work with hundredths

## MATERIALS:

1. Warm-up Practice 1, found after the math journal in the child's worksheets
2. 4-in-1 ruler
3. Meter stick
4. AL Abacus
5. Worksheet 47, Introducing Hundredths

## ACTIVITIES FOR TEACHING:

**Warm-up.** Give the child the warm-up practice sheet. Tell him to do the second multivide on the page. Solutions are on the right.

**Meters.** Give the child the 4-in-1 ruler, meter stick, and abacus. Tell him to open the meter stick. Ask: Are the units the same on both sides of the meter stick? [no] What units are on each side? [centimeters and inches] How many centimeters are on the metric side? [100] Explain that a *meter* is 100 centimeters long.

**Yards.** Ask: How many inches are on the inch side of the meter stick? [36] Tell him that 36 inches is called a *yard*. Ask: Which is longer, a meter or a yard? [meter]

**History of the meter.** Say: In 1790 French scientists decided the unit of length would be one ten-millionth of the distance from the North Pole to the equator. They chose the word "meter," which means measure.

**Decimeters.** Tell him that there is another unit larger than a centimeter, but smaller than a meter that is sometimes used. One-tenth of a meter is called a *decimeter* (DES-uh-MEE-ter).

Write:                    deci meter

and explain that the "deci" part means "tenth." Ask: How does your meter stick show decimeters? [The numbers are larger (and a different font) at the decimeter marks.] Does your ruler show the individual decimeters? [no] How many decimeters long is your ruler? [3] How many decimeters are in a meter? [10] How many centimeters are in a decimeter? [10]

**Measuring on the abacus.** Tell him to use his ruler to measure a row of 10 beads on the abacus. Ask: How long is the row of beads in centimeters? [10] How long is the row in decimeters? [1] How long is the row in meters? [one tenth]

## EXPLANATIONS:

Remind the child to use check numbers with each step as he proceeds through the multivide.

The first multivide on the warm-up practice sheet was completed in a previous lesson.

$$
\begin{array}{r}
7 \\
\times\,3 \\
\hline
21 \ (3) \\
\times\,4 \\
\hline
84 \ (3) \\
\times\,5 \\
\hline
420 \ (6) \\
\times\,6 \\
\hline
2\,520 \ (0) \\
\times\,7 \\
\hline
17\,640 \ (0) \\
\times\,8 \\
\hline
3\,)\,141\,120 \ (0) \\
4\,)\,47\,040 \ (6) \\
5\,)\,11\,760 \ (6) \\
6\,)\,2\,352 \ (3) \\
7\,)\,392 \ (5) \\
8\,)\,56 \ (2) \\
7
\end{array}
$$

**ACTIVITIES FOR TEACHING CONTINUED:**   **EXPLANATIONS CONTINUED:**

Tell him to imagine putting all the beads in a row on a long wire. Ask: How long in centimeters is the row? [100 centimeters] How long in decimeters is the row? [10 decimeters] How long in meters is the row? [1 meter]

***Entering fractions of a meter.*** Tell the child to enter $\frac{2}{100}$ of a meter on his abacus. See left figure below. Repeat for $\frac{4}{100}$ and $\frac{9}{100}$. See below.

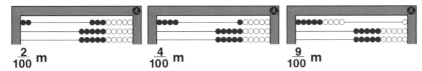

$\frac{2}{100}$ m          $\frac{4}{100}$ m          $\frac{9}{100}$ m

Next, tell him to enter $\frac{2}{10}$ of a meter on his abacus. See the left figure below. Ask: How many hundredths is that? [$\frac{20}{100}$] Tell him to enter $\frac{4}{10}$. Ask: How many hundredths is that? [$\frac{40}{100}$] Tell him to enter $\frac{90}{100}$. Ask: How many tenths is that? [$\frac{9}{10}$] See below.

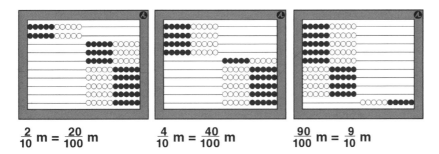

$\frac{2}{10}$ m = $\frac{20}{100}$ m     $\frac{4}{10}$ m = $\frac{40}{100}$ m     $\frac{90}{100}$ m = $\frac{9}{10}$ m

***Worksheet 47.*** Give the child the worksheet and tell him to complete it. The solutions are below.

| | | |
|---|---|---|
| $\frac{1}{100}$ | $\frac{5}{100}$ | $\frac{7}{100}$ |
| $\frac{10}{100}$, $\frac{1}{10}$ | $\frac{30}{100}$, $\frac{3}{10}$ | $\frac{80}{100}$, $\frac{8}{10}$ |
| $\frac{27}{100}$ | $\frac{71}{100}$ | $\frac{49}{100}$ |
| $\frac{8}{100}$ | $\frac{16}{100}$ | $\frac{51}{100}$ |
| $\frac{7}{10}$ | $\frac{9}{10}$ | $\frac{9}{10}$ |
| $\frac{86}{100}$ | $\frac{53}{100}$ | $\frac{86}{100}$ |
| $\frac{98}{100}$ | $\frac{63}{100}$ | $\frac{97}{100}$ |

***In conclusion.*** Ask: What is the length of 10 beads on the abacus? [1 dm] Show with your hands the length of 1 centimeter. Show with your hands the length of 1 decimeter. Show with your hands the length of 1 meter.

If there is additional time following this lesson, play the Corners with Tenths game, found in *Math Card Games* book, F22.2.

# LESSON 75: WORKING WITH HUNDREDTHS

## OBJECTIVES:

1. To review metric terms
2. To subtract tenths and hundredths

## MATERIALS:

1. Warm-up Practice 2, found after the math journal in the child's worksheets
2. Meter stick
3. AL Abacus
4. Worksheet 48, Working with Hundredths

## ACTIVITIES FOR TEACHING:

***Warm-up.*** Give the child the warm-up practice sheet. Tell him to do only the first multivide. Solutions are on the right.

***Reviewing meters.*** Give the child the meter stick and abacus. Ask: How long is the meter stick? [1 m] How many centimeters are in a meter? [100] How many decimeters are in a meter? [10] How many centimeters are in a decimeter? [10] A centimeter is what fraction of a decimeter? [one tenth] A centimeter is what fraction of a meter? [one hundredth]

***Measuring on the abacus.*** Tell him to enter 10 beads on his abacus and ask: How long is the row of beads in centimeters? [10] What would a row of beads measure in meters? [one tenth] How long are 10 rows of beads in meters? [1 m]

Write: $\frac{4}{10} - \frac{1}{100} =$

and tell him to show it on his abacus. [$\frac{39}{100}$] See the left figure below. Also tell him to show it on his meter stick.

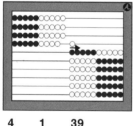

$$\frac{4}{10} - \frac{1}{100} = \frac{39}{100}$$

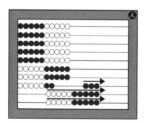

$$1 - \frac{23}{100} = \frac{77}{100}$$

Write: $1 - \frac{23}{100} =$

and tell him to find the answer on his abacus. [$\frac{77}{100}$] See the right figure above.

Write: $\frac{33}{100} - \frac{1}{10} =$

and tell him to solve it on his abacus. [$\frac{23}{100}$] See the figure on the next page.

## EXPLANATIONS:

Remind the child to use check numbers with each step as he proceeds through the multivide.

The second multivide on the warm-up practice sheet will be completed in a future lesson.

```
            8
          × 3
           24 (6)
          × 4
           96 (6)
          × 5
          480 (3)
          × 6
        2 880 (0)
          × 7
       20 160 (0)
          × 8
      161 280 (0)
          × 9
   3) 1 451 520 (0)
    4) 483 840 (0)
    5) 120 960 (0)
     6) 24 192 (0)
      7) 4 032 (0)
       8) 576 (0)
        9) 72 (0)
            8
```

See page ii, number 16 of "Some General Thoughts on Teaching Mathematics," for additional information.

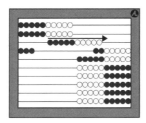

$$\frac{33}{100} - \frac{1}{10} = \frac{23}{100}$$

**Worksheet 48.** Give the child the worksheet and tell him to complete it. The solutions are below.

$$\frac{68}{100} - \frac{2}{100} = \frac{66}{100} \qquad 1 - \frac{84}{100} = \frac{16}{100} \qquad \frac{32}{100} - \frac{1}{10} = \frac{22}{100}$$

$$\frac{9}{100} - \frac{6}{100} = \frac{\mathbf{3}}{\mathbf{100}} \qquad \frac{11}{100} - \frac{1}{100} = \frac{\mathbf{1}}{\mathbf{10}} \qquad \frac{43}{100} - \frac{3}{100} = \frac{\mathbf{4}}{\mathbf{10}}$$

$$\frac{6}{10} - \frac{3}{10} = \frac{\mathbf{3}}{\mathbf{10}} \qquad 1 - \frac{4}{10} = \frac{\mathbf{6}}{\mathbf{10}} \qquad 1 - \frac{83}{100} = \frac{\mathbf{17}}{\mathbf{100}}$$

$$\frac{2}{10} \times 3 = \frac{\mathbf{6}}{\mathbf{10}} \qquad \frac{5}{10} - \frac{3}{100} = \frac{\mathbf{47}}{\mathbf{100}} \qquad \frac{7}{10} - \frac{16}{100} = \frac{\mathbf{54}}{\mathbf{100}}$$

$$\frac{4}{10} - \frac{8}{100} = \frac{\mathbf{32}}{\mathbf{100}} \qquad \frac{33}{100} - \frac{3}{10} = \frac{\mathbf{3}}{\mathbf{100}} \qquad \frac{87}{100} - \frac{1}{10} = \frac{\mathbf{77}}{\mathbf{100}}$$

$$\frac{9}{100} \; \underline{\;\mathbf{>}\;} \; \frac{6}{100} \qquad\qquad \frac{9}{100} + \frac{4}{10} \; \underline{\;\mathbf{>}\;} \; \frac{13}{100}$$

$$\frac{40}{100} \; \underline{\;\mathbf{=}\;} \; \frac{4}{10} \qquad\qquad \frac{81}{100} \; \underline{\;\mathbf{<}\;} \; \frac{8}{10} + \frac{1}{10}$$

$$\frac{7}{10} \; \underline{\;\mathbf{<}\;} \; \frac{87}{100} \qquad\qquad \frac{4}{10} \; \underline{\;\mathbf{=}\;} \; \frac{50}{100} - \frac{1}{10}$$

$$\frac{19}{100} \; \underline{\;\mathbf{<}\;} \; \frac{2}{10} \qquad\qquad 1 - \frac{37}{100} \; \underline{\;\mathbf{>}\;} \; \frac{6}{10}$$

$$\frac{3}{10} \; \underline{\;\mathbf{>}\;} \; \frac{23}{100} \qquad\qquad \frac{1}{10} \; \underline{\;\mathbf{=}\;} \; \frac{5}{100} \times 2$$

**In conclusion.** Ask: If you laid out the little centimeter cubes in a line, how many would you need to make a meter? [100] A centimeter is what fraction of a meter? [one hundredth] How many times longer is a meter than a centimeter? [100]

If there is additional time following this lesson, have the child choose a game to play.

# LESSON 76: DECIMAL FRACTIONS ON THE VERTICAL ABACUS

## OBJECTIVES:

1. To add tenths and hundredths, using the AL Abacus vertically

## MATERIALS:

1. Warm-up Practice 2
2. AL Abacus
3. 1 centimeter cube
4. Worksheet 49, Decimal Fractions on the Vertical Abacus
5. *Math Card Games* book, F22.2

## ACTIVITIES FOR TEACHING:

***Warm-up.*** Give the child the warm-up practice sheet. Tell him to do the second multivide on the page. Solutions are on the right.

***Using the abacus for tenths and hundredths.*** Give the child the abacus. Say: Today we will use side 1 of the abacus, but in a different way. We will turn the abacus clockwise 90 degrees so the AL logo is in the lower right corner. See the left figure below.

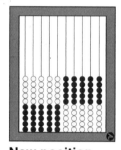 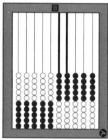 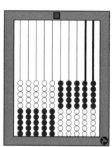

**New position.**   **The tenths.**   **The hundredths.**

Point to the first two wires with the dark-colored beads on top as shown in the center figure above and say: These wires will be the tenths. Put a centimeter cube before the tenths and say: This cube shows where the fractions begin. Then point to the right two wires and say: These wires will be the hundredths. See the right figure above. Repeat for the ones and tens wires as shown below.

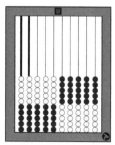 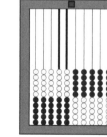

**Tens.**   **Ones.**

***Entering quantities.*** Say: Enter 4 tenths. See the left figure on the next page. Ask: How many hundredths is this? [40 hundredths] Say: Clear and enter 6 hundredths. See the middle figure. Say: Now enter 46 hundredths. See the right figure on the next page.

## EXPLANATIONS:

In this new model the ones and tens are still represented by light-colored beads.

$$
\begin{array}{r}
9 \\
\times\,3 \\
\hline
27 \ (0) \\
\times\,4 \\
\hline
108 \ (0) \\
\times\,5 \\
\hline
540 \ (0) \\
\times\,6 \\
\hline
3\,240 \ (0) \\
\times\,7 \\
\hline
22\,680 \ (0) \\
\times\,8 \\
\hline
181\,440 \ (0) \\
\times\,9 \\
\hline
3)\overline{1\,632\,960} \ (0) \\
4)\overline{544\,320} \ (0) \\
5)\overline{136\,080} \ (0) \\
6)\overline{27\,216} \ (0) \\
7)\overline{4\,536} \ (0) \\
8)\overline{648} \ (0) \\
9)\overline{81} \ (0) \\
9
\end{array}
$$

The previous lesson taught that 4 tenths is equal to 40 hundredths.

## ACTIVITIES FOR TEACHING CONTINUED:

![abacus images]

Entering $\frac{4}{10}$.  Entering $\frac{6}{100}$.  Entering $\frac{46}{100}$.

Write:

$$4\frac{4}{10} \qquad 6\frac{6}{10} \qquad \frac{88}{100}$$
$$+\,4\frac{4}{10} \qquad +\,6\frac{6}{10} \qquad +\,\frac{88}{100}$$

and tell him to find the answers with his abacus and centimeter cube. [$8\frac{8}{10}$, $13\frac{2}{10}$, $1\frac{76}{100}$] Tell him to do it on the abacus, then explain it. Ask: How does trading the tenths and hundredths compare to trading whole numbers? [the same]

**Worksheet 49.** Give the child the worksheet and tell him to complete it. The solutions are below. Tell the child to discuss his answers.

$$\begin{array}{cccc}
23 & 2\frac{3}{10} & 41 & 4\frac{1}{10} \\
+\,36 & +\,3\frac{6}{10} & +\,23 & +\,2\frac{3}{10} \\
\hline
\mathbf{59} & \mathbf{5\frac{9}{10}} & \mathbf{64} & \mathbf{6\frac{4}{10}}
\end{array}$$

$$\begin{array}{cccc}
14 & 1\frac{4}{10} & 39 & 3\frac{9}{10} \\
+\,27 & +\,2\frac{7}{10} & +\,53 & +\,5\frac{3}{10} \\
\hline
\mathbf{41} & \mathbf{4\frac{1}{10}} & \mathbf{92} & \mathbf{9\frac{2}{10}}
\end{array}$$

$$\begin{array}{cccc}
3\frac{9}{10} & \frac{39}{100} & 6\frac{8}{10} & \frac{68}{100} \\
+\,2\frac{8}{10} & +\,\frac{28}{100} & +\,9\frac{7}{10} & +\,\frac{97}{100} \\
\hline
\mathbf{6\frac{7}{10}} & \mathbf{\frac{67}{100}} & \mathbf{16\frac{5}{10}} & \mathbf{1\frac{65}{100}}
\end{array}$$

**Corners™ with Tenths game.** Play the following variation of Corners™ with Tenths game found in *Math Card Games* book, F22.2. Cards joined at the top and bottom are considered to be tenths. Cards joined at the sides are considered to be hundredths.

Say: Use your worksheet to write the scores using fractions with tenths and hundredths. Use your abacus to find the sum. The game is over after 12 turns.

**In conclusion.** Ask: Ten hundredths is equal to how many tenths? [1] Ten tenths is equal to how many ones? [1] Ten ones is equal to how many tens? [1] Ten tens is equal to how many hundreds? [1]

## EXPLANATIONS CONTINUED:

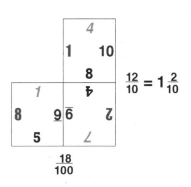

$$\frac{12}{10} = 1\frac{2}{10}$$

Some children may need to write out more steps, while other children can do the scoring mentally.

# LESSON 77: INTRODUCING DECIMAL POINTS

## OBJECTIVES:

1. To introduce the relationship between fractions and decimals
2. To learn the term *decimal point*
3. To understand decimals as an alternate way of writing tenths

## MATERIALS:

1. Warm-up Practice 3
2. AL Abacus
3. 3 to 4 centimeter cubes and Place-value cards
4. Worksheet 50, Introducing Decimal Points
5. *Math Card Games* book, F22.2 and Math journal

## ACTIVITIES FOR TEACHING:

**Warm-up.** Give the child the warm-up practice sheet. Tell him to do only the first section. Solutions are on the right.

**Quick review.** Give the child the abacus, centimeter cubes, and place-value cards. Write:

$$4\frac{9}{10} + \frac{12}{100} =$$

and say: This might have been a score in the Corners™ game you played in the last lesson. Ask: Are you tired of writing 10 and 100 as denominators of these fractions?

**History of decimals.** Say: About 400 years ago, people noticed tenths and hundredths seem to follow so many of the same rules for adding whole numbers. They found they could write them without their denominators. John Napier from Scotland wrote an article in 1619 explaining these numbers, the decimal numbers, that we use today.

**Writing tenths as decimals.** Write:

$$4\frac{6}{10}$$

and say: Enter it on your abacus with the abacus turned clockwise 90° and the centimeter cube on the top center. Instead of writing this number as a fraction, they wrote as a decimal. Write:     4.6

Say: We read it as 4 and 6 tenths. The point, or dot, shows where the fractions begin. It is called a *decimal point*. Tell him that the centimeter cube between the ones and the tenths on his abacus now represents the decimal point. See the figure at the right.

**Entering 4.6.**

**Place-value cards.** Show the child how to compose 4.6 with his place-value cards by placing a centimeter cube as the decimal point. See below.

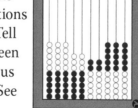

4 . 6

**Composing 4 and 6 tenths with place-value cards.**

## EXPLANATIONS:

| | | |
|---|---|---|
| 58 **(4)** | 58 **(4)** | 58 **(4)** |
| × 6 **(6)** | × 40 **(4)** | × 46 **(1)** |
| **348 (6)** | **2320 (7)** | 348 |
| | | 2320 |
| | | **2668 (4)** |
| | | |
| 279 **(0)** | 279 **(0)** | 279 **(0)** |
| × 5 **(5)** | × 30 **(3)** | × 35 **(8)** |
| **1395 (0)** | **8370 (0)** | 1395 |
| | | 8370 |
| | | **9765 (0)** |

At this point do not read 4.6 as "four point six." This lesson is to help the child understand the relationship between fractions and decimals.

**ACTIVITIES FOR TEACHING CONTINUED:**　　　　**EXPLANATIONS CONTINUED:**

Tell him to enter 9 and 8 tenths on his abacus and to compose it with place-value cards. See left figure below.

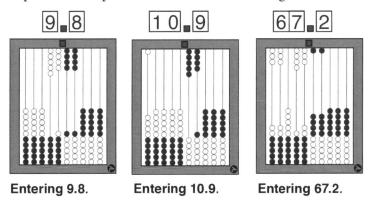

**Entering 9.8.**　　　**Entering 10.9.**　　　**Entering 67.2.**

Repeat for ten and 9 tenths. See the middle figure above.

Repeat for 67 and 2 tenths. See the right figure above.

**Worksheet 50.** Give the child the worksheet and tell him to complete it. The solutions are below.

| $6\frac{7}{10}$ 6.7 | $15\frac{5}{10}$ 15.5 | $20\frac{3}{10}$ 20.3 |
|---|---|---|
| $\frac{4}{10}$ .4 | 32 32 | $12\frac{6}{10}$ 12.6 |

$$
\begin{array}{r} 2\frac{5}{10} \\ + 5\frac{4}{10} \\ \hline 7\frac{9}{10} \end{array}
\qquad
\begin{array}{r} 2.5 \\ + 5.4 \\ \hline 7.9 \end{array}
\qquad
\begin{array}{r} 3\frac{1}{10} \\ + 8\frac{3}{10} \\ \hline 11\frac{4}{10} \end{array}
\qquad
\begin{array}{r} 3.1 \\ + 8.3 \\ \hline 11.4 \end{array}
$$

$$
\begin{array}{r} 5\frac{6}{10} \\ + 2\frac{9}{10} \\ \hline 8\frac{5}{10} \end{array}
\qquad
\begin{array}{r} 5.6 \\ + 2.9 \\ \hline 8.5 \end{array}
\qquad
\begin{array}{r} 7\frac{5}{10} \\ + 8\frac{8}{10} \\ \hline 16\frac{3}{10} \end{array}
\qquad
\begin{array}{r} 7.5 \\ + 8.8 \\ \hline 16.3 \end{array}
$$

$$
\begin{array}{r} 1\frac{15}{10} \\ + 2\frac{9}{10} \\ \hline 5\frac{4}{10} \end{array}
\qquad
\begin{array}{r} 2.5 \\ + 2.9 \\ \hline 5.4 \end{array}
\qquad
\begin{array}{r} 3\frac{4}{10} \\ + \frac{12}{10} \\ \hline 4\frac{6}{10} \end{array}
\qquad
\begin{array}{r} 3.4 \\ + 1.2 \\ \hline 4.6 \end{array}
$$

**Corners™ with Tenths game.** Play Corners™ with Tenths game found in *Math Card Games* book, F22.2. All the numbers on the cards are considered to be tenths. Tell him to use his math journal to write the scores using decimal points. Play the game to the end.

Some children will need to use their abacus to find the sums.

**In conclusion.** Ask: What does a decimal point do? [It tells what part of a number is the fraction.]

# LESSON 78: USING DECIMAL POINTS FOR HUNDREDTHS

## OBJECTIVES:

1. To understand decimals as an alternate way of writing tenths and hundredths
2. To subtract tenths and hundredths in decimal format

## MATERIALS:

1. Warm-up Practice 3
2. AL Abacus and about 10 centimeter cubes
3. Place-value cards
4. *Math Card Games* book, N43 and F22.2, and Math journal
5. Worksheet 51, Using Decimal Points for Hundredths

## ACTIVITIES FOR TEACHING:

**Warm-up.** Give the child the warm-up practice sheet. Tell him to do the second section on the page. Solutions are on the right.

**Writing hundredths as decimals.** Give the child the abacus, centimeter cubes, and place-value cards.

Write: $4\frac{12}{100}$

and ask: How do you think you could write this using a decimal point? Write it: 4.12

Say: We read it as 4 and 12 hundredths. Compose the number with your place-value cards and enter it on your abacus. See the left figure below.

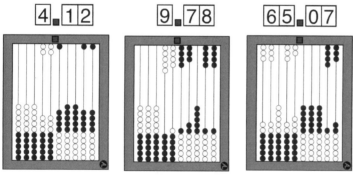

| Entering 4.12. | Entering 9.78. | Entering 65.07. |

Repeat for nine and 78 hundredths. See the middle figure above.

Repeat for 65 and 7 hundredths. (To get the zero, turn a tens card for example, the 30-card, upside down and cover the 3 with the 7.) See the right figure above. Ask: Why did you need a zero before the 7? [Without it, it would be 65 and 7 tenths.]

**Practice.** Write and ask him to read the following:

30.72 [30 and 72 hundredths]

72.8  [72 and 8 tenths]

72.08 [72 and 8 hundredths]

9.40  [9 and 40 hundredths]

## EXPLANATIONS:

| 5678 **(8)** | 5678 **(8)** | 5678 **(8)** |
|---|---|---|
| × 2 **(2)** | × 70 **(7)** | × 72 **(0)** |
| 11 356 **(7)** | 397 460 **(2)** | 11 356 |
| | | 397 460 |
| | | 408 816 **(0)** |
| | 213 459 **(6)** | |
| | × 35 **(8)** | |
| | 1 067 295 | |
| | 6 403 770 | |
| | 7 471 065 **(3)** | |

This question encourages the child to think of the big picture and to continue to think intuitively about math.

Do not at this point read 4.12 as "four point one two." This lesson is to help the child understand the relationship between fractions and decimals.

| ACTIVITIES FOR TEACHING CONTINUED: | EXPLANATIONS CONTINUED: |

**Can You Find game.** Play this variation of the Can You Find game, found in *Math Card Games* book, N43. Use place-value cards with ones and tens and seven centimeter cubes. Below are the numbers to say. Tell the child to compose the number and set it aside. All the cards will be collected at the end of the game.

1. Can you find 90 and 5 tenths?
2. Can you find 8 tenths?
3. Can you find 60 and 87 hundredths?
4. Can you find 50 and 12 hundredths?
5. Can you find 24 and 3 tenths?
6. Can you find 71 and 36 hundredths?
7. Can you find 9 hundredths? (Hint: Turn the 40-card upside down to get a zero.)

**Subtracting tenths and hundredths.** Write:

$$
\begin{array}{r} 4.1 \\ -\ .3 \\ \hline \end{array}
\qquad
\begin{array}{r} 2.37 \\ -\ 1.31 \\ \hline \end{array}
\qquad
\begin{array}{r} 3.26 \\ -\ 1.48 \\ \hline \end{array}
$$

and ask the child to find the differences any way he can. [3.8, 1.06, 1.78] He could do it with the abacus or by thinking in terms in tenths and hundredths as fractions.

**Worksheet 51.** Give the child the worksheet and tell him to do the problems. The solutions are below.

$1\frac{29}{100}$ 1.29     $52\frac{52}{100}$ 52.52     $63\frac{47}{100}$ 63.47

$\frac{83}{100}$ .83     $8\frac{7}{100}$ 8.07     $8\frac{9}{10}$ 8.9

$$
\begin{array}{r} 21.6 \\ -\ 3.5 \\ \hline 18.1 \end{array}
\quad
\begin{array}{r} 9.3 \\ -\ 5.6 \\ \hline 3.7 \end{array}
\quad
\begin{array}{r} 10.0 \\ -\ 8.5 \\ \hline 1.5 \end{array}
\quad
\begin{array}{r} 9.1 \\ -\ 8.3 \\ \hline .8 \end{array}
$$

$$
\begin{array}{r} 11.63 \\ -\ 2.31 \\ \hline 9.32 \end{array}
\quad
\begin{array}{r} 9.47 \\ -\ 2.87 \\ \hline 6.60 \end{array}
\quad
\begin{array}{r} 9.53 \\ -\ 5.28 \\ \hline 4.25 \end{array}
\quad
\begin{array}{r} 7.41 \\ -\ 5.53 \\ \hline 1.88 \end{array}
$$

$$
\begin{array}{r} 5.68 \\ -\ 2.08 \\ \hline 3.60 \end{array}
\quad
\begin{array}{r} 5.15 \\ -\ 2.90 \\ \hline 2.25 \end{array}
\quad
\begin{array}{r} 8.00 \\ -\ 1.25 \\ \hline 6.75 \end{array}
\quad
\begin{array}{r} 3.40 \\ -\ 1.25 \\ \hline 2.15 \end{array}
$$

**Corners™ with Tenths game.** Play this variation of Corners™ with Tenths game found in Math Card Games book, F22.2. Say: Use your math journal to write the scores using decimal points. In this game, all the numbers are considered to be hundredths. A score of 12 is now 12 hundredths, written with a decimal point (.12). Tell him to use his math journal for scoring.

**In conclusion.** Ask: Which is more, 7 tenths or 7 hundredths? [7 tenths] Which is more, 7 tenths or 70 hundredths? [the same] Which is more, 7 or 7 tenths? [7]

# LESSON 79: DECIMAL AND FRACTION PRACTICE

**OBJECTIVES:**
1. To understand decimals as a continuation of the number system
2. To compare decimals

**MATERIALS:**
1. Warm-up Practice 4
2. Worksheet 52, Decimal and Fraction Practice

**ACTIVITIES FOR TEACHING:**

***Warm-up.*** Give the child the warm-up practice sheet. Tell him to do only the first multivide. Solutions are on the right.

***Tens and so forth.*** Say: First we will talk about numbers getting larger by a factor of 10. Write:

1

Ask: What is ten times 1, or what is ten 1s? [10] Write 10 to the left of 1.

10  1

Ask: What is ten times 10? [100] Write 100 to the left of 10.

100  10  1

Ask: What is ten times 100? [1000] Write 1000 to the left of 10:     1000  100  10  1

Point to 1000 and ask: What is 1000 divided by 10? [100]
Point to 100 and ask: What is 100 divided by 10? [10]
Point to 10 and ask: What is 10 divided by 10? [1]

***Tenths and so forth.*** Say: Let's keep going. Point to 1 and ask: What is 1 divided by 10? [one tenth or .1] Write .1 to the right of 1.

1000  100  10  1  .1

Ask: What is one tenth of one tenth? [one hundredth] Write .01 to the right of .1.

1000  100  10  1  .1  .01

Ask: What is one tenth of one hundredth? [one thousandth] Write .001 to the right of 0.01.

1000  100  10  1  .1  .01  .001

Draw lines to connect the numbers as shown.

**EXPLANATIONS:**

Remind the child to use check numbers with each step as he proceeds through the multivide.

```
       11  (2)
     × 16  (7)
       66
      110
      176  (5)
     × 24  (6)
      704
    3 520
    4 224  (3)
     × 27  (0)
   29 568
   84 480
  114 048  (0)
     × 35  (8)
  570 240
3 421 440
2)3 991 680  (0)
3)1 995 840  (0)
4)665 280  (0)
5)166 320  (0)
6)33 264  (0)
7)5 544  (0)
8)792  (0)
9)99  (0)
       11
```

**ACTIVITIES FOR TEACHING CONTINUED:**

**EXPLANATIONS CONTINUED:**

Ask: What does 1000 connect with? [one thousandth]
What does 100 connect with? [one hundredth] What
does 10 connect with? [one tenth] What number is in the
center? [1]

**Worksheet 52.** Give the child the worksheet and tell
him to complete it. The solutions are below.

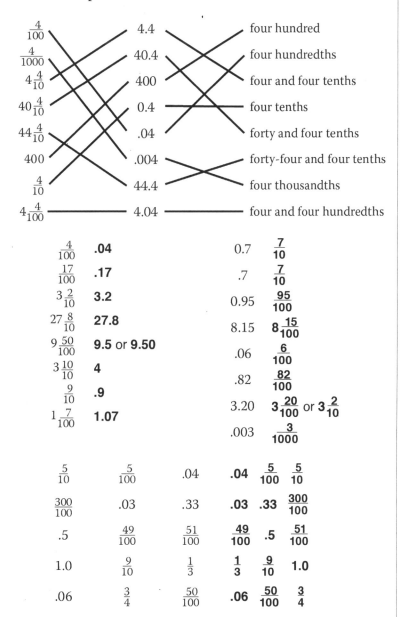

Some people think the "center" of place
value columns is the decimal point, but the
center is the 1!

**In conclusion.** Ask: Why do you think our number
system is called a place value system? [The value of a digit
depends upon its place in the number] Say: True or false:
A digit has greater value the farther it is to the left of the
decimal point. [true]

Our number system uses the Hindu-Arabic
numerals.

If there is additional time following this
lesson, play the Simple Money War game,
found in *Math Card Games* book, M2, or
Money War, M4.

# LESSON 80: HUNDREDTHS OF A DOLLAR

## OBJECTIVES:

1. To work with tenths and hundredths of a dollar
2. To write money amounts for a check

## MATERIALS:

1. Warm-up Practice 4
2. Coins, optional
3. Worksheet 53, Hundredths of a Dollar
4. **A blank check, optional**

## ACTIVITIES FOR TEACHING:

**Warm-up.** Give the child the warm-up practice sheet. Tell him to do the second multivide on the page. Solutions are on the right.

**Review of coins (optional).** Show the child the coins and tell him to identify them by name and value.

**Fractions of a dollar.** Make the table shown below with only the headings on top and coin names on the side.

| Coins | Value in ¢ | Number in Dollar | Fraction of a Dollar | | |
|---|---|---|---|---|---|
| | | | Fraction | Hundredths | Decimal |
| Penny | 1¢ | 100 | $\frac{1}{100}$ | $\frac{1}{100}$ | 0.01 |
| Nickel | | | | | |
| Dime | | | | | |
| Quarter | | | | | |

Ask: What is a penny worth using cents? [1¢] Write 1¢ in the table. Ask: How many pennies equal a dollar? [100] Write 100 in the table. Ask: What fraction of a dollar is a penny? [$\frac{1}{100}$] Write that in the table. Say: When we write money as a decimal, we always write two digits after the decimal point. If the amount is less than a dollar, we write a zero before the decimal point. Write it in the table.

**Worksheet 53.** Give the child the worksheet and tell him to fill in the first row. Repeat for the remaining coins.

| Coins | Value in ¢ | Number in Dollar | Fraction of a Dollar | | |
|---|---|---|---|---|---|
| | | | Fraction | Hundredths | Decimal |
| Penny | 1¢ | 100 | $\frac{1}{100}$ | $\frac{1}{100}$ | 0.01 |
| Nickel | 5¢ | 20 | $\frac{1}{20}$ | $\frac{5}{100}$ | 0.05 |
| Dime | 10¢ | 10 | $\frac{1}{10}$ | $\frac{10}{100}$ | 0.10 |
| Quarter | 25¢ | 4 | $\frac{1}{4}$ | $\frac{25}{100}$ | 0.25 |

## EXPLANATIONS:

```
          12 (3)
        × 28 (1)
          96
         240
         336 (3)
        × 15 (6)
       1 680
       3 360
       5 040 (0)
        × 54 (0)
      20 160
     252 000
     272 160 (0)
        × 16 (8)
   1 632 960
   2 721 600
 2)4 354 560 (0)
 3)2 177 280 (0)
   4)725 760 (0)
   5)181 440 (0)
   6)36 288 (0)
   7)6 048 (0)
     8)864 (0)
     9)108 (0)
          12
```

If there are 20 nickels in a dollar, then one nickel is one twentieth of dollar.

| ACTIVITIES FOR TEACHING CONTINUED: | EXPLANATIONS CONTINUED: |
|---|---|

The solutions are shown on the previous page. Discuss his answers.

**Writing dollar amounts for a check.** If available, show the child a check. Point out where the date, the name of the person receiving the check, and the signature are written.

Say: The dollar amount is written twice, once with numerals and once with words. Write:

$76.19

and say: We read this as seventy-six dollars and nineteen cents.

Say: For the words, the fraction of a dollar is written as a fraction in hundredths of a dollar. Write:

Seventy-six and 19/100 dollars

Say: Note that the fraction is written with the numerator first followed by a slash, and then the denominator 100. The word "dollars" is usually printed on the check. It is correct to write 76 with a dash between the words seventy and six.

Write:   $18.04   $5.00

and say: The numerator always has two digits so this is how we write them. Write:

Eighteen and 04/100 dollars
Five and 00/100 dollars

**Practice.** Tell the child to write 46 dollars, 20 nickels, and 3 pennies in the two ways for a check. [$47.03, Forty-seven and 03/100 dollars]

Repeat for 31 dollars and 2 dimes. [$31.20, Thirty-one and 20/100 dollars]

**Worksheet 53.** Tell him to complete the worksheet. The solutions are at the right.

**In conclusion.** Ask: A penny is what fraction of a dollar? [one hundredth] A nickel is what fraction of a dollar? [one twentieth] A dime is what fraction of a dollar? [one tenth] A quarter is what fraction of a dollar? [one fourth]

Sometimes the zero amount is written as "no/100."

| | |
|---|---|
| 84 dollars and 4 dimes | $84.40 |
| Eighty-four and 40/100 | Dollars |
| 11 dollars and 7 dimes | $11.70 |
| Eleven and 70/100 | Dollars |
| 172 dollars and 1 nickel | $172.05 |
| One hundred seven-two and 05/100 | Dollars |
| 49 dollars and 20 pennies | $49.20 |
| Forty-nine and 20/100 | Dollars |
| 8 dollars and 2 quarters | $8.50 |
| Eight and 50/100 | Dollars |
| 15 dollars and 5 quarters | $16.25 |
| Sixteen and 25/100 | Dollars |
| 18 dollars and 20 nickels | $19.00 |
| Nineteen and 00/100 | Dollars |
| 21 dollars, 10 dimes, and 4 pennies | $22.04 |
| Twenty-two and 04/100 | Dollars |
| 54 dollars, 2 dimes, and 40 nickels | $56.20 |
| Fifty-six and 20/100 | Dollars |
| 34 dollars, 6 quarters, and 10 pennies | $35.60 |
| Thirty-five and 60/100 | Dollars |

# LESSON 81: REVIEW AND GAMES 5

## OBJECTIVES:

1. To review recent topics
2. To develop skills through playing math card games

## MATERIALS:

1. Worksheet 54-A or 54-B, Review 5
2. *Math Card Games* book, A9

---

## ACTIVITIES FOR TEACHING:

**Worksheet 54-A.** Give the child the worksheet. Tell him to listen to the problems and write the answers. Read each problem twice.

five tenths × 2      100 – 18      30 × 30

Tell him to complete the worksheet. Solutions are below.

Write only the answers.

   **1**

   **82**

   **900**

Write the answers.

$2 - \frac{9}{10} = \mathbf{1\frac{1}{10}}$

$\frac{63}{100} + \frac{\mathbf{37}}{\mathbf{100}} = 1$

$3\frac{5}{10} - 1.5 = \mathbf{2}$

Do the arithmetic. Use check numbers.

| 4679 + 13,674 | 8387 − 7793 | 2839 × 7 | 4815 ÷ 3 |
|---|---|---|---|
| **4,679 (8)** | **8387 (8)** | **2839 (4)** | **1605 (3)** |
| **+ 13,674 (3)** | **− 7793 (8)** | **× 7 (7)** | **3) 4815 (0)** |
| **18,353 (2)** | **594 (0)** | **19,873 (1)** | |

Solve the problem.

A turtle walked around the path shown. How many meters did it walk?

$P = 8.3 + 6.8 + 6.4$

$P = 21.5$ m

8.3 m
6.8 m
6.4 m

Put these fractions in order from least to greatest.

$\frac{7}{10}$  $\frac{1}{100}$  .6  $\frac{1}{2}$  $\frac{24}{8}$  $\frac{7}{7}$

$\mathbf{\frac{1}{100}}$  $\mathbf{\frac{1}{2}}$  **.6**  $\mathbf{\frac{7}{10}}$  $\mathbf{\frac{7}{7}}$  $\mathbf{\frac{24}{8}}$

Circle the numbers that are greater than one.

(**1.96**)  $\frac{63}{100}$  $\frac{2}{3}$  $\frac{6}{6}$  $\left(\frac{12}{10}\right)$  $\left(\frac{111}{100}\right)$

Circle the prime number in each row.

27  25  49  (61)

(17)  58  93  40

87  88  (89)  85

Write >, <, or = on the lines.

$0.46 \mathbf{=} .46$

$\frac{2}{7} \mathbf{<} \frac{4}{7}$

$1 + \frac{7}{10} \mathbf{>} \frac{163}{100}$

$1 + \frac{1}{100} \mathbf{=} 1.01$

$\frac{7}{10} \mathbf{<} \frac{7}{8}$

$\frac{1}{100} + \frac{7}{10} \mathbf{=} .71$

5 dimes $\mathbf{<}$ $0.60

$0.86 \mathbf{>} \frac{8}{10}$

## EXPLANATIONS:

Ask the child to correct any errors during the lesson.

---

## ACTIVITIES FOR TEACHING CONTINUED:

***Corners™ game.*** Play this variation of the regular Corners game, found in *Math Card Games* book, A9. Cards joined at the top and bottom are considered to be dollars. Cards joined at the sides are considered to be cents. See the example at the right.

***Worksheet 54-B.*** Give the child the worksheet. Tell him to listen to the problems and write the answers. Read each problem twice.

two tenths × 5    100 − 31    20 × 40

Tell him to complete the worksheet. Solutions are below.

## EXPLANATIONS CONTINUED:

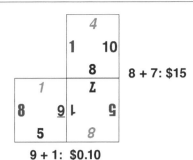

8 + 7: $15

9 + 1: $0.10

---

Write only the answers.

**1**

**69**

**800**

Write the answers.

$2 - \frac{7}{10} = \mathbf{1\frac{3}{10}}$

$\frac{56}{100} + \frac{\mathbf{44}}{\mathbf{100}} = 1$

$4\frac{3}{10} - 1.3 = \mathbf{3}$

Do the arithmetic. Use check numbers.

| 7956 + 21,786 | 9674 − 8685 | 7594 × 8 | 5624 ÷ 4 |
|---|---|---|---|
| **7,956 (0)** | **9674 (8)** | **7594 (7)** | **1406 (2)** |
| **+ 21,786 (6)** | **− 8685 (0)** | **× 8 (8)** | 4)**5624 (8)** |
| **29,742 (6)** | **989 (8)** | **60,752 (2)** | |

Solve the problem.

A tortoise walked around the rectangular path shown. How many meters did it walk?

13.9 m

3.8 m

**P = (13.9 + 3.8) × 2**

**P = 35.4 m**

Put these fractions in order from least to greatest.

$\frac{1}{10}$    $\frac{100}{100}$    .6    $\frac{1}{4}$    $\frac{20}{4}$    $\frac{1}{7}$

$\mathbf{\frac{1}{10}}$    $\mathbf{\frac{1}{7}}$    $\mathbf{\frac{1}{4}}$    **.6**    $\mathbf{\frac{100}{100}}$    $\mathbf{\frac{20}{4}}$

Circle the numbers that are greater than one.

0.99    ⓪$\frac{103}{100}$    ⓪$\frac{4}{3}$    $\frac{8}{8}$    ⓪$\frac{21}{10}$    $\frac{74}{100}$

Circle the prime number in each row.

21    ㉓    39    15

⑦    18    99    36

49    45    81    ㉙

Write >, <, or = on the lines.

.27 **=** 0.27

$\frac{3}{9}$ **>** $\frac{2}{9}$

$1 + \frac{2}{10}$ **<** $\frac{123}{100}$

$2 + \frac{2}{100}$ **=** 2.02

$\frac{6}{12}$ **<** $\frac{6}{8}$

$\frac{5}{100} + \frac{8}{10}$ **=** .85

5 nickels **>** $0.05

0.94 **>** $\frac{9}{10}$

# LESSON 82: ORDER OF OPERATIONS WITH A CALCULATOR

## OBJECTIVES:

1. To follow the order of operations while using a calculator
2. To introduce the memory functions on a calculator

## MATERIALS:

1. Warm-up Practice 5
2. Casio SL-450S calculator
3. Worksheet 55, Order of Operations with a Calculator

## ACTIVITIES FOR TEACHING:

**Warm-up.** Give the child the warm-up practice sheet. Tell him to do only the first multivide. Solutions are on the right.

**Order of operations.** Write:

$$n = 2 + (3 \times 4)$$
$$m = 2 + 3 \times 4$$

If necessary, remind the child that multiplication must be done before addition. Ask: What is *n* and *m*? [14]

Give the child the calculator and tell him to try it on the calculator. Ask: What answer do you get when you add 2 + 3 and then multiply by 4? [20] What happens when you multiply 3 by 4 and then add 2? [14] Say: These basic calculators do not follow the rules for order of operations. More expensive calculators, such as scientific calculators, will give the right answer because they will multiply first and then add.

Write: $8 + 7 \times 5 =$

Tell him to use his calculator to find the answer. [43]

**Calculator memory.** Change the problem to:

$$8 \times 8 + 7 \times 5 =$$

and ask him how he could do it. Let him think for a few minutes. Say: To solve this equation on your calculator without writing down numbers, you need to use calculator memory.

Tell him: If you see an *M* in the upper left corner, press (MRC) (MRC) to clear memory. Then press (8) (×) (8) (M+). The *M* will show. It is not necessary to press the (=) key. Continue with 7 × 5: press (7) (×) (5) (M+). To get the answer to the equation, press (MRC), which will show 99.

Repeat for: $6 \times 9 + 5 \times 8 = [94]$

Ask: What does the (M+) key do? [adds to memory] What do you think the (M−) key does? [subtracts from memory]

## EXPLANATIONS:

This lesson is virtually a repeat of Lesson 42 from Level D. If may skipped if the review is not necessary.

Scientific calculators will give the correct answer for 2 + 3 × 4 by multiplying 3 × 4 first then adding the 2. They are programmed to follow the order of operations when the equal sign is pressed; basic calculators usually are not.

```
                13 (4)
              × 56 (2)
                78
               650
               728 (8)
              × 18 (0)
             5 824
             7 280
            13 104 (0)
            × 24 (6)
            52 416
           262 080
           314 496 (0)
           × 15 (6)
         1 572 480
         3 144 960
      9)4 717 440 (0)
      8)524 160 (0)
      7)65 520 (0)
      6)9 360 (0)
      5)1 560 (3)
      4)312 (6)
      3)78 (6)
      2)26 (8)
         13
```

Encourage the child to learn about the calculator intuitively.

Intuition is a method of learning that is becoming increasingly more important in our technological world. To learn intuitively is to try new procedures by combining common sense with a willingness to take a risk. It implies the hope that what is learned is worth the inevitable frustration.

| ACTIVITIES FOR TEACHING CONTINUED: | EXPLANATIONS CONTINUED: |
|---|---|

Change the problem to:

$$6 \times 9 - 5 \times 8 = [14]$$

and ask: How can you do it now? [Use the (M−) key instead of the (M+) key to subtract the second expression.]

**Worksheet 55.** Give the child the worksheet and tell him to do the three problems in the first box on his worksheet.

$6 + 17 \times 8 = \mathbf{142}$

$34 \times 8 + 52 \times 4 = \mathbf{480}$

$34 \times 78 - 773 \times 3 = \mathbf{333}$

Continue with the next box of three problems:

$(17 + 35) \times 8 = \mathbf{416}$

$7 \times 6 + 7 \times 3 + 7 \times 11 = \mathbf{140}$

$7 \times (6 + 3 + 11) = \mathbf{140}$

Ask: Why do the last two have the same answer? [the distributive property]

Tell him to look at the last box of four equations and ask: How are they different from each other? [only the parentheses] Do you think the answers are the same? Tell him to find the answers and then explain.

$(3 + 5) \times (4 + 7) = \mathbf{88}$

$3 + 5 \times (4 + 7) = \mathbf{58}$

$3 + 5 \times 4 + 7 = \mathbf{30}$

$(3 + 5) \times 4 + 7 = \mathbf{39}$

Tell him to complete the worksheet. The remaining solutions are:

**182**
**80**
**144**
**144**
**1701**
**2520**
**1660**
**2458**
**10 + 7 × 4 + 12 × 3 = $74**
**n = 160**

***In conclusion.*** Ask: What feature of a calculator remembers numbers while you are calculating other numbers? [memory] What key do you press to add to memory? [(M+)] What key do you press to subtract from memory? [(M−)] What key do you press to clear memory? [(MRC) (MRC)]

Allow the child to explore and develop her intuitive learning. Encourage her to try various processes, to risk frustration, then to continue to success.

The distributive property works for numbers being added or subtracted and then multiplied. The sum or difference is the same when two numbers are added then multiplied or multiplied by each number then added or subtracted.

The solution could also be written as $1 \times 10 + 7 \times 4 + 12 \times 3 = \$74$.

If there is additional time following this lesson, have the child choose a game to play.

# LESSON 83: DOLLARS AND CENTS ON A CALCULATOR

## OBJECTIVES:

1. To observe a calculator's representations of decimals
2. To introduce the terms *trailing zeros* and *leading zeros*
3. To solve money problems using memory on a calculator

## MATERIALS:

1. Warm-up Practice 5
2. Casio SL-450S calculator
3. Worksheet 56, Dollars and Cents on a Calculator

## ACTIVITIES FOR TEACHING:

**Warm-up.** Give the child the warm-up practice sheet. Tell him to do the second multivide on the page. Solutions are on the right.

**The zeros in decimals on a calculator.** Give the child the calculator. Say: Turn your calculator on by pressing the (AC) button. Ask: What does your calculator show? [0] Say: Press 3 and ask: What does your calculator show now? [3] What happened to the zero? [It disappeared.]

Write: 3.60

and tell the child to enter it on his calculator and to press (=). Ask: What does the calculator show? [3.6] What happened to the zero? [It disappeared.] Is it necessary? [no, 3.6 is the same as 3.60] Say: The extra zeros after a decimal are called *trailing zeros,* which do not change the number. The calculator does not show the trailing zeros.

Tell the child to enter 002. Ask: What happened? [Only the 2 is entered.] Next tell him to enter 0.25 and then enter .25 without the 0. Ask: What happened? [Both show 0.25.] Tell him the zeros before a digit from 1 to 9 are called *leading zeros*. Ask: Does the calculator show a leading zero before a whole number? [no] Does the calculator show a leading zero before the decimal point in a number less than one? [yes]

**Dollar fractions on a calculator.** Ask: What fraction of a dollar is a penny? [one hundredth] Say: Divide 1 by 100 on your calculator and ask: What do you get? [0.01] How do you write that as money using a dollar sign? [the same, $0.01]

Ask: What fraction of a dollar is a nickel? [one twentieth] Say: Divide 1 by 20 on your calculator and ask: What do you get? [0.05] How do you write that as money? [the same, $0.05]

Ask: What fraction of a dollar is 2 dimes? [two tenths] Say: Divide 2 by 10 on your calculator and ask: What do you get? [0.2] How do you write that as money? [$0.20]

## EXPLANATIONS:

You could say that calculators do not like extra zeros.

```
           14 (5)
         × 56 (2)
           84
          700
          784 (1)
          × 3 (3)
        2 352 (3)
         × 60 (0)
      141 120 (0)
         × 36 (0)
      846 720
    4 233 600
  9)5 080 320 (0)
  8)  564 480 (0)
  7)   70 560 (0)
  6)   10 080 (0)
  5)    1 680 (6)
  4)      336 (3)
  3)       84 (3)
  2)       28 (1)
           14
```

| ACTIVITIES FOR TEACHING CONTINUED: | EXPLANATIONS CONTINUED: |
|---|---|

**Worksheet 56.** Give the child the worksheet and tell him to do Problems 1 to 3. The solutions are below.

|  | 3 dimes | 4 nickels | 2 quarters | 5 quarters | 8 quarters | 4 pennies |
|---|---|---|---|---|---|---|
| Calculator | 0.3 | 0.2 | 0.5 | 1.25 | 2. | 0.04 |
| Dollars | $0.30 | $0.20 | $0.50 | $1.25 | $2.00 | $0.04 |

2. $a = 3.60 \div 12$
   $a = \$0.30$

3. $p = 20.80 \div 8$
   $p = \$2.60$

**Reviewing calculator memory.** Write:

$$2.3 \times 5 + 6.01 \times 7 =$$

and say: Use your calculator to find the answer without writing anything on paper. Ask the child to explain how to do it. [Be sure memory is cleared; no *M* will show. (To clear press (MRC) (MRC).) First multiply 2.3 × 5. Enter it in memory with (M+). Next multiply 6.01 by 7 and add it to memory with (M+). To find the sum press (MRC); 53.57 will show.]

**Problem 4.** Tell the child to do Problem 4 on the worksheet. Tell him to explain his solution. Two possible equations are:

4. $c = 18 \times (0.59 + 0.16)$ or $c = 18 \times 0.59 + 18 \times 0.16$
   $c = \$13.50$

For the first equation, add the .59 and .16 and then multiply by 18. For the second equation, multiply 18 by .59 and put it in memory with (M+). Next multiply 18 by .16 and add it to memory with (M+). To find the sum press (MRC); 13.5 will show.

**Worksheet 56.** Tell the child to complete the worksheet. Discuss his solutions, which are shown below.

5. $g = (9.98 + 1.55 + 0.25) = \$11.78$
   $g = \$11.78 \div 2 = \$5.89$

6. $m = 5 - 0.20 \times 6 - 0.25 \times 5 - 0.05 \times 9$
   $m = \$2.10$

7. $a = 10.50 - 4 - 0.89 \times 2 - 0.49 \times 8$
   $a = \$0.80$

**In conclusion.** Ask: If you write a zero before the number 6, does the number change? [no] If you write a zero after the number 6, does the number change? [yes] If you write a zero after the number 6 tenths, does the number change? [no] If you write a zero between the decimal point and the 6 in the number 6 tenths, does the number change? [yes]

# LESSON 84: DECIMALS ON A NUMBER LINE

## OBJECTIVES:

1. To compare various decimal numbers
2. To find decimal numbers on a number line
3. To find decimal equivalents

## MATERIALS:

1. Warm-up Practice 6
2. Worksheet 57, Decimals on a Number Line
3. Casio SL-450S calculator
4. *Math Card Games* book, F23

## ACTIVITIES FOR TEACHING:

**Warm-up.** Give the child the warm-up practice sheet. Tell him to do only the first multivide. Solutions are on the right.

**Two ways of looking at numbers.** Write:

$$23 = \underline{\quad} \text{ tens} + \underline{\quad} \text{ ones}$$

and ask: How many tens and ones is 23? [2 tens + 3 ones] Then write:

$$23 = \underline{\quad} \text{ ones}$$

and ask: How many ones altogether are in 23? [23 ones] How do you know? [2 tens = 20 ones]

Say: We can also think about decimals in more than one way. Write:

$$0.45 = \underline{\quad} \text{ tenths} + \underline{\quad} \text{ hundredths}$$

and ask: How many tenths and hundredths in 45 hundredths? [4 tenths + 5 hundredths] How else can we think of it? [45 hundredths] How do you know? [four tenths is forty hundredths]

Tell the child to write 0.98 in two ways.

[0.98 = 9 tenths + 8 hundredths] and

[0.98 = 98 hundredths]

Ask: What whole number is 0.98 close to? [1]

**Comparing.** Write:

$$0.2 \quad 0.17$$

and ask: Which is greater and how do you know? [0.2 is greater because 0.2 is the same as 0.20 and 0.20 is greater than 0.17]

Next write:

$$0.5 \quad 0.05$$

and ask: Which is greater and how do you know? [0.5 is greater because 0.5 is five tenths and is much greater than 5 hundredths]

## EXPLANATIONS:

```
              16 (7)
            × 28 (1)
             128
             320
             448 (7)
            × 48 (3)
           3 584
          17 920
          21 504 (3)
            × 18 (0)
         172 032
         215 040
         387 072 (0)
            × 15 (6)
       1 935 360
       3 870 720
     9)5 806 080 (0)
     8)  645 120 (0)
     7)   80 640 (0)
     6)   11 520 (0)
     5)    1 920 (3)
     4)      384 (6)
     3)       96 (6)
     2)       32 (5)
               16
```

| ACTIVITIES FOR TEACHING CONTINUED: | EXPLANATIONS CONTINUED: |
|---|---|

Now write:

$$1.5 \qquad 1\frac{1}{2}$$

and again ask: Which is greater and how do you know? [the same; .5 is one half]

Write:

$$2.4 \qquad 4.2$$

and ask: Which is greater and how do you know? [4.2, 4 is greater than 2] Be sure the child understands that 2.4 means 2 plus .4 and 4.2 is 4 plus .2.

**Worksheet 57.** Give the child the worksheet and tell him to do the problems. Discuss his solutions, which are shown below.

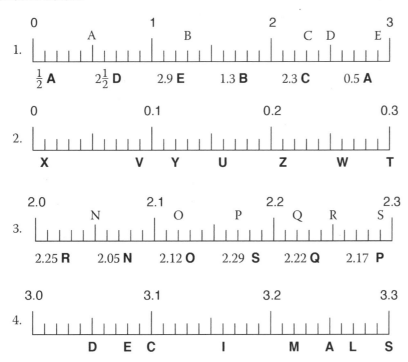

1.
$\frac{1}{2}$ **A**   $2\frac{1}{2}$ **D**   2.9 **E**   1.3 **B**   2.3 **C**   0.5 **A**

2.

3.
2.25 **R**   2.05 **N**   2.12 **O**   2.29 **S**   2.22 **Q**   2.17 **P**

4.
D  E  C  I  M  A  L  S

**Hardest Fraction War game.** Give the child the calculator. Play this variation of Hardest Fraction War game, found in *Math Card Games* book, F23. Use the two cards to form a proper fraction, where the smaller number is the numerator. Players find the decimal equivalent by dividing the numerator by the denominator on their calculator. The player having the greater decimal takes all four cards.

**In conclusion.** Ask: Which is more, 3 tenths or 30 hundredths? [the same] Which is more, 4 or 4 tenths? [4] Which is more, one half or 50 hundredths? [the same] Which is more, 6 tenths or 6 hundredths? [6 tenths]

# LESSON 85: MEASURING IN TENTHS OF AN INCH AND A MILE

## OBJECTIVES:

1. To measure and add with tenths of an inch
2. To learn that 12 inches equal 1 ft
3. To introduce a *mile*

## MATERIALS:

1. Warm-up Practice 6
2. 4-in-1 ruler
3. Worksheet 58, Measuring in Tenths of an Inch and a Mile

## ACTIVITIES FOR TEACHING:

***Warm-up.*** Give the child the warm-up practice sheet. Tell him to do the second multivide on the page. Solutions are on the right.

***Finding decimal tenths of an inch on a ruler.*** Give the child the 4-in-1 ruler. Tell him to find the scale that shows tenths of a inch.

Tell him to find nine tenths of an inch on the ruler. See the figure below.

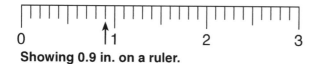

Showing 0.9 in. on a ruler.

Write:           .9 in.     .9″

and say: The inch abbreviation is either "in." or with a type of apostrophe after the number.

Next write (without saying it aloud):

1.6″

and tell the child to find it on his ruler. See the figure below.

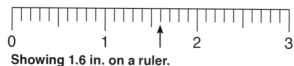

Showing 1.6 in. on a ruler.

Repeat for 2.4″ and 0.1″.

***Worksheet 58.*** Give the child the worksheet and ask him to measure in tenths of an inch the sides of the three figures. The figures and measurements are shown below.

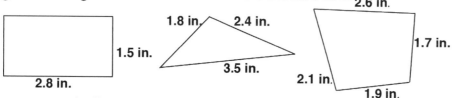

rectangle: *P* = (1.5 + 2.8) × 2 = 8.6 in.
triangle: *P* = 1.8 + 2.4 + 3.5 = 7.7 in.
quadrilateral: *P* = 2.6 + 1.7 + 1.9 + 2.1 = 8.3 in.

## EXPLANATIONS:

```
       17 (8)
     × 96 (6)
       102
     1 530
     1 632 (3)
     × 18 (0)
    13 056
    16 320
    29 376 (0)
    × 35 (8)
   146 880
   881 280
 1 028 160 (0)
     × 6 (6)
9)6 168 960 (0)
8)685 440 (0)
7)85 680 (0)
6)12 240 (0)
5)2 040 (6)
4)408 (3)
3)102 (3)
2)34 (7)
   17
```

165

| ACTIVITIES FOR TEACHING CONTINUED: | EXPLANATIONS CONTINUED: |

**A foot.** Tell the child his ruler is 1 ft. long. Ask: How many inches in a foot? [12 in.] If a line is 8.3 in long, how much longer must it be to be a foot long? [3.7 in.]

**A mile.** Say: A mile is 5280 feet long. Originally the Romans said a mile was 1000 strides. A stride is the distance a person covers when the heel of one foot touches the ground until that same heel touches the ground again. A stride is two steps.

Write:                    5280 ft

and ask: How many feet in one tenth of a mile? [528 ft] If appropriate, discuss mile markers on highways that are in tenths.

Say: A city block is about 500 feet long. Ask: About how many blocks would you need to walk to make a mile? [10] Why do we have to say **about** 10? [Blocks are not all the same.]

Say: Some people try to walk 10,000 steps a day. About how many miles is this? [5 miles]

**Problem.** Tell the child to solve this problem two different ways.

  Find how many feet are in five tenths of a mile.

Then tell him to explain his answer. One way is to multiply 528 × 5. [2640 ft] Another way is to find half of a mile by dividing 5280 ÷ 2. [2640 ft]

**Worksheet 58.** Tell the child to complete the worksheet. The solutions are shown below.

| | |
|---|---|
| 5.8 in. + 2.7 in. = **8.5 in.** | 0.8 in. + 5.3 in. = **6.1 in.** |
| 5.5 in. + 7.9 in. = **13.4 in.** | 4.3 in. + 7 in. = **11.3 in.** |
| 8.2 in. − 2.6 in. = **5.6 in.** | 8.4 in. − 2.7 in. = **5.7 in.** |
| 2.5 in. − 0.6 in. = **1.9 in.** | 6.7 in. − 5.5 in. = **1.2 in.** |
| 9.5 in. + **2.5 in.** = 1 ft | 2.2 in. + **9.8 in.** = 1 ft |
| 10.8 in. + **1.2 in.** = 1 ft | 7.4 in. + **4.6 in.** = 1 ft |

**In conclusion.** Ask: How many tenths are in a inch? [10] How many tenths of an inch are in a foot? [120] How many tenths are in a mile? [10] A city block is about what fraction of a mile? [one tenth]

If there is additional time following this lesson, play the Hardest Fraction War game, found in *Math Card Games* book, F23.

# LESSON 86: DECIMAL PARTS OF A METER

## OBJECTIVES:

1. To measure tenths of a centimeter
2. To introduce a *millimeter*
3. To add meters, decimeters, centimeters, and millimeters

## MATERIALS:

1. Warm-up Practice 7
2. 4-in-1 ruler
3. Meter stick
4. Worksheet 59, Decimal Parts of a Meter

## ACTIVITIES FOR TEACHING:

***Warm-up.*** Give the child the warm-up practice sheet. Tell him to do only the first multivide. Solutions are on the right.

***Finding tenths of a centimeter.*** Give the child the 4-in-1 ruler and the meter stick. On the ruler tell the child to find the scale that shows tenths of a centimeter as shown below.

Tell him to find two and three tenths (2.3). See the left arrow in the figure below.

**Showing 2.3 cm and 4.9 cm.**

Write:                              4.9 cm

and ask him to find it on the ruler. See the right arrow in the figure above.

***Decimal fractions of a meter.*** Ask: What do we call one-tenth of a meter? [decimeter] How do we write it as a decimal fraction? [0.1 m] What do we call one hundredth of a meter? [centimeter] How do we write 1 cm in terms of a meter as a decimal fraction? [0.01 m] How would you write 2.3 cm as part of a meter? [0.023 m] How would you write 4.9 cm as part of a meter? [0.049 m]

***Millimeters.*** Say: If we break the centimeter into 10 pieces, we have a millimeter. The prefix "milli" means thousand. Think of mile as one thousand steps or a millipede with supposedly one thousand feet. Write the word millimeter and its abbreviation, "mm."

                    millimeter      mm

Ask: How small is a millimeter? [space between the small lines of a centimeter on a ruler] How many millimeters are in a meter? [1000] What fraction of a meter is a millimeter? [one thousandth] Write it as a decimal fraction:                    [0.001]

## EXPLANATIONS:

```
                18 (0)
              × 35 (8)
                90
               540
               630 (0)
              × 27 (0)
             4 410
            12 600
            17 010 (0)
             × 16 (7)
           102 060
           170 100
           272 160 (0)
             × 24 (6)
         1 088 640
         5 443 200
   9) 6 531 840 (0)
   8)  725 760 (0)
   7)   90 720 (0)
   6)   12 960 (0)
   5)    2 160 (0)
   4)      432 (0)
   3)      108 (0)
   2)       36 (0)
               18
```

## ACTIVITIES FOR TEACHING CONTINUED:

## EXPLANATIONS CONTINUED:

***Worksheet 59.*** Give the child the worksheet and tell him to complete it. The solutions are shown below.

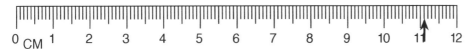

How many millimeters is 1 dm + 1 cm + 1 mm? **111 mm**
Write it as a decimal fraction of a centimeter. **11.1 cm**
Write it as a decimal fraction of a meter. **0.111 m**

|  | Decimal fraction of a meter | Sum |
|---|---|---|
| 1 dm + 2 cm | 0.1 + 0.02 | 0.12 m |
| 1 dm + 4 mm | **0.1 + .004** | **0.104 m** |
| 2 dm + 16 mm | **0.2 + .016** | **0.216 m** |
| 1 m + 2 dm | **1 + 0.2** | **1.2 m** |
| 4 m + 3 cm | **4 + .03** | **4.03 m** |
| 2 m + 3 dm + 12 cm | **2 + .3 + .12** | **2.42** |
| 3 m + 7 dm + 7 mm | **3 + .7 + .007** | **3.707** |
| 2 m + 5 cm + 1 mm | **2 + .05 + .001** | **2.051** |
| 5 m + 2 mm | **5 + .002** | **5.002** |

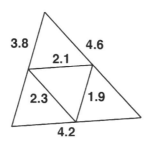

| Large Triangle | | | Small Triangles | | |
|---|---|---|---|---|---|
| cm | mm | m | cm | mm | m |
| 3.8 | 38 | 0.038 | 1.9 | 19 | 0.019 |
| 4.6 | 46 | 0.046 | 2.3 | 23 | 0.023 |
| 4.2 | 42 | 0.042 | 2.1 | 21 | 0.021 |

***In conclusion.*** Ask: How many millimeters are in a meter? [1000] How do you write one millimeter as decimal fraction of a meter? [.001] How many millimeters are in a centimeter? [10] How do you write it as decimal fraction of a centimeter? [.1]

If there is additional time following this lesson, play the Concentrating on Tenths game, found in *Math Card Games* book, F21.

# LESSON 87: FUEL PRICES

**OBJECTIVES:**

1. To learn to read gasoline prices
2. To understand how to work with a fraction of a cent

**MATERIALS:**

1. Worksheet 60, Fuel Prices
2. Casio SL-450S calculator

---

| ACTIVITIES FOR TEACHING: | EXPLANATIONS: |
|---|---|

***Warm-up.*** Give the child the worksheet. Tell him to do only the warm-up section. Solutions are below.

| $123 | $124 | $125 | $126 |
|---|---|---|---|
| $123.23 | $124.24 | $124.70 | $125.67 |
| $122.50 | $124.00 | $124.91 | $126.03 |
| $122.90 | $123.99 | $124.61 | $125.99 |
| $123.47 | $123.56 | $125.46 | $125.72 |

Rounding was taught in Lesson 16.

***Reading gas station signs.*** Tell the child to look at the worksheet. See below. Ask: Have you ever seen signs like these? [at gas stations]

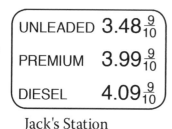

UNLEADED $3.48\frac{9}{10}$

PREMIUM $3.99\frac{9}{10}$

DIESEL $4.09\frac{9}{10}$

Jack's Station

UNLEADED $3.49^9$

PREMIUM $3.99^9$

DIESEL $4.05^9$

Jill's Station

Discuss the following points:

- The numbers are prices for one gallon of fuel. The dollar sign and sometimes the decimal point are omitted.

- Two of the prices are for different types of gasoline and one price is for diesel.

- People in North America often say "gas" when they mean "gasoline," which is not a gas like air is.

- The $\frac{9}{10}$ means $\frac{9}{10}$ of one cent, which is also one thousandth of a dollar.

- The small 9s are also $\frac{9}{10}$ of one cent and also are thousands of a dollar.

| ACTIVITIES FOR TEACHING CONTINUED: | EXPLANATIONS CONTINUED: |

**Working with fractions of a cent.** Ask: What does one gallon of diesel cost at Jack's Station? [4 dollars and $9\frac{9}{10}$ cents] Explain that gas stations charge the next whole cent only if the price is a half of a cent or more. Ask: If you needed 1 gallon of diesel for your lawn mower, what would you pay? [$4.10] What is the cost of a gallon of diesel at Jill's Station? [4 dollars and $5\frac{9}{10}$ cents] What do you think you would actually pay? [$4.06]

Give the child the calculator. Tell him to find the cost of 4 gallons of diesel at Jill's Station. The procedure is to enter 4.059 $\times$ 4 $=$ . The display shows 16.236. After rounding the answer is $16.24.

**Worksheet 60.** Tell the child to complete the worksheet. The solutions are shown below.

1. $\frac{9}{10}$ of one cent

2. $\frac{9}{10}$ of one cent

3. **Premium**

| Number of Gallons | Unleaded Gasoline | |
| --- | --- | --- |
| | Jack's | Jill's |
| 1 | $3.49 | $3.50 |
| 5 | $17.45 | $17.50 |
| 10 | $34.89 | $34.99 |
| 20 | $69.78 | $69.98 |

| Number of Gallons | Diesel | |
| --- | --- | --- |
| | Jack's | Jill's |
| 30 | $122.97 | $121.77 |
| 100 | $409.90 | $405.90 |
| 200 | $819.80 | $811.80 |
| 300 | $1229.70 | $1217.70 |

4. **20¢**

5. **$59.99**

6. **$60.00**

**In conclusion.** Ask: Is there much difference in cost if the price is $3.99$\frac{9}{10}$ or $4.00? [no] Why do stations use $3.99$\frac{9}{10}$ instead of $4.00? [It seems to be cheaper.]

Using the calculator memory was taught in Lesson 61.

If there is additional time following this lesson, play the Concentrating on Tenths game, found in *Math Card Games* book, F21.

# LESSON 88: REVIEW AND GAMES 6

## OBJECTIVES:

1. To review recent topics
2. To develop skills through playing math card games

## MATERIALS:

1. Worksheet 61-A or 61-B, Review 6
2. 4-in-1 ruler
3. Casio SL-450S calculator
4. *Math Card Games* book, F23

## ACTIVITIES FOR TEACHING:

**Worksheet 61-A.** Give the child the worksheet and ruler. Tell him to listen to the problems and write the answers. Read each problem twice.

$1.50 \times 2$ $\qquad$ $101 - 27$ $\qquad$ $.1 \times 30$

Tell him to complete the worksheet. Solutions are below.

---

Write only the answers.

**$3.00**

**74**

**3**

Write the answers.

$2 - 50¢ =$ **$1.50**

$1.69 +$ **0.31** $= 2$

$2\frac{5}{10} \times 2 =$ **5**

Do the calculations.

$3542 - 1576$

$$\begin{array}{r} 3542 \\ -\ 1576 \\ \hline 1966 \end{array}$$

$9056 + 37 + 249$

$$\begin{array}{r} 9056 \\ 37 \\ +\ 249 \\ \hline 9342 \end{array}$$

$2835 \div 7$

$$\begin{array}{r} 405 \\ 7\overline{)2835} \end{array}$$

$49 + 49 + 49 + 49$

$$\begin{array}{r} 49 \\ \times\ 4 \\ \hline 196 \end{array} \quad \text{or} \quad \begin{array}{r} 50 \\ \times\ 4 \\ \hline 200 \\ -\ 4 \\ \hline 196 \end{array}$$

Solve the problem.

| UNLEADED | 2.49⁹ |
| PREMIUM | 2.69⁹ |
| DIESEL | 3.05⁹ |

Robin bought 10 gallons of premium gasoline. How much was the change from a hundred dollar bill?

**$2.699 × 10 = $26.99**

**$100 − 26.99 = $73.01**

Fill in the tables below.

| m | dm | cm | mm |
|---|---|---|---|
| **1** | **10** | 100 | **1000** |
| 0.5 | **5** | 50 | 500 |
| $\frac{9}{10}$ | 9 | **90** | **900** |

1 yard (yd) is 3 feet (ft). Use fractions.

| yd | ft | in. |
|---|---|---|
| 1 | **3** | **36** |
| $\frac{1}{2}$ | **$1\frac{1}{2}$** | 18 |
| $\frac{2}{3}$ | 2 | **24** |

Use your ruler and find the perimeter of the triangle in centimeters. Also find the perimeter in millimeters.

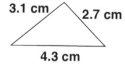

**3.1 cm** **2.7 cm**

**4.3 cm**

**P = 3.1 + 2.7 + 4.3**

**P = 10.1 cm**

**P = 101 mm**

## EXPLANATIONS:

Some of the questions on this review have not been explicitly taught, but the underlying concepts were taught.

Ask the child to correct any errors during the lesson.

Some of the child's measurements may vary slightly, which will effect the perimeter.

**ACTIVITIES FOR TEACHING CONTINUED:**

**EXPLANATIONS CONTINUED:**

*Hardest Fraction War game.* Give the child the calculator. Play this variation of Hardest Fraction War game, found in *Math Card Games* book, F23. Use the two cards to form a proper fraction, where the smaller number is the numerator. Players find the decimal equivalent by dividing the numerator by the denominator on their calculator. The player having the greater decimal takes all four cards.

*Worksheet 61-B.* Give the child the worksheet and ruler. Tell him to listen to the problems and write the answers. Read each problem twice.

$$\$2.50 \times 2 \qquad 101 - 38 \qquad .1 \times 20$$

Tell him to complete the worksheet. Solutions are below.

---

Write only the answers.

**\$5.00**

**63**

**2**

Write the answers.

$\$2.50 - \$1 = $ **\$1.50**

$1.57 + $ **0.43** $ = 2$

$1\frac{5}{10} \times 4 = $ **6**

Do the calculations.

$4786 - 3797$

$$\begin{array}{r} 4786 \\ -\ 3797 \\ \hline \mathbf{989} \end{array}$$

$8704 + 68 + 457$

$$\begin{array}{r} 8704 \\ 68 \\ +\ 457 \\ \hline \mathbf{9229} \end{array}$$

$5624 \div 8$

$$8\overline{)5624}\ \ \mathbf{703}$$

$59 + 59 + 59 + 59$

$$\begin{array}{r} 59 \\ \times\ 4 \\ \hline \mathbf{236} \end{array} \text{ or } \begin{array}{r} 60 \\ \times\ 4 \\ \hline 240 \\ -\ 4 \\ \hline \mathbf{236} \end{array}$$

Solve the problem.

| UNLEADED | 2.99⁹ |
| PREMIUM | 3.19⁹ |
| DIESEL | 3.05⁹ |

Alex bought 10 gallons of unleaded gasoline. How much was the change from a hundred dollar bill?

**$\$2.999 \times 10 = \$29.99$**

**$\$100 - \$29.99 = \$70.01$**

Fill in the tables below.

| m | dm | cm | mm |
|---|---|---|---|
| **1** | **10** | 100 | **1000** |
| 1.5 | **15** | **150** | **1500** |
| $\frac{1}{10}$ | 1 | **10** | **100** |

1 yard (yd) is 3 feet (ft). Use fractions.

| yd | ft | in. |
|---|---|---|
| 1 | **3** | **36** |
| $\frac{1}{2}$ | $1\frac{1}{2}$ | **18** |
| $\frac{1}{3}$ | **1** | 12 |

Use your ruler and find the perimeter of the triangle in centimeters. Also find the perimeter in millimeters.

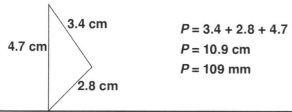

**3.4 cm**

**4.7 cm**

**2.8 cm**

$P = 3.4 + 2.8 + 4.7$

$P = 10.9$ cm

$P = 109$ mm

Some of the child's measurements may vary slightly, which will effect the perimeter.

# LESSON 89: INTRODUCTION TO PERCENTAGES

## OBJECTIVES:
1. To introduce the term *percent*
2. To understand percents as a fraction of 100

## MATERIALS:
1. Warm-up Practice 7
2. AL Abacus
3. Worksheet 62, Introduction to Percentage

## ACTIVITIES FOR TEACHING:

**Warm-up.** Give the child the warm-up practice sheet. Tell him to do the second multivide on the page. Solutions are on the right.

**The word percent.** Say: Today we will talk about percents. The word *cent* means *hundred*: one hundred cents is one dollar and a century is 100 years. The word *percent* means *per-cent*, or per hundred, or out of a hundred.

Ask: What do you think 100 percent means? [100 per 100, the whole] What do you think 50 percent means? [50 out of 100, or one half]

Say: There is a special symbol that means percent. Show him how to construct it. First draw a little circle near the top, like a degree symbol, then a slanted line, and finally, another little circle at the bottom. The top circle is often connected to the slanted line. See below.

$$^{\circ} \quad ^{\circ}\!\!/ \quad \% \qquad ^{\circ} \quad \overline{7} \quad \%$$

**Steps for drawing the two styles of the percent symbol.**

**Expressing fractions in percents.** Give the child the abacus. Ask: How many beads are on the abacus? [100] Say: So, this means we can use the abacus as the model for percents.

Tell him to enter half of the beads. Ask: How much is one half of 100? [50] Explain that this means 50 per, or out of, 100 and we say it as 50 percent. Ask: So what percent is one half? [50%] See the figure below on the left. Write: $\frac{1}{2}$ = 50%

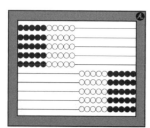
**Showing 50%.**

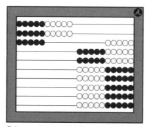
**Showing 25%.**

## EXPLANATIONS:

In British English the word *percent* is spelled *per cent*.

```
              19 (1)
           × 54 (0)
              76
             950
           1 026 (0)
           × 16 (7)
           6 156
          10 260
          16 416 (0)
           × 28 (1)
         131 328
         328 320
         459 648 (0)
           × 15 (6)
       2 298 240
       4 596 480
    9)6 894 720 (0)
    8)766 080 (0)
    7)95 760 (0)
    6)13 680 (0)
    5)2 280 (3)
    4)456 (6)
    3)114 (6)
    2)38 (2)
         19
```

**ACTIVITIES FOR TEACHING CONTINUED:**

**EXPLANATIONS CONTINUED:**

Ask: How much is $\frac{1}{4}$ of 100? [25] How do we say $\frac{1}{4}$ in percent language? [25 percent] See the right figure on the previous page. Write it:

$$\frac{1}{4} = 25\%$$

Ask: Does this remind you of something else? [money: half dollar and quarter] Tell him to find the percents for $\frac{1}{5}$ [20%] and $\frac{1}{10}$. [10%]

Ask: How could you find the percent for $\frac{1}{8}$? Tell him to find a solution and explain it. One way is to think of $\frac{1}{8}$ as half of $\frac{1}{4}$. Half of 25% is $12\frac{1}{2}\%$. Another way is to think $\frac{1}{8}$ of 80 is 10, leaving 20, and 20 divided by 8 is $2\frac{1}{2}$. Adding $10 + 2\frac{1}{2}$ gives $12\frac{1}{2}\%$.

Tell him to find the percent for $\frac{1}{3}$. The second procedure for the $\frac{1}{8}$ works for finding $\frac{1}{3}$. One third of 90 is 30; one third of 9 is 3; and one third of the remaining 1 is $\frac{1}{3}$. So $\frac{1}{3} = 33\frac{1}{3}\%$.

A third way to look at the equation is $(90 + 10) \times \frac{1}{3} = 30 + 3\frac{1}{3} = 33\frac{1}{3}$.

***Worksheet 62.*** Give the child the worksheet and tell him to complete it. The solutions are shown below.

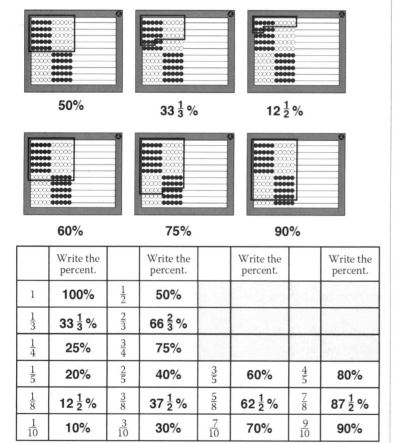

| | Write the percent. | | Write the percent. | | Write the percent. | | Write the percent. |
|---|---|---|---|---|---|---|---|
| 1 | **100%** | $\frac{1}{2}$ | **50%** | | | | |
| $\frac{1}{3}$ | **$33\frac{1}{3}\%$** | $\frac{2}{3}$ | **$66\frac{2}{3}\%$** | | | | |
| $\frac{1}{4}$ | **25%** | $\frac{3}{4}$ | **75%** | | | | |
| $\frac{1}{5}$ | **20%** | $\frac{2}{5}$ | **40%** | $\frac{3}{5}$ | **60%** | $\frac{4}{5}$ | **80%** |
| $\frac{1}{8}$ | **$12\frac{1}{2}\%$** | $\frac{3}{8}$ | **$37\frac{1}{2}\%$** | $\frac{5}{8}$ | **$62\frac{1}{2}\%$** | $\frac{7}{8}$ | **$87\frac{1}{2}\%$** |
| $\frac{1}{10}$ | **10%** | $\frac{3}{10}$ | **30%** | $\frac{7}{10}$ | **70%** | $\frac{9}{10}$ | **90%** |

This worksheet will be needed again in Lesson 92.

***In conclusion.*** Ask: Fifty percent is the same as what fraction? [one half] Twenty percent is the same as what fraction? [one fifth] Ninety percent is the same as what fraction? [nine tenths]

If there is additional time following this lesson, play the Percentages Memory game, found in *Math Card Games* book, F46.

# LESSON 90: PERCENTAGE OF A RECTANGLE

## OBJECTIVES:

1. To find the percentage of the area of a rectangle
2. To estimate fractions and percents

## MATERIALS:

1. Warm-up Practice 8
2. Worksheet 63, Percentage of a Rectangle

## ACTIVITIES FOR TEACHING:

**Warm-up.** Give the child the warm-up practice sheet. Tell him to do only the first multivide. Solutions are on the right.

**Percentage of a rectangle.** Draw two identical rectangles. Tell the child to crosshatch one half of the left rectangle. See the left figure below. Then tell him to crosshatch fifty percent of the right rectangle. See the right figure below.

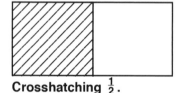 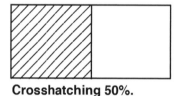

**Crosshatching $\frac{1}{2}$.**   **Crosshatching 50%.**

Ask: Which rectangle has more area crosshatched? [the same]

Draw two more rectangles. Tell the child to crosshatch $33\frac{1}{3}$% of one and to crosshatch $66\frac{2}{3}$% of the other. See below.

 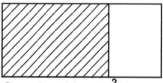

**Crosshatching $33\frac{1}{3}$%.**   **Crosshatching $66\frac{2}{3}$%.**

Draw two more rectangles and tell the child to estimate where 10% would be. Ask: What fraction would that be? [$\frac{1}{10}$] See the left figure below. Repeat for 90%. [$\frac{9}{10}$] See the right figure below.

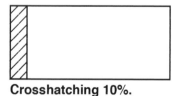 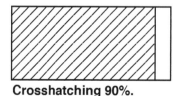

**Crosshatching 10%.**   **Crosshatching 90%.**

## EXPLANATIONS:

See Lesson 44 for estimating the fraction areas.

$$
\begin{array}{r}
21 \ (3) \\
\times 24 \ (6) \\
\hline
84 \\
\underline{420} \\
504 \ (0) \\
\times 18 \ (0) \\
\hline
4\ 032 \\
\underline{5\ 040} \\
9\ 072 \ (0) \\
\times 15 \ (6) \\
\hline
45\ 360 \\
\underline{90\ 720} \\
136\ 080 \ (0) \\
\times 56 \ (2) \\
\hline
816\ 480 \\
\underline{6\ 804\ 000} \\
\end{array}
$$

9)7 620 480 (0)
8)846 720 (0)
7)105 840 (0)
6)15 120 (0)
5)2 520 (0)
4)504 (0)
3)126 (0)
2)42 (6)
21

| **ACTIVITIES FOR TEACHING CONTINUED:** | **EXPLANATIONS CONTINUED:** |

***Finding a fraction.*** Draw a long rectangle and place marks at the following points: $\frac{1}{2}$, $\frac{1}{4}$, $\frac{1}{8}$, $\frac{3}{4}$, $\frac{2}{3}$, and at the end ($\frac{8}{8}$). See the figure below.

The fractions are given in this order for ease of estimating.

Ask: Which mark shows $\frac{1}{2}$? Write it at the half mark as shown below.

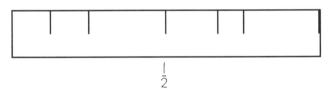

Ask: Which mark shows $\frac{1}{4}$? Tell him to write it at the one fourth mark. See below. Ask: How did you make your estimate? [halfway between left end and the one half]

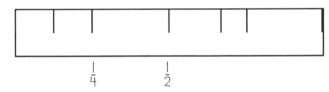

Repeat for the remaining fractions. See below.

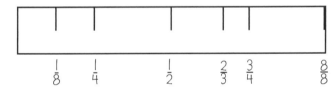

***Worksheet 63.*** Give the child the worksheet and tell him to complete it. The solutions are shown below.

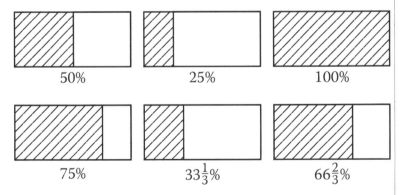

50%   25%   100%

75%   $33\frac{1}{3}$%   $66\frac{2}{3}$%

2. **E I G H T Y**
3. **E Q U A L S**
4. **P R O D U C T**

***In conclusion.*** Ask: What fraction is half of a half? [$\frac{1}{4}$] What percentage is half of a half? [25%] What percentage is two out of five? [40%]

If there is additional time following this lesson, play the Percentages Memory game, found in *Math Card Games* book, F46.

# LESSON 91: FINDING PERCENTAGES

## OBJECTIVES:

1. To find the percentage of various numbers in the hundred chart

## MATERIALS:

1. Warm-up Practice 8
2. Worksheet 64, Finding Percentages
3. *Math Card Games* book, F50

## ACTIVITIES FOR TEACHING:

***Warm-up.*** Give the child the warm-up practice sheet. Tell him to do the second multivide on the page. Solutions are on the right.

***Percent of ten.*** Write the numbers 1 to 10:

    1   2   3   4   5   6   7   8   9   10

Ask: What percent of these numbers are even? [50%] How do you know? [half are even and half is 50%] What percent of the first five numbers are even? [40%, 2 out of 5] What percentage of the numbers are greater than 7? [30%, 3 out of 10] What percentage of the numbers have a 1? [20%, 1 and 10, 2 out of 10] What percentage of the even numbers have a 1? [20%, 10, 1 out of 5]

***Worksheet 64.*** Give the child the worksheet and tell him to complete it.

1. What percentage of the numbers have only 1 digit? **9%**
2. What percentage of the numbers have 3 digits? **1%**
3. What percentage of the numbers have 2 digits? **90%**
4. What percentage of the numbers are even numbers? **50%**
5. What percentage of the numbers are odd numbers? **50%**
6. What percentage of the numbers are multiples of 10? **10%**
7. What percentage of the numbers are multiples of 5? **20%**
8. What percentage of the multiples of 5 are even? **50%**
9. What percentage of the numbers are not multiples of 5? **80%**
10. What percentage of the numbers > 80? **20%**
11. What percentage of the numbers < 15? **14%**
12. What percentage of the numbers are perfect squares? **10%**
13. What percentage of the perfect squares are even? **50%**
14. What percentage of the numbers are multiples of 9? **11%**
15. What percentage of the multiples of 9 are multiples of 3? **100%**
16. What percentage of the numbers in the 1st row are prime? **40%**

***One Hundred Percent game.*** Play the One Hundred Percent game, found in *Math Card Games* book, F50.

***In conclusion.*** Ask: Thirty percent plus what is 100%? [70%] Thirty-three and one third percent plus what is 100% [$66\frac{2}{3}$] Fifteen percent plus what is 100%? [85%]

## EXPLANATIONS:

$$
\begin{array}{r}
22 \ (4) \\
\times 36 \ (0) \\
\hline
132 \\
660 \\
\hline
792 \ (0) \\
\times 56 \ (2) \\
\hline
4\ 752 \\
39\ 600 \\
\hline
44\ 352 \ (0) \\
\times 3 \ (3) \\
\hline
133\ 056 \ (0) \\
\times 60 \ (0) \\
\hline
9\overline{)7\ 983\ 360} \ (0) \\
8\overline{)887\ 040} \ (0) \\
7\overline{)110\ 880} \ (0) \\
6\overline{)15\ 840} \ (0) \\
5\overline{)2\ 640} \ (3) \\
4\overline{)528} \ (6) \\
3\overline{)132} \ (6) \\
2\overline{)44} \ (8) \\
22
\end{array}
$$

For some children, you may want to omit the $16\frac{2}{3}$ and $83\frac{1}{3}$ cards.

# LESSON 92: PERCENTAGES ON A CALCULATOR

## OBJECTIVES:
1. To practice using percentage equivalents
2. To use the % key on a calculator

## MATERIALS:
1. Casio SL-450S calculator
2. AL Abacus
3. Worksheet 62, Introduction to Percentages, from Lesson 89
4. *Math Card Games* book, F46

| ACTIVITIES FOR TEACHING: | EXPLANATIONS: |
|---|---|

**Warm-up.** Ask: Fifty percent plus what is 100%? [50%] Sixty-six and two thirds percent plus what is 100% [$33\frac{1}{3}$]

**Percentage on a calculator.** Give the child the calculator. Ask: If you enter one fourth of the beads on the abacus, how many beads are entered? [25] Demonstrate if necessary. See the figure on the right. Ask: What is this as a decimal? [0.25] What is this as a percent? [25%]

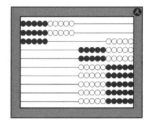

**Showing 25%.**

Tell him to divide 1 by 4 on his calculator. Ask: What did you get? [0.25] Say: Now divide 1 by 4, but instead of pressing ⊜, press ⊗. Ask: What did you get? [25]

Write:    $\frac{1}{4}$    0.25    25%

Say: Use your calculator to find the percent for one eighth. [12.5] Because .5, five tenths, is one half, one eighth is $12\frac{1}{2}$%.

**Thirds and sixths in percents.** Say: Use your calculator to find 1 divided by 3. [0.333333] Now find one third in percents. [33.333333] So, one third is $33\frac{1}{3}$%. Tell him to compare this to the chart data on Worksheet 62.

Repeat for finding 2 divided by 3 [0.6666666] and two thirds in percents. [66.666666] Say: Two thirds is $66\frac{2}{3}$%. Compare the numbers to the worksheet.

Tell him to find one sixth in percents. [16.666666] Ask: How do you write it? [$16\frac{2}{3}$%] Tell him to add the $\frac{1}{6}$ fraction and percentage to the bottom of Worksheet 62.

Repeat for five sixths. [83.333333, $83\frac{1}{3}$%] Tell him to add the $\frac{5}{6}$ fraction and percentage to the worksheet.

**Percentage Memory game.** Have him play the Percentage Memory game, found in *Math Card Games* book, F46. Tell him to use the table at the bottom of Worksheet 62 as a reference.

**In conclusion.** Ask: What is half of 25 percent? [$12\frac{1}{2}$%] What fraction is that? [$\frac{1}{8}$] What fraction is $\frac{1}{2} + \frac{1}{8}$? [$\frac{5}{8}$] What percentage is that? [$62\frac{1}{2}$%]

# LESSON 93: PERCENTAGES IN GEOGRAPHY

**OBJECTIVES:**

1. To find percentages in a geography context

**MATERIALS:**

1. U.S. Map and Alphabetical List of States, Appendix p. 3 and 4
2. Worksheet 65, Percentages in Geography

| ACTIVITIES FOR TEACHING: | EXPLANATIONS: |
|---|---|
| **Warm-up.** Ask: What percent is 100 of 100? [100%] What percent is half of 100? [50%] What percent is a fourth of 100? [25%] What is that fraction? [$\frac{1}{4}$] | |

**Warm-up.** Ask: What percent is 100 of 100? [100%] What percent is half of 100? [50%] What percent is a fourth of 100? [25%] What is that fraction? [$\frac{1}{4}$]

Ask: What percent is 50 of 50? [100%] What percent is half of 50? [50%] What is half of 50? [25]

Ask: What percent is 10 of 50? [20%] What fraction is 10 of 50? [$\frac{10}{50}$ or $\frac{1}{5}$] What percent is 20 of 50? [40%] What fraction is 20 of 50? [$\frac{20}{50}$ or $\frac{2}{5}$] What percent is 30 of 50? [60%] What fraction is 30 of 50? [$\frac{30}{50}$ or $\frac{3}{5}$] What percent is 40 of 50? [80%] What fraction is 40 of 50? [$\frac{40}{50}$ or $\frac{4}{5}$]

**United States map and list of states.** Give the child the U.S. map and list of the states. Tell him to find the state he lives in.

Say: Forty-eight of the states are contiguous; that means they are next to each other. Ask: Which two states are not contiguous? [Alaska and Hawaii] How many states are there altogether? [50] What country is between the 48 contiguous states and Alaska? [Canada] How many states border Illinois? [five] What percentage of the 50 states border Illinois? [10%, 5 out of 50]

Tell him to find the following on the map:

The west coast

The east coast

Pacific Ocean

Atlantic Ocean

Gulf of Mexico

Great Lakes

Mississippi River

Explain that a river is usually the cause of a jagged border between two states.

| ACTIVITIES FOR TEACHING CONTINUED: | EXPLANATIONS CONTINUED: |
|---|---|

**Worksheet 65.** Give the child the worksheet and tell him to complete it. The solutions are shown below.

1. What percentage of the states' names start with the letter *M*? **16%**

2. What percentage of the states' names start with the letter *N*? **16%**

3. What percentage of the names starting with *N* have two words? **75%** (6 out of 8, all but Nebraska and Nevada)

4. What percentage of the states' names start with letters other than *M* or *N*? **68%**

5. What percentage of the states' names have two words? **20%**

6. What percentage of the states' names have only one word? **80%**

7. What percentage of the states were part of the 13 original colonies? **26%**

8. What percentage of the states joined the union after the original colonies? **74%**

9. What percentage of the states border the Mississippi River? **20%**

10. What percentage of the states have a coastline on the Pacific Ocean? **10%** (includes Alaska and Hawaii)

11. What percentage of the states border either the Atlantic Ocean or Gulf of Mexico? **36%**

12. What percentage of the states border Canada? **26%** (includes Alaska)

13. What percentage of the states border the Great Lakes? **16%**

14. What percentage of the states border both a Great Lake and an ocean? **2%** (New York)

15. What percentage of the states border Mexico? **8%**

16. What percentage of the states border only other states? **28%**

17. What percentage of the states border Kentucky? **14%**

18. What percentage of the states do not border any other state? **4%** (only Alaska and Hawaii)

19. What percentage of the states are in North America? **98%** (all but Hawaii)

20. What percentage of the states are in South America? **0%**

21. What percentage of the states have borders that are only straight lines? **6%** (Wyoming, Utah, Colorado)

22. What percentage of the states have borders that are an arc of a circle? **4%** (southeastern Pennsylvania and northern Delaware)

**In conclusion.** Say: In 17 states, the largest city is the capital city. Ask: In what percentage of the states, is the capital city not the largest city? [66%]

If there is additional time following this lesson, play the Percentages Old Main game, found in *Math Card Games* book, F47.

# LESSON 94: PERCENTAGE PROBLEMS

## OBJECTIVES:
1. To solve common problems involving percentages

## MATERIALS:
1. Warm-up Practice 9
2. Worksheet 66, Percentage Problems
3. *Math Card Games* book, F48

## ACTIVITIES FOR TEACHING:

**Warm-up.** Give the child the warm-up practice sheet. Tell him to do only the first multivide. Solutions are on the right.

**Worksheet 66.** Give the child the worksheet and ask him to read and solve the first problem. Then tell him to explain it.

> 1. Some shoes are on sale for 50% off. The original price (the price before the sale) is $48.30. What is the sale price? [$24.15]

Once the child realizes 50% means half off, the task is to find half of $48.30. It can be done piecemeal; half of 40, half of 8, and half of 30¢ or it can be done with short division.

Repeat for the remaining problems.

> 2. The Reader's Bookstore is selling a book at 10% off. How much did the buyer save if the original price is $22? [$2.20] What is the sale price? [sale price is $19.80]

This problem has two parts. The savings is $22 × 10%, which is $2.20. To determine the sales price, the child must remember to subtract to find the actual amount paid: $22 − $2.20 = $19.80.

> 3. Lee can't decide which gift to buy. The red one is $5 and is 10% off. The green one is $6 and is 20% off. Which one is cheaper? [Red is cheaper.]

The red one is $5 × 10%, which is $0.50. Again subtraction is necessary to find the actual price paid: $5 − $0.50 is $4.50. The green one is $6 × 20%, which is $1.20 and $6 − $1.20 is $4.80.

## EXPLANATIONS:

```
            23 (5)
          × 48 (3)
           184
           920
          1104 (6)
          × 18 (0)
          8 832
         11 040
         19 872 (0)
          × 15 (6)
         99 360
        198 720
        298 080 (0)
          × 28 (1)
      2 384 640
      5 961 600
   9)8 346 240 (0)
   8)927 360 (0)
   7)115 920 (0)
   6)16 560 (0)
   5)2 760 (6)
   4)552 (3)
   3)138 (3)
   2)46 (1)
       23
```

| ACTIVITIES FOR TEACHING CONTINUED: | EXPLANATIONS CONTINUED: |

4. Prices have gone up 10% at the Little Store. What is the new price for cereal, which used to cost $4.00? [$4.40]

Finding 10% of $4 can be accomplished, if necessary, by thinking of 400¢: 400¢ × 10% = 40¢ and $4 + 40¢ = $4.40.

5. A jacket is on sale at a store for $35.88. There is a tag on it saying it was marked down 50%. What was the original price? Hint: first solve the problem with easier numbers. [$71.76]

Using easier numbers often helps with problem solving. If a certain amount is half, then the whole is twice that. So, $35.88 × 2 = $71.76.

**Percentage War game.** Have him play the Percentage War game, found in *Math Card Games* book, F48.

**In conclusion.** Ask: Which is more, one half or 40%? [one half] Which is more, one eighth or 20%? [20%] Which is more, two thirds or three fifths? [two thirds]

# LESSON 95: MORE PERCENTAGE PROBLEMS

## OBJECTIVES:

1. To solve more common problems involving percentages
2. To learn about tipping and sales tax

## MATERIALS:

1. Warm-up Practice 9
2. Worksheet 67, More Percentage Problems
3. *Math Card Games* book, F48

## ACTIVITIES FOR TEACHING:

**Warm-up.** Give the child the warm-up practice sheet. Tell him to do the second multivide on the page. Solutions are on the right.

**Worksheet 70.** Give the child the worksheet and ask him to read and solve the first problem. Then tell him to explain it.

> 1. In a certain class 50% of the children are girls. There are 12 girls. How many children are in the class? [24 children]

If 50% are girls, then 50% must be boys. The total number will be 12 × 2 = 24 children.

Repeat for the remaining problems.

> 2. The usual tip at a restaurant is 15% of the cost of the food. Many people figure it out by first finding 10%, then finding 5%, which is half of 10%, and adding them together. What is the tip if the food costs $8.00? [$1.20]

Ten percent of $8 is $0.80. Half of that is $0.40. Adding $0.80 and $0.40 is $1.20.

> 3. What is the 15% tip if the food bill is $12.00? What is the total cost? [$13.80]

Tip is $1.20 + $0.60 = $1.80. Total is $12 + $1.80 = $13.80.

> 4. In some places people pay sales tax on certain things they buy. If the sales tax is 5%, what is the total bill for a car that cost $4000? [$4200]

Ten percent of $4000 is $400. Half of that is $200. Total is $4000 + $200 = $4200 total cost.

## EXPLANATIONS:

```
              24 (6)
            × 18 (0)
             192
             240
             432 (0)
             × 6 (6)
           2 592 (0)
            × 35 (8)
          12 960
          77 760
          90 720 (0)
            × 96 (6)
         544 320
       8 164 800
    9)8 709 120 (0)
    8)967 680 (0)
    7)120 960 (0)
    6)17 280 (0)
    5)2 880 (0)
    4)576 (0)
    3)144 (0)
    2)48 (3)
       24
```

**ACTIVITIES FOR TEACHING CONTINUED:**

**EXPLANATIONS CONTINUED:**

5. The original price for a game is $10.00. In Store A it went on sale at 10% off and then it went on sale again with 50% off of the sale price. In Store B it went on sale at 50% off and then it went on sale again with 10% off of the sale price. Which store has the better price? [the same, $4.50]

At Store A, the price after the first reduction is $10 \times 90\% = \$9$. After the second price reduction, it is $\$9 \times 50\% = \$4.50$.

At Store B, the price after the first reduction is $\$10 \times 50\% = \$5$. After the second price reduction, it is $\$5 \times 90\% = \$4.50$.

Note that the final price for Store A is $\$10 \times 50\% \times 90\%$ and for Store B it is $\$10 \times 90\% \times 50\%$, which gives the same result.

**Percentage War game.** Have him play the Percentage War game, found in *Math Card Games* book, F48.

**In conclusion.** Ask: Which is more, one half or 60%? [60%] Which is more, three eighth or 20%? [three eighths] Which is more, two thirds or four fifths? [four fifths]

# Lesson 96: Fraction Circles

## OBJECTIVES:

1. To find fractions in circles
2. To draw common fractions of a circle

## MATERIALS:

1. Fraction Circle and Percentage Circle, Appendix p. 5
2. **Scissors**
3. Worksheet 68, Fraction Circles

## ACTIVITIES FOR TEACHING:

***Warm-up.*** Say: A polygon is a flat closed figure made with straight lines. Ask: Is a triangle a polygon? [yes] Say: A quadrilateral is a polygon with four sides. Ask: Is a triangle a quadrilateral? [no, it does not have four sides]

Say: A parallelogram is a quadrilateral with opposite sides parallel. Ask: Is a trapezoid a parallelogram? [no, it does not have two sets of parallel sides]

Say: A rectangle is a parallelogram with right angles. Ask: Is a square a rectangle? [yes] What makes a square special? [it has equal sides] Say: A rhombus has equal sides but may not have right angles. Think of a diamond; it has equal sides but not right angles. See figure on the right.

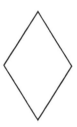

***Fraction Circle and Percentage Circle.*** Give the child the Fraction Circle and Percentage Circle appendix page and scissors. Tell him to cut out the four large circles and to assemble the fraction circle with a shaded circle as shown below.

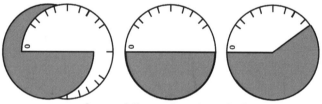

**Assembling a fraction circle.**

***Fraction circles.*** Explain that the fraction of the circle we will be talking about is the visible part of the white circle. Tell him to find fractions $\frac{1}{2}$, $\frac{1}{4}$, and $\frac{2}{3}$. See below. Continue with $\frac{1}{8}$ and $\frac{7}{8}$.

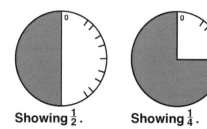

Showing $\frac{1}{2}$.  Showing $\frac{1}{4}$.

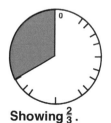

Showing $\frac{2}{3}$.

## EXPLANATIONS:

The back side of the appendix page has a shaded rectangular area. This will prevent show through during estimation activities.

Although numbers are not shown in the figures here, they are on the paper circles.

Only the fraction circle will be used in this lesson. The percentage circle will be used in the next lesson.

Both circles will be used in future lessons.

| **ACTIVITIES FOR TEACHING CONTINUED:** | **EXPLANATIONS CONTINUED:** |

Ask: Which fraction on the circle is closest to 1? [$\frac{9}{10}$]
Which is more, $\frac{3}{4}$ or $\frac{7}{8}$? [$\frac{7}{8}$]

Tell the child to name the fractions between $\frac{1}{2}$ and
$\frac{3}{4}$. [$\frac{3}{5}, \frac{5}{8}, \frac{2}{3}, \frac{7}{10}$] Tell him to find $\frac{1}{4}$, then to double it.
Ask: What is the new fraction? [$\frac{1}{2}$]

**Worksheet 68.** Give the child the worksheet. Tell him to look at the row of figures. See below.

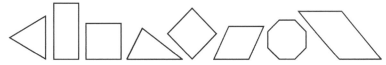

Ask: What fraction of the figures are triangles? [$\frac{1}{4}$ (first and fourth figures in the row of eight)] Tell him to show it with his fraction circle. See the left figure below.

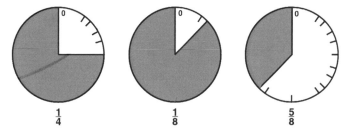

Ask: What fraction of the figures have no sides equal?
[$\frac{1}{8}$, (fourth figure in the row)] Tell him to show it with his fraction circle. See the middle figure above.

Ask: What fraction of the figures are parallelograms? [$\frac{5}{8}$ (second, third, fifth, sixth, and eighth figures)] Tell him to show it with his fraction circle. See the right figure above.

**Worksheet 68.** Tell the child to do the worksheet. The solutions are below.

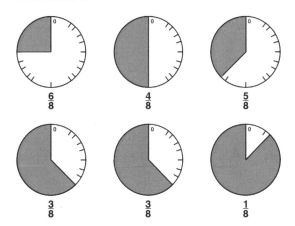

Second problem: The octagon has perpendicular lines. They may not meet at a vertex, but they are perpendicular.

**In conclusion.** Ask: In a collection of figures, could you have more squares than rectangles? [no] In a collection of figures, could the fraction of rectangles be nine eighths? [no] In a collection of figures, could you have more triangles than rectangles? [yes]

If there is additional time following this lesson, play the Simplifying Fractions game, found in *Math Card Games* book, F29.

# LESSON 97: PERCENTAGE CIRCLES

## OBJECTIVES:
1. To find percentages in circles
2. To draw common percentages of a circle

## MATERIALS:
1. Fraction and Percentage Circles from previous lesson
2. Worksheet 69, Percentage Circles
3. Tangrams, optional
4. Fraction card deck

## ACTIVITIES FOR TEACHING:

***Warm-up.*** Say: A quadrilateral is a polygon with four sides. A parallelogram is a quadrilateral with opposite sides parallel. Tell the child to show parallel lines with his arms.

Ask: Is a triangle a parallelogram? [no, it does not have four sides or opposite parallel sides] Is a circle a parallelogram? [no, it does not have four sides] Is a rectangle a parallelogram? [yes]

Say: A rhombus has four equal sides but may not have right angles. Tell the child to show a right angle with his arms. Ask: Can a triangle be a rhombus? [no, it only has three sides] Can a square be a rhombus? [yes]

***Percentage circles.*** Tell the child to put together his percentage circle, if it is not already assembled. Tell him to find 50%, 25%, and 66$\frac{2}{3}$%. See below. Continue with 75% and 90%.

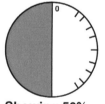 

**Showing 50%.**  **Showing 25%.**  **Showing 66$\frac{2}{3}$%.**

Ask: Which percentage mark on the circle is the smallest? [10%] What is twice 10%? [20%] What percentage is one half? [50%]

***Worksheet 69.*** Give the child the worksheet. Tell him to look at the row of figures. See below.

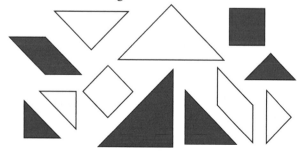

## EXPLANATIONS:

Although numbers are not shown in the figures here, they are on the paper circles.

Some children may prefer to use the actual tangrams. They will need all but one of the largest triangle from each color.

**ACTIVITIES FOR TEACHING CONTINUED:**

**EXPLANATIONS CONTINUED:**

Ask: What percentage of the tangram pieces are light-colored? [50%] How do you know? [half are light-colored, or six twelfths, which is one half] What percentage of the tangram pieces are squares? [two twelfths, which is one sixth, $16\frac{2}{3}$ %] What percentage of the tangram pieces are parallelograms? [four twelfths, which is one third (squares are parallelograms), $33\frac{1}{3}$ %] What percentage of the tangram pieces are triangles? [eight twelfths, which is two thirds, $66\frac{2}{3}$ %]

**Worksheet 69.** Tell him to do the worksheet. The solutions are below.

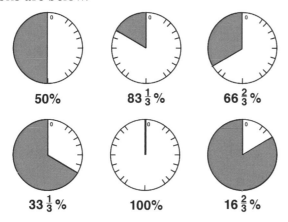

50%  $83\frac{1}{3}$ %  $66\frac{2}{3}$ %

$33\frac{1}{3}$ %  100%  $16\frac{2}{3}$ %

**Percentage and Fraction War game.** Play the Percentage and Fraction War game. Use a stack of fraction cards and the stack of 20 percentage cards. He will also need his percentage and fraction circles.

The first player takes a card from the fraction stack and shows the fraction on his fraction circle. The second player takes a card from the percentage stack and shows the percentage on her percentage circle. The players then compare values. The player with the higher value takes both cards, setting them aside on separate piles. Wars, where the cards played have the same value, are resolved by putting one extra card down before playing another card.

When the percentage stack is depleted, reuse the percentage cards. Now the first player uses the percentage cards and the second player uses the fraction cards.

The winner is the player with the most fraction cards.

**In conclusion.** Ask: Which is more, one fourth or 40%? [40%] Which is more, two thirds or 23%? [two thirds] Which is more, 50% of 100 or 100% of 50? [same]

# LESSON 98: PERCENTAGE AND FRACTIONS TOTALING ONE

## OBJECTIVES:

1. To find percentages in circles
2. To discover the sum of the fractions in a circle is one
3. To discover the sum of the percentages in a circle is 100%

## MATERIALS:

1. Fraction and Percentage Circles from previous lessons
2. Worksheet 70, Percentage and Fractions Totaling One
3. *Math Card Games* book, F48

## ACTIVITIES FOR TEACHING:

***Warm-up.*** Ask: What is 25% equal to in fractions? [one fourth] What is 50% equal to? [one half] What is 75% equal to? [three fourths]

Ask: Which is less, one sixth or 60%? [one sixth] Which is less, three fourths or 34%? [34%] Which is less, 50% or one half? [same]

***Guessing fractions and clocks.*** Tell the child to take his fraction circle and to turn it over so the fractions are not visible. Tell him to show $\frac{1}{4}$ and then turn it over to see how close he is to the actual fraction. See the figures below.

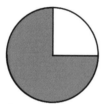 

**Guessing 25%.**　　**Checking 25%.**

Tell the child to keep the circle at $\frac{1}{4}$ and put the 0 at the top. Ask: If the fraction circle were a clock, what number would the minute hand be pointing to? [3] What fraction of an hour has passed since the beginning of an hour? [$\frac{1}{4}$] What is another word for one fourth? [quarter] Say: This is why some people say it is a quarter past the hour. Repeat for $\frac{1}{2}$ and $\frac{3}{4}$.

Ask: What fraction of a circle would the 4 on a clock be? [one third] How do you know? [four twelfths is one third] Say: Turn your fraction circle to the blank side and set it where you think the 4 position on a clock is. Turn it back and ask: Was it close to one third?

## EXPLANATIONS:

These circles will be used again in Lesson 104.

| ACTIVITIES FOR TEACHING CONTINUED: | EXPLANATIONS CONTINUED: |
|---|---|

**ACTIVITIES FOR TEACHING CONTINUED:**

***Combining fraction and percentage circles.*** Tell the child to combine the fraction and percentage circles by putting the fraction circle on top of the percentage circle as shown below.

**Combining the fraction and percentage circles.**

Say: Set the percentage circle to 75%. Ask: What does the fraction circle say? [$\frac{1}{4}$] What happens when you add them? [They total 1, or 100%.] Tell him to try it with other fractions and percentages. [They always add to 1.]

***Worksheet 70.*** Give the child the worksheet. Tell him to read the instructions very carefully. The solutions are on the right.

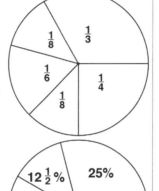

Ask: When you added the fractions and the percentages, did you get the answer you expected? Ask the child to explain how he added them.

$\frac{1}{8} + \frac{1}{8} + \frac{1}{4} + \frac{1}{3} + \frac{1}{6} = 1$

The two $\frac{1}{8}$ s = $\frac{1}{4}$ and two $\frac{1}{4}$s = $\frac{1}{2}$.

Also $\frac{1}{3} + \frac{1}{6} = \frac{1}{2}$.

Lastly, the two $\frac{1}{2}$ s = 1.

For the percentages:

$12\frac{1}{2}\% + 25\% + 10\% + 12\frac{1}{2}\% + 40\%$
$= 1.$

Adding the two $12\frac{1}{2}$ s is 25.

Then $25 + 25 + 10 + 40 = 100\%$.

***Percentage and Fraction War game.*** Play either Percentage War from *Math Card Games* book, F48, or the Percentage and Fraction War game from the previous lesson.

***In conclusion.*** Ask: On a clock, what fraction of an hour has passed if the minute hand is at 6? [one half] What fraction of an hour has passed if the minute hand is at 4? [one third] What fraction of an hour has passed if the minute hand is at 8? [two thirds]

# LESSON 99: REVIEW AND GAMES 7

## OBJECTIVES:
1. To review recent topics
2. To develop skills through playing math card games

## MATERIALS:
1. Worksheet 71-A or 71-B, Review 6
2. *Math Card Games* book, F48

| ACTIVITIES FOR TEACHING: | EXPLANATIONS: |
|---|---|

**Worksheet 71-A.** Give the child the worksheet. Tell him to listen to the problems and write the answers. Read each problem twice.

$2.50 × 4        101 − 45        .5 × 20

Tell him to complete the worksheet. Solutions are below.

Ask the child to correct any errors during the lesson.

---

Write only the answers.

**$10.00**

**56**

**10**

Write the answers.

50% of 12 = **6**

40% + **60%** = 1

574 + 78 = **652**

Do the calculations.

10,000 − 4682

**10,000**
**− 4,682**
**5,318**

7934 + 784 + 8538

**7934**
**784**
**+ 8538**
**17,256**

2359 ÷ 7

**337**
**7)2359**

7946 × 8

**7946**
**× 8**
**63,568**

Answer the questions about the tangram pieces.

What fraction of the pieces are triangles? **3/5**

What fraction of the pieces are parallelograms? **2/5**

What fraction of the triangles are identical? **2/3**

What percentage of the pieces do not have a right angle? **20%**

What percentage of the pieces are polygons? **100%**

Match the fractions to the corresponding percentages.

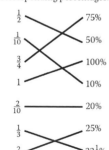

$\frac{1}{2}$ — 75%

$\frac{1}{10}$ — 50%

$\frac{3}{4}$ — 100%

1 — 10%

$\frac{2}{10}$ — 20%

$\frac{1}{3}$ — 25%

$\frac{2}{8}$ — $33\frac{1}{3}$%

Skylar had a tray of 24 tomato seedlings. Skylar gave $\frac{1}{4}$ of them to a friend, $\frac{1}{3}$ of them to another friend, and $\frac{1}{6}$ of them to a third friend. What fraction of the seedlings did Skylar have left? How many seedlings did Skylar have left?

$\frac{1}{4} + \frac{1}{3} + \frac{1}{6} +$ _____ = 1

**Skylar has $\frac{1}{4}$ left.**

**$\frac{1}{4}$ of 24 = 6 seedlings left**

---

191

## ACTIVITIES FOR TEACHING CONTINUED:

**EXPLANATIONS CONTINUED:**

***Percentage War game.*** Play the Percentage War game, found in *Math Card Games* book, F48.

***Worksheet 71-B.*** Give the child the worksheet. Tell him to listen to the problems and write the answers. Read each problem twice.

$2.50 × 3          101 − 72          .2 × 30

Tell him to complete the worksheet. Solutions are below.

---

Write only the answers.

**$7.50**

**29**

**6**

Write the answers.

25% of 8 = **2**

70% + **30%** = 1

369 + 87 = **456**

Do the calculations.

10,000 − 4759

$$\begin{array}{r} 10,000 \\ -\ 4,759 \\ \hline 5,241 \end{array}$$

6378 + 782 + 7963

$$\begin{array}{r} 6378 \\ 782 \\ +\ 7963 \\ \hline 15,123 \end{array}$$

7152 ÷ 8

$$8\overline{)7152} \quad 894$$

4792 × 7

$$\begin{array}{r} 4792 \\ \times\ 7 \\ \hline 33,544 \end{array}$$

Answer the questions about the tangram pieces.

What fraction of the pieces are right triangles? $\frac{1}{2}$

What fraction of the pieces are parallelograms? $\frac{1}{2}$

What fraction of the pieces are rectangles? $\frac{1}{4}$

What percentage of the quadrilaterals are squares? **50%**

What percentage of the pieces are hexagons? **0%**

Match the fractions to the corresponding percentages.

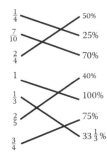

$\frac{1}{4}$          50%

$\frac{7}{10}$          25%

$\frac{2}{4}$          70%

1          40%

$\frac{1}{3}$          100%

$\frac{2}{5}$          75%

$\frac{3}{4}$          $33\frac{1}{3}$%

Leslie had 12 pumpkin seeds to plant. Leslie gave $\frac{1}{4}$ of them to a younger sister, $\frac{1}{6}$ of them to a younger brother, and $\frac{1}{4}$ of them to a friend. What fraction of the seeds did Leslie have left to plant? How many seeds did Leslie plant?

$$\frac{1}{4} + \frac{1}{6} + \frac{1}{4} + \underline{\hspace{1cm}} = 1$$

**Leslie has $\frac{1}{3}$ left.**

**$\frac{1}{3}$ of 12 = 4 seeds planted**

© Activities for Learning, Inc. 2016

# LESSON 100: MEASURING ANGLES

**OBJECTIVES:**

1. To introduce the term *angle*
2. To measure angles with the goniometer
3. To measure and add the angles in a triangle

**MATERIALS:**

1. Warm-up Practice 10
2. Goniometer
3. 45 triangle and 30-60 triangle
4. Worksheet 72, Measuring Angles

## ACTIVITIES FOR TEACHING:

**Warm-up.** Give the child the warm-up practice sheet. Tell him to do only the first multivide. Solutions are on the right.

**The goniometer.** Give the child the goniometer and triangles. Tell him that a goniometer (GON-ee-OM-i-ter) measures the *angles*. An angle is the space between two lines at their vertex, or intersecting point.

Lay the goniometer flat on a surface and demonstrate how to open it by holding the bottom part with your right hand and gently opening the top part with your left hand. See the left figure below.

**The goniometer.**

Tell him to open his goniometer so the inside edges are perpendicular to make a right angle. See the right figure above. Tell him to look at the number inside the little magnifying bubble and ask: What number do you see? [90] Tell him to read it as 90 degrees. Tell him to continue to open the goniometer to twice 90°. Ask: What is the angle? [180°]

**Measuring angles.** Tell him to measure the angles in the triangles with his goniometer. See the figures below.

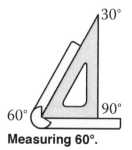

**Measuring 60°.**

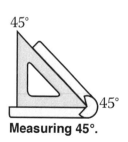

**Measuring 45°.**

Ask: Which triangle has two angles that are congruent, or the same? [45 triangle]

## EXPLANATIONS:

Goniometers were briefly introduced in Level D, Lesson 116.

If the two parts of the goniometer come apart, they can be snapped back together. Align the part with the bump on top of the other part and press down.

```
        22 (4)
      × 27 (0)
       154
       440
       594 (0)
      × 35 (8)
      2 970
     17 820
     20 790 (0)
      × 24 (6)
     83 160
    415 800
    498 960 (0)
      × 16 (7)
    2 993 760
    4 989 600
 9)7 983 360 (0)
 8) 887 040 (0)
 7) 110 880 (0)
 6) 15 840 (0)
 5) 2 640 (3)
 4) 528 (6)
 3) 132 (6)
 2) 44 (8)
      22
```

Congruent is defined as fitting exactly on top.

**ACTIVITIES FOR TEACHING CONTINUED:**

**EXPLANATIONS CONTINUED:**

***Combining angles.*** Tell him to place the 90° angle of the 45 triangle next to the 60° angle of the 30-60 triangle. See the left figure shown below. Ask: What do you think the angle is now? [60 + 90 = 150°] Tell him to use his goniometer to check. [150°] See the right figure below.

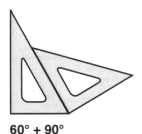

**60° + 90°**

**Measuring 150°.**

Tell him to place the 45° angle next to the 60° angle. Ask: What is the combined angle? [105°] Tell him to use his goniometer to check. [105°] See the left figure below.

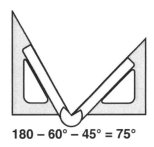

**60° + 45° = 105°.**

**180 − 60° − 45° = 75°**

Tell him to place the two triangles on a straight line with the right angles on the outside as in the right figure above. Ask: How could you find the angle between them? [180 − 60° − 45° = 75°] Tell him to check with his goniometer. [75°]

***Worksheet 72.*** Give the child the worksheet and tell him to complete it. He will need a goniometer. The solutions are below.

If the worksheets are coil bound, it may be easier to remove the page so that the goniometer lays flat on the page.

| | | |
|---|---|---|
| 45 + 60 = 105° | 45 + 30 = 75° | 90 + 90 = 180° |
| 45 + 90 = 135° | 30 + 90 = 120° | 90 + 60 = 150° |
| 180 − 45 − 60 = 75° | 45 − 30 = 15° | 60 − 45 = 15° |

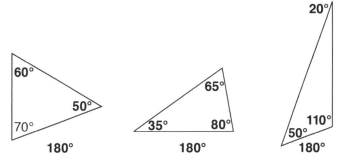

***In conclusion.*** Ask: What are the angles in the 45 triangle? [45°, 45°, 90°] What are the angles in the 30-60 triangle? [30°, 60°, 90°] How many degrees are in a right angle? [90°]

If there is additional time following this lesson, play the Subtracting from One Hundred game, found in *Math Card Games* book, S33.

# LESSON 101: ISOSCELES TRIANGLES

## OBJECTIVES:

1. To review the term *congruent*
2. To learn the term *isosceles*
3. To learn the term *equilateral*
4. To discover that triangles with equal angles have equal sides

## MATERIALS:

1. 1 set of tangrams
2. Worksheet 73, Isosceles Triangles
3. Goniometer
4. Geoboard, optional

---

## ACTIVITIES FOR TEACHING:

***Warm-up.*** Ask: What are the angles in the 30-60 triangle? [30°, 60°, 90°] What are the angles in the 45 triangle? [45°, 45°, 90°] How many degrees are in a right angle? [90°]

Say: Congruent means fitting exactly on top. Ask: Are the 30-60 triangle and 45 triangle congruent? [no] Does the 45 triangle have two congruent sides? [yes] Does an the 30-60 triangle have any congruent sides? [no] Does a square have congruent sides? [yes] Does a square have congruent angles? [yes]

***The word "isosceles" and "equilateral."*** Tell the child that today he will work with *isosceles* and *equilateral* triangles. Say: An isosceles triangle has two equal sides. An equilateral triangle has three equal sides.

***Making isosceles triangles with tangrams.*** Give the child the tangrams. Tell him he will need the two small triangles, the medium triangle, and one large triangle. Ask: Are these tangram triangle isosceles or equilateral triangles? [isosceles]

Show him how to put the longer sides of the small triangles together as shown in the left figure below. Then slowly separate them until the width at the bottom is equal to a side of the medium triangle. See below.

**Making an equilateral triangle with tangrams.**

Ask: What special triangle is inside, framed by the tangrams? [equilateral triangle]

Say: Next replace the medium triangle with the long side of the large triangle. See the left figure on the next page. Increase the angle between the small triangles until the top sides form a straight line. See the second figure on the next page. Tell him it is called an isosceles right triangle.

## EXPLANATIONS:

The derivation of isosceles comes from two words. The "iso" part is Greek for "equal" and the "sceles" is Greek for "legs."

The equilateral triangle can be made with a third small triangle from the second tangram set. See below.

---

**ACTIVITIES FOR TEACHING CONTINUED:** | **EXPLANATIONS CONTINUED:**

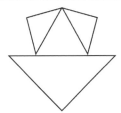 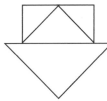 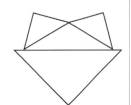

**Equilateral triangle.** **Isosceles right triangle.** **Obtuse triangle.**

Continue increasing the angle. Say: When the triangle has an angle greater than 90°, it is called an *obtuse triangle*. See the right figure above.

***Worksheet 73.*** Give the child the worksheet and goniometer. Say: For this worksheet, triangles that are turned around or flipped over are not different. Show the child by taking a triangle and flip and rotate it such as shown below, stating that these triangles are not different. Tell him to do the worksheet.

He will need to use a goniometer to complete the first part of the worksheet. The solutions are below.

If the worksheets are coil bound, it may be easier to remove the page so that the goniometer lays flat on the page.

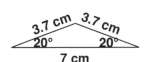 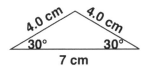 

3.7 cm 3.7 cm 20° 20° **7 cm**   4.0 cm 4.0 cm 30° 30° **7 cm**   4.6 cm 4.6 cm 40° 40° **7 cm**

2. **The sides are congruent.**

Some children may benefit from using a geoboard with one rubber band. Block off the unneeded portion with rubber bands to work in the 3 × 3 area as shown below.

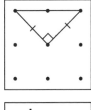  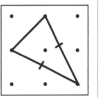 

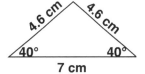

4. isosceles triangles: **5**   right triangles: **4**

***In conclusion.*** Ask: What do you call a triangle that has two congruent sides? [isosceles triangle] What do you call a triangle that has two congruent angles? [isosceles triangle] What do you call a triangle that has two congruent sides and a right angle? [isosceles right triangle]

If there is additional time following this lesson, have the child choose a game to play.

# LESSON 102: CLASSIFYING TRIANGLES

## OBJECTIVES:
1. To classify triangles by sides and by angles
2. To learn the terms *scalene*, *acute*, and *obtuse*

## MATERIALS:
1. Warm-up Practice 10
2. Worksheet 74 , Classifying Triangles
3. Goniometer
4. 4-in-1 ruler

## ACTIVITIES FOR TEACHING:

***Warm-up.*** Give the child the warm-up practice sheet. Tell him to do the second multivide on the page. Solutions are on the right.

***Classifying triangles by side.*** Give the child the worksheet. Tell him that we can group triangles by comparing their sides or by comparing their angles.

Tell him to look at the tables on his worksheet, which are shown below.

| Triangles by Sides | | Triangles by Angles | |
|---|---|---|---|
| 3 sides congruent | Equilateral | < 90° | Acute |
| 2 sides congruent | Isosceles | = 90° | Right |
| 0 sides congruent | Scalene | > 90° | Obtuse |

Say: There is a new term in the first chart. A *scalene* (skay-LEEN) triangle has no sides congruent. Ask: If a triangle has two sides the same length, is it a scalene triangle? [no] Ask: What do you call a triangle with two sides the same? [isosceles]

Ask: How many congruent sides does an equilateral triangle have? [three] Is an equilateral triangle isosceles? [yes] Tell him that some people do not agree that an equilateral triangle is an isosceles triangle, however mathematicians agree it is. Ask: What is a triangle with three unequal sides called? [scalene]

***Classifying triangles by angles.*** Tell him to look at the second chart on his worksheet. Ask: How does this chart classify triangles? [by angles] What do we call angles that are less than 90°? [acute (a-CUTE)] Tell him that some people remember the word *acute* because the capital letter "A" has an acute angle.

Ask: What is an angle greater than 90° called? [obtuse (ob-TUSE)] If you put two 30° angles together, would it be obtuse? [no, 30 + 30 is less than 90] If you put two 60° angles together, would it be obtuse? [yes, 60 + 60 is greater than 90]

## EXPLANATIONS:

$$
\begin{array}{r}
23 \ (5) \\
\times 16 \ (7) \\
\hline
138 \\
230 \\
\hline
368 \ (8) \\
\times 28 \ (1) \\
\hline
2\,944 \\
7\,360 \\
\hline
10\,304 \ (8) \\
\times 54 \ (0) \\
\hline
41\,216 \\
515\,200 \\
\hline
556\,416 \ (0) \\
\times 15 \ (6) \\
\hline
2\,782\,080 \\
5\,564\,160 \\
\hline
\end{array}
$$

$$
\begin{array}{r}
9)\overline{8\,346\,240} \ (0) \\
8)\overline{927\,360} \ (0) \\
7)\overline{115\,920} \ (0) \\
6)\overline{16\,560} \ (0) \\
5)\overline{2\,760} \ (6) \\
4)\overline{552} \ (3) \\
3)\overline{138} \ (3) \\
2)\overline{46} \ (1) \\
23
\end{array}
$$

Mathematically, obtuse angles must be more than 90° and must be less than 180°. Obviously, being greater than 180° is not a concern in triangles.

| ACTIVITIES FOR TEACHING CONTINUED: | EXPLANATIONS CONTINUED: |
|---|---|

*Name my triangle.* Play this guessing game with the child.

Say: I'm a triangle with sides of 3 cm, 4 cm, and 5 cm. Ask: What kind of a triangle am I? [scalene triangle]

Say: I'm a triangle with sides of 4 cm, 4 cm, and 4 cm. Ask: What kind of a triangle am I? [equilateral and isosceles triangle]

Say: I'm a triangle with angles of 40°, 40°, and 100°. Ask: What kind of a triangle am I? [isosceles obtuse triangle]

Say: I'm a triangle with angles of 50°, 50°, and 80°. Ask: What kind of a triangle am I? [isosceles acute triangle]

Ask the child to make up some of his own descriptions.

*Worksheet 74.* Give the child the goniometer and ruler. Tell him to do the worksheet. The solutions are below.

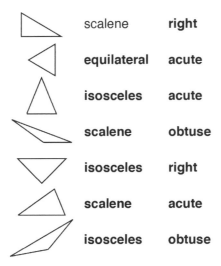

| scalene | **right** |
|---|---|
| **equilateral** | **acute** |
| **isosceles** | **acute** |
| scalene | **obtuse** |
| **isosceles** | **right** |
| scalene | **acute** |
| **isosceles** | **obtuse** |

Does an isosceles scalene triangle exist? Why or why not? **No. Isosceles means two sides equal and scalene means no sides equal.**

Does an equilateral right triangle exist? Why or why not? **No. Three sides can't be equal if the triangle has a right angle.**

*In conclusion.* Ask: What kind of a triangle has all of its angles less than 90°? [acute triangle] What kind of a triangle has an angle more than 90°? [obtuse triangle] What kind of a triangle has all of its angles equal to 60°? [equilateral triangle] What kind of a triangle does not have any sides congruent? [scalene triangle]

If there is additional time following this lesson, have the child choose a game to play.

# LESSON 103: CLASSIFYING POLYGONS

## OBJECTIVES:

1. To classify polygons as *regular polygon* or *irregular polygon*

## MATERIALS:

1. Worksheet 75, Classifying Polygons
2. 4-in-1 ruler
3. Goniometer

## ACTIVITIES FOR TEACHING:

***Warm-up.*** Ask: An acute triangle has what kind of angles? [all of its angles are less than 90°] An obtuse triangle has what kind of angle? [one angle is more than 90°] What kind of a triangle has all of its angles equal to 60°? [equilateral triangle]

Ask: What do we call something that exactly fits on top? [congruent] What is special about the angles of a equilateral triangle? [congruent angles] What is special about the sides of a equilateral triangle? [congruent lengths] What kind of a triangle does not have any sides congruent? [scalene triangle]

***Triangle review.*** Say: Yesterday we talked about classifying triangles by sides and angles. There are special names for triangles depending upon whether or not their sides are congruent. Ask: What are these names? [scalene, isosceles, equilateral] Say: There are special names for triangles depending upon whether their angles are less than, equal to, or greater than 90°. Ask: What are these names? [acute, right, obtuse]

***Polygon review.*** Say: A triangle is a polygon, but many polygons have more than three sides as we've discussed before. A polygon is a closed figure made of straight lines.

Draw the following figures.

| Yes | No | Yes | No |

**Are these polygons?**

Ask: Is the first figure a polygon? [yes] Is the second figure a polygon? [no] Why not? [not closed] Is the third figure a polygon? [yes] Is the fourth figure a polygon? [no] Why not? [all the lines are not straight]

## EXPLANATIONS:

| ACTIVITIES FOR TEACHING CONTINUED: | EXPLANATIONS CONTINUED: |
|---|---|

**Worksheet 79.** Give the child the worksheet. Tell him to look at the polygon chart at the top of the page. See the figure below.

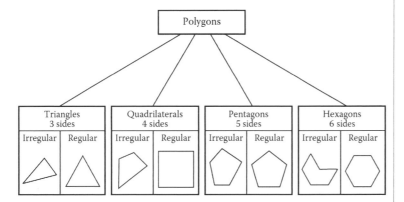

**Classifying polygons.** Say: Polygons can be classified whether they are regular or irregular. A *regular polygon* has all of the sides equal and all angles equal. *Irregular* means not regular.

Tell the child to read the top part of each small chart. [triangle, 3 sides; quadrilaterals, 4 sides; pentagons, 5 sides; hexagons, 6 sides] Ask: Could the charts be extended in the left direction? [no, a polygon cannot have only two sides] Could the charts be extended in the right direction? [yes] Name an example. [octagon]

Ask: What does the bottom half of each small chart show? [a figure that is irregular and a figure that is regular]

**Worksheet 75.** Give the child the ruler and goniometer. Tell him to do the worksheet and to use a ruler or goniometer for measuring. The solutions are below.

1. Which of the figures below are polygons? **A, B, D, F**
2. Explain why the others are not polygons. **C is not closed; E does not have all straight lines.**
3. Which pentagons above have congruent sides? **GI**
4. Which pentagons above have congruent angles? **HI**
5. Which pentagons above are regular pentagons? **I**
6. What is another name for a regular triangle? **equilateral triangle**
7. What is another name for a regular quadrilateral? **square**
8. Which of the polygons in the first question are regular polygons? **B, D, F**

*If the worksheets are coil bound, it may be easier to remove the page so that the goniometer lays flat on the page.*

**In conclusion.** Ask: What does congruent mean? [exactly fits on top] What two attributes must a polygon have to be regular? [congruent sides and congruent angles] Is a stop sign a regular polygon? [yes]

*If there is additional time following this lesson, play the Quotient Race game, found in* Math Card Games *book, D4.*

# LESSON 104: CLASSIFYING ANGLES

## OBJECTIVES:

1. To introduce the terms *straight angle*, *reflex angle*, and *full angle*
2. To learn the sum of the angles in a circle is 360°
3. To make a protractor
4. To understand how a protractor is set up by construction one

## MATERIALS:

1. Worksheet 76, Classifying Angles
2. **Scissors**
3. Large shaded circles, Lesson 98
4. **A protractor, if available**
5. Drawing board and T-square
6. Goniometer

## ACTIVITIES FOR TEACHING:

***Warm-up.*** Say: I'm a triangle with sides of 3 cm, 4 cm, and 5 cm. Ask: What kind of a triangle am I? [scalene triangle]

Say: I'm a triangle with angles of 20°, 20°, and 140°. Ask: What kind of a triangle am I? [isosceles obtuse triangle]

Say: I'm a triangle with angles of 55°, 55°, and 70°. Ask: What kind of a triangle am I? [isosceles acute triangle]

Say: I'm a triangle with sides of 8 cm, 8 cm, and 8 cm. Ask: What kind of a triangle am I? [equilateral and isosceles triangle]

***Worksheet 76.*** Give the child the worksheet and scissors. Tell him to cut out the triangles on the bottom right and save them for the next lesson. Then tell him to cut out the circle in the bottom left corner and to assemble it with a shaded circle used in Lesson 98.

***Measuring angles.*** Tell him to hold his angle circle with the zero at the right. Explain that angles start at that position and move counterclockwise in algebra and in higher mathematics.

Tell him to find 30° and 60° with his angle circles. Ask: What are angles less than 90° called? [acute] See the left figure below. Tell him to find 90° and ask: What is this angle called? [right] See the middle figure. Tell him to find 145° and ask: What is this angle called? [obtuse] See the right figure.

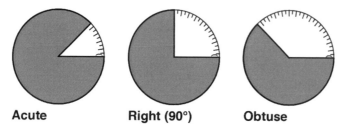

| Acute | Right (90°) | Obtuse |

Tell him to find 180°. Ask: What does that angle look like? [straight line] Say: It is called a *straight angle*. See the left figure on the next page.

## EXPLANATIONS:

A 3 cm, 4 cm, and 5 cm triangle would also be an acute triangle.

Angles start at the "3 o'clock" position because of the x-axis. Clocks and geographers start at the top and go clockwise.

The angle 145° is found halfway between 140° and 150°.

These circles will be used in future lessons.

201

## ACTIVITIES FOR TEACHING CONTINUED:

**Straight (180°)**    **Reflex**    **Full (360°)**

Tell him to find 30° more than a straight angle. See the middle figure above. Say: This is called a *reflex angle*. Reflex angles are not used very often.

Tell him to find 360°. See the right figure above. Say: Sometimes that angle is called a *full angle*, but usually it is just called a 360.

**Constructing a protractor.** Tell the child he will now make a protractor. If available, show him what a commercial protractor looks like. Explain that it measures angles, like a goniometer. A sample protractor is shown on the worksheet.

**Worksheet 76.** Give the child the drawing board, T-square, and goniometer. Tell him to construct his protractor. Demonstrate drawing the 105° line with a goniometer, shown in the left figure below. Emphasize that the point on the protractor is the vertex of the angle. See the right figure below to construct angles less than 90°.

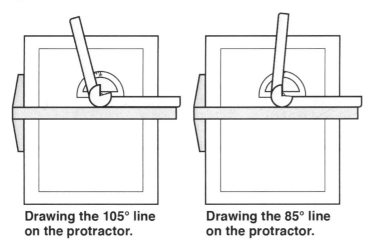

**Drawing the 105° line on the protractor.**    **Drawing the 85° line on the protractor.**

Tell the child that this protractor will be used in the next lesson.

**In conclusion.** Ask: How many degrees are in a right angle? [90°] How many degrees are in a straight angle? [180°] Can angles be more than 180°? [yes] How many degrees are in a whole circle? [360°]

## EXPLANATIONS CONTINUED:

If appropriate, discuss how some sports refer to "doing a 360."

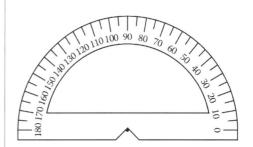

Most protractors have two scales, one from 0 to 180 and the other from 180 to 0. Many people have a problem trying to decide which scale to use. By constructing his own with one scale, the child will come to understand how to use it.

See page ii, number 5 of "Some General Thoughts on Teaching Mathematics," for additional information.

If there is additional time following this lesson, have the child choose an addition game to play.

© Activities for Learning, Inc. 2016

# LESSON 105: ANGLES IN A CIRCLE

## OBJECTIVES:

1. To discover the sum of the angles in a circle is 360°
2. To use the protractor for measuring angles

## MATERIALS:

1. Warm-up Practice 11
2. Worksheet 77-1 and 77-2, Angles in a Circle
3. Protractor and angle circle, Worksheet 76
4. Goniometer, optional
5. Triangles from Worksheet 76
6. Geared clock

## ACTIVITIES FOR TEACHING:

***Warm-up.*** Give the child the warm-up practice sheet. Tell him to do only the first multivide. Solutions are on the right.

***Worksheet 77-1.*** Give the child both worksheets. Tell him to do the first worksheet, using the protractors he made in the last lesson. Solutions are shown below.

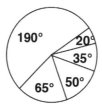

Sum of angles in each circle is **360°**.

Ask: Did you ever wonder why there are 360° in a circle? Explain that the Babylonians really liked the number 60 because 2, 3, 4, 6, 10, and 12 were factors. They knew that a year was about 360 days, and 360 is six 60s. That is why we have 360 degrees in a circle and 60 minutes in an hour and 60 seconds in a minute.

***Triangles from Worksheet 76.*** Tell the child to take one of triangles he cut out in the last lesson and tear off the three corners. See the left figure below.

**Corners torn off and placed side-by-side.**

Tell the child to put the vertices together and ask: What do you get? [a straight line] How many degrees is it? [180°] See the right figure above. Ask: Do you think this works with all triangles?

Tell him to try it with the second triangle and put those vertices together. Ask: What do you get? [same, 180°] How many degrees are in this triangle? [180°] Ask: Do you think this works with all triangles? [yes]

## EXPLANATIONS:

Some children may need to use their goniometer rather than their protractor.

```
                    24 (6)
                  × 15 (6)
                    120
                    240
                    360 (0)
                  × 24 (1)
                  1 440
                  7 200
                  8 640 (0)
                  × 56 (2)
                 51 840
                432 000
                483 840 (0)
                  × 18 (0)
              3 870 720
              4 838 400
          9) 8 709 120 (0)
          8) 967 680 (0)
          7) 120 960 (0)
          6) 17 280 (0)
          5) 2 880 (0)
          4) 576 (0)
          3) 144 (0)
          2) 48 (3)
                    24
```

| ACTIVITIES FOR TEACHING CONTINUED: | EXPLANATIONS CONTINUED: |
|---|---|

**Angles on a clock.** Use the clock and move the minute hand from 12 to 3. Tell the child that angles on clocks are measured clockwise. Tell him to show the same angle on his angle circles. Ask: What is the angle? See the figures below.

**Moving from 12 to 3, 90°.**

Ask: If the hand moves from 12 to 1, what is the angle? [30°] How do you know? [one third of 90 and it measures 30°] Ask: If the hand moves from 12 to 6, what is the angle? [180°] How do you know? [half way around and it's a straight angle] Ask: If the hand moves from 12 to 7, what is the angle? [210°] How do you know? [180 + 30 = 210°] See the figures below.

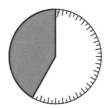

**Moving from 12 to 7, 180 + 30 = 210°.**

**Worksheet 77-2.** Tell the child to do the second worksheet. Tell him to use tools for drawing the lines and measuring the angles. The solutions are below.

| | | |
|---|---|---|
| From 12 to 3: **90°** | From 12 to 1: **30°** | From 12 to 2: **60°** |
| From 12 to 6: **180°** | From 3 to 12: **270°** | From 1 to 8: **210°** |
| From 6 to 10: **120°** | From 7 to 12: **150°** | From 7 to 3: **240°** |

If the worksheets are coil bound, it may be easier to remove the page so that the goniometer lays flat on the page.

**In conclusion.** Ask: How many degrees are in a triangle? [180°] How many degrees are in a circle? [360°] How many degrees does a hand on a clock move through when it moves from 3 to 9? [180°] How many degrees does a hand on a clock move through when it moves from 3 to 10? [210°]

If there is additional time following this lesson, have the child choose a subtraction game to play.

# LESSON 106: ANGLES ON A GEOBOARD

## OBJECTIVES:

1. To introduce the terms *central angle* and *inscribed angle*
2. To discover that in a circle the inscribed angle is half the central angle
3. To become more familiar working with angles

## MATERIALS:

1. Geoboard and rubber bands
2. Goniometer
3. Worksheet 78, Angles on a Geoboard

---

### ACTIVITIES FOR TEACHING:

**Warm-up.** Ask: What do you call an angle less than 90°? [acute angle] What do you call an angle more than 90°? [obtuse triangle] What do you call an angle that is exactly 90°? [right angle]

Ask: If you add a 90° angle and a 30° angle, what is the new angle? [120°] What kind of angle is this? [obtuse angle] If you add a 40° angle and a 15° angle, what is the new angle? [55°] What kind of angle is this? [acute angle] If you add a 25° angle and a 65° angle, what is the new angle? [90°] What kind of angle is this? [right angle]

**Central angles.** Give the child the geoboard, rubber bands, and goniometer.

Tell him to use the circle side of the geoboard and to place a rubber band from the center to the peg directly to the right. See the left figure below.

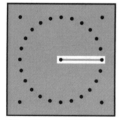 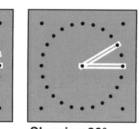

**Starting at 0°.**      **Showing 15°.**      **Showing 30°.**

Then tell him to place a second rubber band from the center peg to the next peg on the circle in the counterclockwise direction. See the middle figure above. Say: Use your goniometer to find the angle between the two rubber bands. [15°] Say: An angle with its vertex at the center of a circle is called a *central angle*.

Tell him to move the second rubber band to the next peg. See the right figure above. Ask: What is the central angle? [30°] If you were going to make a clock, would you need all the pegs for the hour numbers? [no, only half]

**Inscribed angles.** Tell him to move the vertex of the angle to a peg on the circle. See the left figure on the next page. Say: An angle whose vertex is on the circle is called

### EXPLANATIONS:

The fact that the inscribed angle stays the same when the vertex is moved, while the endpoints stay the same, is truly amazing. Help the child appreciate it.

---

| **ACTIVITIES FOR TEACHING CONTINUED:** | **EXPLANATIONS CONTINUED:** |

an *inscribed angle.* Measure the angle. [15°] Tell him to move only the vertex to other pegs and measure the angles. [15°] See the right two figures.

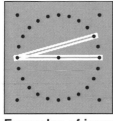 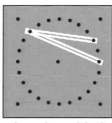 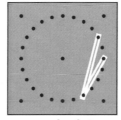

**Examples of inscribed angles with the same endpoints.**

Tell him to make and measure inscribed angles with other endpoints and compare the angles. [same]

***Comparing inscribed angles and central angles.***
Now tell the child to make an inscribed angle on his geoboard and to add a central angle with the same endpoints. See examples below.

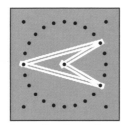 

**Inscribed angles with their central angles.**

Make the following chart.

| Central Angle | 60° | 120° | | | | |
|---|---|---|---|---|---|---|
| Inscribed Angle | 30° | 60° | | | | |

Tell the child to measure both angles and record his results. Tell him to try other inscribed and central angles and record his results in the chart. Ask: What pattern do you see? [central angle is twice the inscribed angle]

***Worksheet 78.*** Give the child the worksheet and tell him to complete it. The solutions are below.

| | | |
|---|---|---|
| **30°** | **30°** | **30°** |
| **60°, 120°** | **30°, 60°** | **45, 90°** |
| **The inscribed angle is half of the central angle.** | | |
| **90°** | **90°** | **90°** |

***In conclusion.*** Ask: What do you call the angle whose vertex is in the center of a circle? [central angle] What do you call the angle whose vertex is on the circle? [inscribed angle] If the central angle is 30°, what is the inscribed angle? [15°] If the central angle is 45, what is the inscribed angle? [22.5°]

To combine two rubber bands to make a longer rubber band, follow the steps below.

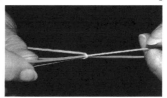

**Insert the first rubber band under the second rubber band.**

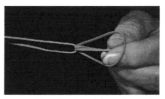

**Loop the first rubber band back through itself.**

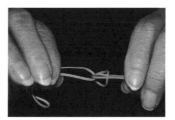

**Pull on the ends of the rubber bands.**

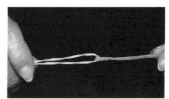

**Voila! A longer rubber band.**

If the worksheets are coil bound, it may be easier to remove the page so that the goniometer lays flat on the page.

If there is additional time following this lesson, have the child choose a multiplication game to play.

# LESSON 107: REGULAR POLYGONS ON A GEOBOARD

## OBJECTIVES:

1. To learn the term *adjacent*
2. To calculate central angles
3. To use central angles to make regular polygons on a geoboard

## MATERIALS:

1. Warm-up Practice 11
2. Geoboard and rubber bands
3. Goniometer
4. Worksheet 79, Regular Polygons on a Geoboard

## ACTIVITIES FOR TEACHING:

**Warm-up.** Give the child the warm-up practice sheet. Tell him to do the second multivide on the page. Solutions are on the right.

**Hexagon on the geoboard.** Give the child the geoboard, rubber bands, and goniometer to him.

Tell him to use the circle side of the geoboard to make a 60° angle. See the left figure below. Say: Make another 60° angle adjacent to the first angle. *Adjacent* means next to. See the middle figure below.

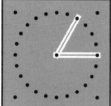  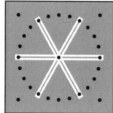

**One 60° angle.**    **Two 60° angles.**    **Six 60° angles.**

Tell the child to keep going and make as many 60° angles as he can. See the right figure above. Ask: How many 60° angles can you make? [6] What is the sum of the six central angles? [60 × 6 = 360°]

Tell him to connect the endpoints of the angles. See the figure below.

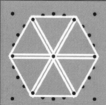

**A hexagon.**

Ask: What figure did you make? [hexagon] Is it a regular polygon? [yes] How do you know? [sides and angles are congruent] If you didn't know the central angle for a hexagon, how could you figure it out? [360 divided by 6 = 60°] What other polygons do you see? [equilateral triangles]

## EXPLANATIONS:

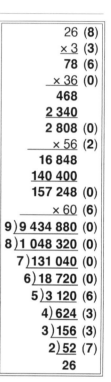

$$
\begin{array}{r}
26 \ (8) \\
\times\, 3 \ (3) \\
\hline
78 \ (6) \\
\times\, 36 \ (0) \\
\hline
468 \\
\underline{2\,340} \\
2\,808 \ (0) \\
\times\, 56 \ (2) \\
\hline
16\,848 \\
\underline{140\,400} \\
157\,248 \ (0) \\
\times\, 60 \ (6) \\
\hline
9\,)\,9\,434\,880 \ (0) \\
8\,)\,1\,048\,320 \ (0) \\
7\,)\,131\,040 \ (0) \\
6\,)\,18\,720 \ (0) \\
5\,)\,3\,120 \ (6) \\
4\,)\,624 \ (3) \\
3\,)\,156 \ (3) \\
2\,)\,52 \ (7) \\
26
\end{array}
$$

| ACTIVITIES FOR TEACHING CONTINUED: | EXPLANATIONS CONTINUED: |
|---|---|

***Equilateral triangle on the geoboard.*** Ask: How can you find the central angle for an equilateral triangle? [divide 360 by 3, 120°] Tell the child to make the three adjacent central angles on his geoboard. See the left figure below. Tell him to connect the endpoints. See the right figure.

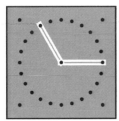 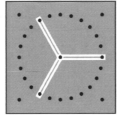 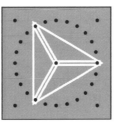

**One 120° angle.**    **Three 120° angles.**    **Equilateral triangle.**

***Worksheet 79.*** Give the child the worksheet. Tell him to complete it. Say: It is not necessary to draw all the central angles. The solutions are below.

If the worksheets are coil bound, it may be easier to remove the page so that the goniometer lays flat on the page.

Each figure can have many different orientations.

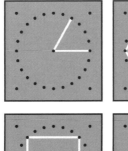 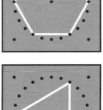

 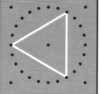

Central angle **90°**    Central angle **120°**

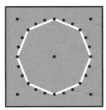 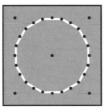

Central angle **45°**    Central angle **30°**

***In conclusion.*** Ask: If you wanted to make a regular decagon, a figure with 10 sides, what would the central angle be? [360 divided by 10 = 36°] How many central angles would the regular decagon have? [10] Can you make a regular decagon on your geoboard? [no] Why not? [cannot make a 36° angle] Can you make an irregular decagon? [yes]

If there is additional time following this lesson, have the child choose a division game to play.

# LESSON 108: REVIEW AND GAMES 8

## OBJECTIVES:
1. To review recent topics
2. To develop skills through playing math card games

## MATERIALS:
1. Worksheet 80-A or 80-B, Review 8
2. *Math Card Games* book, F48

| ACTIVITIES FOR TEACHING: | EXPLANATIONS: |
|---|---|

**ACTIVITIES FOR TEACHING:**

***Worksheet 80-A.*** Give the child the worksheet. Tell him to listen to the problems and write the answers. Read each problem twice.

$0.25 × 5        105 − 82        12 × 20

Tell him to complete the worksheet. Solutions are below.

Write only the answers.

**$1.25**

**23**

**240**

Write the answers.

50% of 16 = **8**

55% + **45%** = 1

693 + 58 = **751**

Do the calculations.

12,345 − 9483

**12,345**
**− 9,483**
**2,862**

29 + 784 + 8538

**29**
**784**
**+ 8538**
**9351**

5932 ÷ 7

**847** r3
7)**5932**

6582 × 9

**6582**
**× 9**
**59,238**

Find the missing angle. Write an equation.

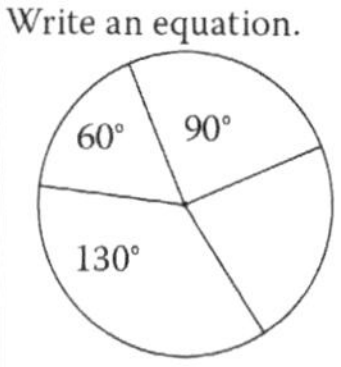

60°  90°
130°

***a = 360 − 130 − 60 − 90***
***a = 80°***

Write T for true or F for false before each statement.

**T** An equilateral triangle has equal angles.

**T** A rhombus has equal sides.

**F** A square is not a regular polygon.

**T** The central angles of a regular polygon are congruent.

**F** A hexagon with congruent sides is always a regular polygon.

**F** A circle is a regular polygon.

**F** An irregular polygon cannot have congruent angles.

Classify the triangles. Classifications can have more than one answer.

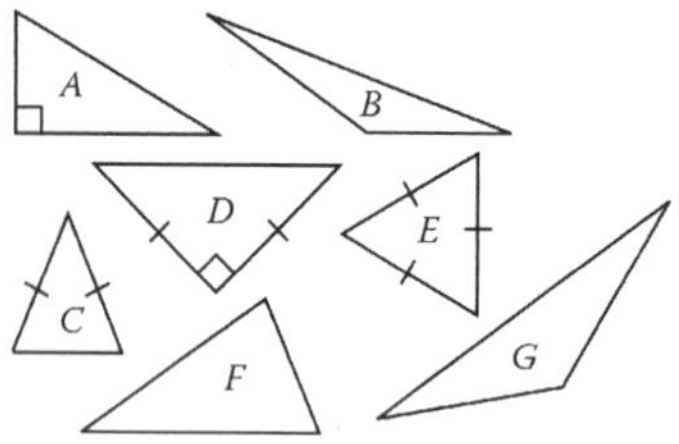

A    B
D    E
C
F    G

Equilateral **E**
Isosceles **C, D, E**
Scalene **A, B, F, G**
Acute **C, E, F**
Right **A, D**
Obtuse **B, G**

Which angle is greatest? 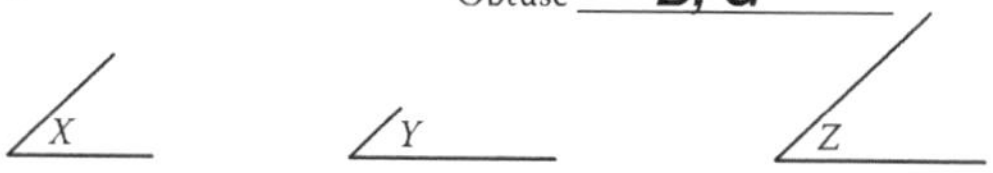
X    Y    Z
**all the same**

**EXPLANATIONS:**

Ask the child to correct any errors during the lesson.

A regular hexagon must have congruent angles as well as congruent sides.

The equation can also be written
$a = 360 − (130 + 60 + 90)$

An equilateral triangle is also isosceles because it has two congruent sides.

## ACTIVITIES FOR TEACHING CONTINUED:

**EXPLANATIONS CONTINUED:**

***Percentage War game.*** Play the Percentage War game, found in *Math Card Games* book, F48.

***Worksheet 80-B.*** Give the child the worksheet. Tell him to listen to the problems and write the answers. Read each problem twice.

$0.25 × 6      103 − 79      13 × 20

Tell him to complete the worksheet. Solutions are below.

---

Write only the answers.

__**$1.50**__

__**24**__

__**260**__

Write the answers.

50% of 18 = __**9**__

35% + __**65%**__ = 1

768 + 78 = __**846**__

Do the calculations.

13,574 − 5968

**13,574**
**− 5,968**
**7,606**

17 + 904 + 6587

**17**
**904**
**+ 6587**
**7508**

2759 ÷ 8

**344 r7**
8)**2759**

7586 × 7

**7586**
**× 7**
**53,102**

Find the missing angle. Write an equation.

100°
80°  70°

**a = 360 − 80 − 100 − 70**
**a = 110°**

Write T for true or F for false before each statement.

**T** An equilateral triangle has equal sides.

**F** A rhombus always has equal angles.

**F** A rectangle can never be a regular polygon.

**T** The least number of sides a polygon can have is three.

**F** A hexagon with congruent angles is always a regular polygon.

**F** A circle is a special polygon.

**T** A trapezoid is an irregular polygon.

A rectangle can be a square.

A regular hexagon must have congruent sides as well as congruent angles.

The equation can also be written
$a = 360 − (80 + 100 + 70)$

Classify the triangles. Classifications can have more than one answer.

Acute __**B, E, F**__
Right __**A, C**__
Obtuse __**D, G**__
Equilateral __**B**__
Isosceles __**A, B, E, G**__
Scalene __**C, D, F**__

An equilateral triangle is also isosceles because it has two congruent sides.

Which angle is least? **all the same**

X    Y    Z

# LESSON 109: SQUARE UNITS

## OBJECTIVES:

1. To construct a square yard
2. To compare square yards with square feet and square inches
3. To construct a square meter
4. To compare square meter with square decimeters and square centimeters

## MATERIALS:

1. Worksheet 81, Square Units
2. Meter stick
3. One tile
4. Tangrams, both sets
5. **Two rulers**

## ACTIVITIES FOR TEACHING:

*Warm-up.* Give the child the worksheet. Tell him to do just the warm-up section. The solutions are below.

$$
\begin{array}{r}
523\ \textbf{(1)} \\
\times\,68\ \textbf{(5)} \\
\hline
4184 \\
31380 \\
\hline
35{,}564\ \textbf{(5)}
\end{array}
\qquad
\begin{array}{r}
2346\ \textbf{(6)} \\
\times\,93\ \textbf{(3)} \\
\hline
7038 \\
211140 \\
\hline
218{,}178\ \textbf{(0)}
\end{array}
$$

*Yards and feet.* Give the child the meter stick, tile, tangrams, and ruler. Tell him to look at his meter stick and ask: What is the unit of measurement on the side of the meter stick with 100 spaces? [centimeters] What is another name for 100 centimeters? [meter] What is the unit of measurement on the side with 36 spaces? [inches] Say: A *yard* has 36 inches. Ask: Which is longer, a meter or a yard? [a meter]

Then tell him to use his ruler find how many feet are in a yard. [3] See the figure on the right.

**Showing 1 yard is 3 feet.**

## EXPLANATIONS:

If there are three rulers available, the child can lay all three end to end to show a yard.

Ask: How many feet are in 2 yards? [6 ft] Ask: How many feet are in 8 yards? [24 ft] Ask: How many yards are in 9 feet? [3 yards]

*Square yards.* Tell the child to use the meter stick and make a square yard as shown below.

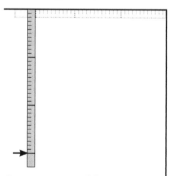

**A square yard in a corner using one meterstick.**

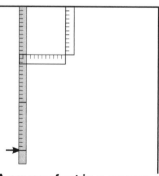

**A square foot in a square yard.**

Then tell him to use two rulers to make a square foot inside the square yard as shown above on the right. Ask: How many square feet are in a square yard? [3 × 3 = 9]

| **ACTIVITIES FOR TEACHING CONTINUED:** | **EXPLANATIONS CONTINUED:** |

**Meters and decimeters.** Tell the child to turn his meter stick over to the meter side. Say: The longest side of the large tangram triangle is 1 decimeter long.

Tell him to measure and find how many decimeters are in 1 meter? [10] See the figure on the right.

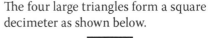

**Showing 1 decimeter.**

**Square meters.** Tell him to use the meter stick and make a square meter. See the left figure below.

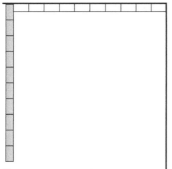 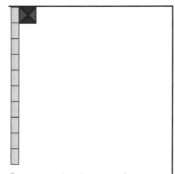

**Square meter in a corner using one meterstick.**

**Square decimeter in a square meter.**

The four large triangles form a square decimeter as shown below.

Then tell him to make a square decimeter with four large triangles and put it inside the square meter. See the right figure above. Ask: How many square decimeters are in a square meter? [10 × 10 = 100]

**Worksheet 81.** Tell the child to do the worksheet. The solutions are below.

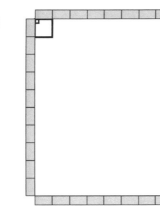

How many feet are in a yard? **3**
How many sq ft in a sq yard? **9**
How many inches in a foot? **12**
How many sq in. in a sq ft? **144**
How many inches in a yard? **36**
How many sq in. in a sq yard? **1296**

How many decimeters in a meter? **10**
How many dm² in a square meter (m²)? **100**
How many centimeters in a decimeter? **10**
How many cm² in a dm²? **100**
How many centimeters in a meter? **100**
How many cm² in a m²? **10,000**

**In conclusion.** Ask: Which is longer, a yard or a meter? [meter] Which has more area, a square yard or a square meter? [square meter] What do we call one third of a yard? [foot] What do we call one tenth of a meter? [decimeter]

If there is additional time following this lesson, play the Corners game, found in *Math Card Games* book, A9.

# Lesson 110: Area Problems

**OBJECTIVES:**
1. To solve area problems

**MATERIALS:**
1. Worksheet 82, Area Problems

---

| **ACTIVITIES FOR TEACHING:** | **EXPLANATIONS:** |
|---|---|

**Warm-up.** Give the child the worksheet. Tell him to do just the warm-up section. The solutions are below.

```
    618 (6)         3618 (0)
  × 49 (4)         × 52 (7)
    5562            7236
   24720          180900
   30,282 (6)     188,136 (0)
```

**Worksheet 82.** Tell the child to solve Problem 1 on the worksheet and then to explain his work. The solution is shown below.

1. Which desk is larger, one that is 13 dm long by 11 dm wide, or one that is a square measuring 1 m and 2 dm on a side?

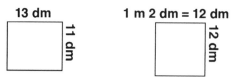

**13 dm** — 11 dm

**1 m 2 dm = 12 dm** — 12 dm

$A_1 = 13 \text{ dm} \times 11 \text{ dm} = 143 \text{ dm}^2$

$A_2 = 12 \text{ dm} \times 12 \text{ dm} = 144 \text{ dm}^2$

**The square desk is larger.**

**Problem 2.** Tell him to solve Problem 2 and then to explain his work. The solution is shown below.

2. A room is 117 m². One side is 9 m long. How long is the other side?

**9 m**

$A = 9 \text{ m} \times s = 117 \text{ m}^2$

$s = 117 \div 9 = 13 \text{ m}$

| **ACTIVITIES FOR TEACHING CONTINUED:** | **EXPLANATIONS CONTINUED:** |

***Buying carpeting.*** Explain that in the United States, carpeting is sold by the square yard, not by the square foot. Area is measured in feet and then converted to square yards.

***Problem 3.*** Tell the child to solve Problem 3 and then to explain his work. The solution is shown below.

3. A room is 18 ft by 18 ft. What will the carpet cost if carpeting is $11.95 per square yard?

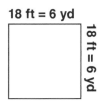

**18 ft = 6 yd**
**18 ft = 6 yd**

**$A$ = 6 yd × 6 yd = 36 sq yd**
**Cost is: $11.95 × 36 = $430.20**

Tell him to solve Problems 4 and 5. The solutions are below.

4. Jacob measured a bedroom and found it was 9 ft by 15 ft. What will the carpet cost if carpeting is $9.95 per square yard?

**9 ft = 3 yd**
**15 ft = 5 yd**

**$A$ = 3 yd × 5 yd = 15 sq yd**
**Cost is: $9.95 × 15 = $149.25**

5. Isabel measured a hallway. It measures 36 ft by 36 inches. Hallway carpeting costs $8.50 a square yard. The installer charges $3.25 a square yard. What is the total cost?

**36 in. = 1 yd**
**36 ft = 12 yd**

**$A$ = 12 yd × 1 yd = 12 sq yd**
**Cost per yard is: $8.50 + 3.25 = $11.75**
**Total cost is: $11.75 × 12 = $141.00**

The cost of the carpeting and the installation can be calculated separately and added together.

***In conclusion.*** Ask: How do you change feet into yards? [divide by 3] How do you change square feet into square yards? [divide by 9] How do you change yards into feet? [multiply by 3] How do you change square yards into square feet? [multiply by 9]

If there is additional time following this lesson, play the Corners game, found in *Math Card Games* book, A9.

# LESSON 111: DISTANCE PROBLEMS

## OBJECTIVES:

1. To work with changing linear units within the same measuring system
2. To introduce the term *kilometer*
3. To solve distance problems

## MATERIALS:

1. Worksheet 83, Distance Problems

## ACTIVITIES FOR TEACHING:

**Warm-up.** Give the child the worksheet. Tell him to do just the warm-up section. The solutions are below.

$$
\begin{array}{r}
249\ (6) \\
\times\, 27\ (0) \\
\hline
1743 \\
4980 \\
\hline
6{,}723\ (0)
\end{array}
\qquad
\begin{array}{r}
6249\ (3) \\
\times\, 38\ (2) \\
\hline
49992 \\
187470 \\
\hline
237{,}462\ (6)
\end{array}
$$

**Worksheet 83.** Tell the child to look at the tables on the worksheet, which are shown below.

| Miles (mi) | Yards (yd) | Feet (ft) |
|---|---|---|
| 1 | 1760 | 5280 |
| 2 | | |
| 7 | | |
| | | 528 |
| $\frac{1}{2}$ | | |
| $\frac{1}{4}$ | | |
| $n$ | | |

| Kilometers (km) | Meters (m) |
|---|---|
| 1 | 1000 |
| 2 | |
| 3 | |
| 4 | |
| 10 | |
| | 500 |
| $n$ | |

Ask: Which table uses the United States customary system? [left table] Which table uses the metric system? [right table]

Tell the child to look at the first table. Ask: How many yards are in a mile? [1760] How many feet are in a mile? [5280] How could you find the number of yards in 2 miles? [multiply 1760 by 2]

Tell him to look at the second table. Ask: How many meters are in a kilometer? [1000] Tell him that the prefix *kilo-* means thousand.

Tell the child to fill in the tables on his worksheet. Say: A shaded rectangle means nothing needs to be written there. The solutions are on the next page.

## EXPLANATIONS:

Although many people accent kilometer on the second syllable, to be consistent with other metric lengths, (centimeter, decimeter, and millimeter) kilometer should be pronounced KIL-o-me-ter.

Words for measuring tools, such as odometer, thermometer, speedometer, and goniometer are accented on the third to the last syllable, for example, o-DOM-e-ter.

**ACTIVITIES FOR TEACHING CONTINUED:**  |  **EXPLANATIONS CONTINUED:**

| Miles (mi) | Yards (yd) | Feet (ft) |
|---|---|---|
| 1 | 1760 | 5280 |
| 2 | **3520** | **10,560** |
| 7 |  | **36,960** |
| 0.1 | **176** | 528 |
| $\frac{1}{2}$ | **880** | **2640** |
| $\frac{1}{4}$ | **440** | **1320** |
| $n$ | **1760 × $n$** | **5280 × $n$** |

| Kilometers (km) | Meters (m) |
|---|---|
| 1 | 1000 |
| 2 | **2000** |
| 3 | **3000** |
| 4 | **4000** |
| 10 | **10,000** |
| 0.5 ($\frac{1}{2}$) | 500 |
| $n$ | **1000 × $n$** |

Tell him the number of feet in seven miles has special significance. Ask: What is the number of feet in seven miles, rounded to the nearest thousand? [37,000 ft] Say: The cruising altitude that many planes fly at is 37,000 ft. Pilots worldwide measure altitude in feet, not with metric units. Ask: How many miles high are many planes when they're at cruising speed? [7 miles]

**Problem 1.** Tell the child to solve Problem 1 and then to explain his work. The solution is shown below.

1. McKenzie ran 880 yards on Monday, 2 miles on Tuesday, 440 yards four times on Wednesday, and 1.5 miles on Thursday. How many yards did she run during the week? How many miles did she run?

> $M = 880 + (1760 × 2) + (440 × 4) + 1760 + 880$
> $M = 8800$ yd
> $M = 5$ mi

**Problem 2.** Tell him to solve Problem 2 and then to explain his work. The solution is shown below.

2. Sydney raced on her unicycle 400 m around a track on Monday, twice around the same track on Tuesday and Wednesday, and rode 2 km on Thursday. How many meters did she ride during the week? How many kilometers did she ride?

> $S = 400$ m $+ (400$ m $× 4) + 2000$ m
> $S = 4000$ m
> $S = 4$ km

**In conclusion.** Name five metric units that measure length. [kilometer, meter, decimeter, centimeter, and millimeter] Name four United States customary units that measure length. [mile, yard, feet, and inch]

If there is additional time following this lesson, play Find the Products game, found in *Math Card Games* book, P33.

# LESSON 112: CAPACITY PROBLEMS

## OBJECTIVES:

1. To work with changing capacity units within the same measuring system
2. To introduce the terms *pint* and *milliliter*
3. To solve capacity problems

## MATERIALS:

1. Worksheet 84, Capacity Problems

## ACTIVITIES FOR TEACHING:

**Warm-up.** Ask: What are some United States customary units that measure length? [mile, yard, feet, and inch] What are some metric units that measure length? [kilometer, meter, decimeter, centimeter, and millimeter]

**Worksheet 84.** Give the child the worksheet and tell him to look at the pictures of the gallon, half gallon, and quart containers. Discuss where he may have seen them before. Then have him look at the pictures of the measuring cups with the cups and ounces on one side and milliliters on the other. Finally, have him look at the tables below the pictures, which are shown below.

| Gallons | Quarts (qt) | Cups | Pints | Cups | Ounces (oz) | Liters (L) | Milliliters (ml) |
|---------|-------------|------|-------|------|-------------|------------|------------------|
| 1 | 4 | | 1 | 2 | | 1 | 1000 |
| | 1 | 4 | | 1 | 8 | 2 | |
| 1 | | | 1 | | | | 3000 |
| 2 | | | 2 | | | 0.5 | |
| $\frac{1}{2}$ | | | | | 24 | 1.5 | |
| | | 12 | | 6 | | | 100 |
| | 16 | | | | 64 | | 200 |
| $n$ | | | $n$ | | | $n$ | |

Ask: What kind of things can be measured with these units? [liquids] Tell him they are also used to measure things that can be poured, such as rice, wheat, and even ice cream.

Ask: Which tables uses the United States customary system? [left two tables] Which tables uses the metric system? [right table]

Tell the child to look at the first two tables. Ask: How many quarts are in a gallon? [4] How many cups are in a quart? [4] How could you find the number of cups in a gallon? [4 × 4 = 16] How many cups are in a pint? [2] What is the name for half a quart? [pint]

Tell the child to look at the last table. Ask: How many *milliliters* are in a liter? [1000] Tell him that just as 1

## EXPLANATIONS:

| ACTIVITIES FOR TEACHING CONTINUED: | EXPLANATIONS CONTINUED: |

millimeter is one-thousandth of a meter, 1 milliliter is one-thousandth of a liter. Ask: Do you notice something unusual about the abbreviation for liter? [capital letter]

Tell him the abbreviation for liter is one place where a capital letter is required. In the United States customary system, there are no standards for the abbreviations.

Tell him to fill in the three tables. Say: A shaded rectangle means nothing needs to be written. The solutions are below.

Sometimes, in the U.S., people will use "mL" for milliliter, but the international standard is "ml."

| Gallons | Quarts (qt) | Cups | Pints | Cups | Ounces (oz) | Liters (L) | Milliliters (ml) |
|---|---|---|---|---|---|---|---|
| 1 | 4 | | 1 | 2 | | 1 | 1000 |
| | 1 | 4 | | 1 | 8 | 2 | **2000** |
| 1 | **4** | **16** | 1 | 2 | **16** | 3 | 3000 |
| 2 | **8** | **32** | 2 | 4 | **32** | 0.5 | **500** |
| $\frac{1}{2}$ | **2** | **8** | $1\frac{1}{2}$ | 3 | 24 | 1.5 | **1500** |
| $\frac{3}{4}$ | **3** | 12 | 3 | 6 | **48** | **0.1** | 100 |
| 4 | 16 | **64** | 4 | 8 | 64 | **0.2** | 200 |
| $n$ | **4 × $n$** | **16 × $n$** | $n$ | **2 × $n$** | **16 × $n$** | $n$ | **1000 × $n$** |

**Problem 1.** Tell the child to solve Problem 1 and then to explain his work. The solution is shown below.

1. Eileen is making a punch with a 12-oz can of lemonade, 4 cups cranberry juice, and 1 qt of soda. How many cups of punch will this recipe make? How many servings will there be if each serving is 4 oz?

These quantities and units were taken from an actual recipe.

$E = 1\frac{1}{2}c + 4c + 4c$

$E = 9\frac{1}{2}c$

**Since 4 oz is half of a cup,**

$E = 9\frac{1}{2} \times 2 = 19$ **servings**

**Problem 2.** Tell the child to solve Problem 2 and then to explain his work. The solution is shown below.

2. Zane is mixing a drink using 2 cans with 275 ml frozen cranberry concentrate, 1 L of orange juice, 60 ml of lime juice, and 1.5 L of soda. Will there be enough of the drink for 17 people to each have 180 ml?

$Z = (275\ ml \times 2) + 1000\ ml + 60\ ml + 1500\ ml$

$Z = 3110\ ml$

$Z = 180 \times 17 = 3060\ ml$

**Yes, there is enough.**

**In conclusion.** Ask: What unit would you use to measure water for a bathtub, gallons or ounces? [gallons] What unit would you use to measure water to cook rice for a family, gallons or cups? [cups]

If there is additional time following this lesson, play Find the Products game, found in *Math Card Games* book, P33.

# LESSON 113: WEIGHT PROBLEMS

**OBJECTIVES:**

1. To work with changing weight units within the same measuring system
2. To introduce the terms *ton* and *kilogram*
3. To solve capacity problems

**MATERIALS:**

1. Worksheet 85, Weight Problems

---

**ACTIVITIES FOR TEACHING:**

**Warm-up.** Give the child the worksheet. Tell him to do just the warm-up section. The solutions are below.

$$
\begin{array}{r}
275\ \textbf{(5)} \\
\times\,63\ \textbf{(0)} \\
\hline
825 \\
16500 \\
\hline
17{,}325\ \textbf{(0)}
\end{array}
\qquad
\begin{array}{r}
7275\ \textbf{(3)} \\
\times\,74\ \textbf{(2)} \\
\hline
29100 \\
509250 \\
\hline
538{,}350\ \textbf{(6)}
\end{array}
$$

**Worksheet 85.** Tell the child to look at the tables on the worksheet, which are shown below.

| Pound (lb) | Ounces (oz) |
|---|---|
| 1 | 16 |
| 2 | |
| 7 | |
| 75 | |
| 76 | |
| $\frac{1}{4}$ | |
| $\frac{1}{2}$ | |
| $n$ | |

| Ton | Pound (lb) |
|---|---|
| 1 | 2000 |
| 2 | |
| 5 | |
| 10 | |
| $n$ | |

| Kilogram (kg) | Gram (g) |
|---|---|
| 1 | 1000 |
| 2 | |
| 3 | |
| | 6000 |
| | 4000 |
| | 100 |
| | 500 |
| $n$ | |

Ask: What are we measuring with these units? [how heavy something is] Tell him these units measure the force of gravity on an object.

Ask: Which tables uses the United States customary system? [left two tables] Which tables use the metric system? [right table]

Tell the child to look at the first two tables. Ask: How many ounces are in a pound? [16] Ask: Where did we use ounces before? [8 ounces in a cup] Say: There are two types of ounces. To tell them apart, "fl" is sometimes written before the ounces that measure liquids or other fluids. Eight fluid ounces of water weighs 8 ounces, but 8 fluid ounces of honey weighs 12 ounces.

Ask: How many pounds are in a ton? [2000] Tell him there are other kinds of tons. For example, a metric ton is 2204 pounds.

**EXPLANATIONS:**

Ounces that measure weight technically are call avoirdupois ounces (av oz).

---

**ACTIVITIES FOR TEACHING CONTINUED:**

**EXPLANATIONS CONTINUED:**

Tell the child to look at the last table. Ask: How many grams are in a *kilogram*? [1000] Tell him that just as 1 kilometer is one thousand meters, 1 kilogram is one thousand grams.

Tell him to fill in the tables. The solutions are below.

| Pound (lb) | Ounces (oz) |
|---|---|
| 1 | 16 |
| 2 | 32 |
| 7 | 112 |
| 75 | 1200 |
| 76 | 1216 |
| $\frac{1}{4}$ | 4 |
| $\frac{1}{2}$ | 8 |
| $n$ | 16 × $n$ |

| Ton | Pound (lb) |
|---|---|
| 1 | 2000 |
| 2 | 4000 |
| 5 | 10,000 |
| 10 | 20,000 |
| $n$ | 2000 × $n$ |

| Kilogram (kg) | Gram (g) |
|---|---|
| 1 | 1000 |
| 2 | 2000 |
| 3 | 3000 |
| 6 | 6000 |
| 4 | 4000 |
| 0.1 | 100 |
| 0.5 | 500 |
| $n$ | 1000 × $n$ |

**Problem 1.** Tell him to solve Problem 1 and then to explain his work. The solution is shown below.

1. Ryan's bicycle weighs 15 pounds. His car weighs 200 times that much. How many pounds does his car weigh? How many tons does his car weigh?

> **$c$ = 15 lb × 200**
> **$c$ = 3000 lb**
> **$c$ = 1 and a half tons**

The abbreviation for both pound and pounds is "lb". Using lbs is considered incorrect. In other words, units do not have plural forms.

**Problem 2.** Tell the child to solve Problem 2 and then to explain his work. The solution is shown below.

2. Each little centimeter cube weighs 1 gram. One hundred cubes come in a package. How many packages do you need to weigh 10 kilograms?

> **One package weighs 100 g.**
> **Ten packages weigh 1000 g = 1 kg**
> **So, 100 packages are needed for 10 kg.**

**In conclusion.** Ask: Why does 1 fluid ounce of honey weigh more than 1 fluid ounce of water? [It is heavier.] Could a person ever weigh a ton? [no] How many pounds does a three ton Asian elephant weigh? [6000]

If there is additional time following this lesson, play Multiplying Three One-Digit Numbers game, found in *Math Card Games* book, P36.

# LESSON 114: TIME PROBLEMS

**OBJECTIVES:**

1. To work with changing time units
2. To introduce the terms *elapsed* and *millisecond*
3. To solve time problems

**MATERIALS:**

1. Worksheet 86, Time Problems
2. Casio SL-450S calculator, optional

---

**ACTIVITIES FOR TEACHING:**

**EXPLANATIONS:**

*Warm-up.* Give the child the worksheet. Tell him to do just the warm-up section. The solutions are below.

$$
\begin{array}{r}
451\ \textbf{(1)} \\
\times 86\ \textbf{(5)} \\
\hline
2706 \\
36080 \\
\hline
38{,}786\ \textbf{(5)}
\end{array}
\qquad
\begin{array}{r}
8451\ \textbf{(0)} \\
\times 97\ \textbf{(7)} \\
\hline
59157 \\
760590 \\
\hline
819{,}747\ \textbf{(0)}
\end{array}
$$

*Worksheet 86.* Tell the child to look at the tables on the worksheet, which are shown below.

| Day | Hour (hr) | Minute (min) |
|-----|-----------|--------------|
| 1   | 24        |              |
|     | 1         | 60           |
| 1   |           |              |
| 2   |           |              |
|     | 12        |              |
| 7   |           |              |
| 365 |           |              |
| *n* |           |              |

| Minute (min) | Second (sec) | Millisecond (msec) |
|--------------|--------------|--------------------|
| 1            | 60           |                    |
|              | 1            | 1000               |
| 1            |              |                    |
|              |              | 500                |
| 2            |              |                    |
|              |              | 6000               |
| 60           |              |                    |
| *n*          |              |                    |

Ask: What are we measuring with these units? [time] Tell him there are two ways of talking about time. One is naming a particular moment in time, such as 8:30 on a certain date. The other way is measuring the amount of *elapsed* time that has passed, such as 30 minutes, 8 hours, 4 days, or 10 years. Ask: Is the time you were born a particular time or elapsed time? [particular time] Is your age a particular time or elapsed time? [elapsed time]

Ask: Which tables use the United States customary system? [both tables] Which table uses the metric system? [neither] Tell him that in the 1790s, the country of France changed to the metric system. They even made their day metric by having 10 hours in a day with each hour having 100 minutes and each minute having 100 seconds. The metric day was given up a year or two later.

**ACTIVITIES FOR TEACHING CONTINUED:**

**EXPLANATIONS CONTINUED:**

Tell the child to look at the tables. Ask: How many minutes are in an hour? [60] How many hours are in a day? [24]

Tell the child to look at the last column. Ask: How many *milliseconds* are in a second? [1000] Where else have you seen the prefix *milli-*? [millimeter, milliliter]

Tell him to fill in the tables. The solutions are below.

| Day | Hour (hr) | Minute (min) |
|---|---|---|
| 1 | 24 | |
| | 1 | 60 |
| 1 | 24 | 1440 |
| 2 | 48 | 2880 |
| $\frac{1}{2}$ | 12 | 720 |
| 7 | 168 | 10,080 |
| 365 | 8760 | 525,600 |
| $n$ | 24 × $n$ | 1440 × $n$ |

| Minute (min) | Second (sec) | Millisecond (msec) |
|---|---|---|
| 1 | 60 | |
| | 1 | 1000 |
| 1 | 60 | 60,000 |
| | $\frac{1}{2}$ | 500 |
| 2 | 120 | 120,000 |
| 0.1 or $\frac{1}{10}$ | 6 | 6000 |
| 60 | 3600 | 3,600,000 |
| $n$ | 60 × $n$ | 60,000 × $n$ |

A calculator may be used for some of these calculations.

**Problem 1.** Tell the child to solve Problem 1 and then to explain his work. The solution is shown below.

1. Kenna spends 5 hours a day in school Monday to Friday. How many hours is that in a week? How many hours during a week is she not in school?

> *time in school* = 5 × 5 = 25 hr
> *hr in a week* = 7 × 24 = 168 hr
> *time not in school* = 168 − 25 = 143 hr

**Problem 2.** Tell him to solve Problem 2 and then to explain his work. The solution is shown below.

2. Dez had a job for a year (52 weeks) except for 2 weeks of vacation. She worked 8 hours a day 5 days a weeks. How many hours did she work in a year?

> *D worked* = 8 hr × 5 = 40 hr a week
> *D worked* = 40 hr × 50 weeks
> *D worked* = 2000 hr in a year

**In conclusion.** Ask: How many hours pass from 8 o'clock in the morning until 8 o'clock the next morning? [24 hours] How many minutes pass from 8 o'clock in the morning until 9 o'clock the same morning? [60 minutes] How many seconds are there between 12:02 p.m. and 12:04 p.m.? [120 seconds]

If there is additional time following this lesson, play the Before the Hour game, found in *Math Card Games* book, C30.

# LESSON 115: LINE PLOTS

## OBJECTIVES:

1. To make line plots
2. To solve problems using information from a line plot

## MATERIALS:

1. Worksheet 87, Line Plots
2. Calendars, Appendix p. 6
3. Geometric solids, optional

| ACTIVITIES FOR TEACHING: | EXPLANATIONS: |
|---|---|
| **Warm-up.** Say: A line plot is a type of chart that shows a picture of data. First you draw a line. Then you draw little marks for the number of categories. Maybe the categories are numbers; maybe they are colors or names. Then you record the data on the chart and it is easy to see the information. | Line plots were taught in RightStart Mathematics Level C and Level D, second edition. |

**Leap years.** Give the child the worksheet and the calendars.

Ask: What do we call how long it takes the earth to go around the sun? [a year] How long is a year? [about 365 and a fourth days] What was done to the calendar to take care of the extra part of a day? [leap day every four years] How many days in a non-leap year? [365] How many days in a leap year? [366]

Recite the "Thirty Days Has September" rhyme with the child:

> **Thirty Days Has September**
> *Thirty days has September,*
> *April, June, and November.*
> *The rest have thirty-one to carry,*
> *But only twenty-eight for February,*
> *Except in leap year, that's the time*
> *When February has twenty-nine.*

Ask: How can you tell that a year is a leap year? [February has 29 days] Say: Another way to tell that a year is a leap year is that the last two digits are a multiple of 4. So, 2000, 2004, 2012, and 1908 are all leap years.

**Worksheet 87, Problem 1.** Tell the child to read the first problem on the worksheet. Ask: What does S, M, T, W, Th, F, and S mean? [days of the week]

Tell him to look at the calendar of the non-leap year and ask: What day of the week is January 1st? [in 2017, Sunday] Tell him to put an X by that day of the week on his line plot. See the figure on the next page.

| ACTIVITIES FOR TEACHING CONTINUED: | EXPLANATIONS CONTINUED: |

First Day of the Months in a Non-leap Year

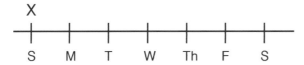

Depending upon the year, the initial X will vary.

Continue with February and March before telling him to complete the year. A sample year is shown below.

First Day of the Months in a Non-leap Year

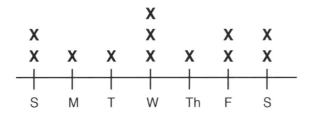

All non-leap years will have three months that start on the same day of the week because February, March, and November start on the same day.

**Problem 2.** Tell him to make a line plot for a leap year. An example is shown below.

First Day of the Months in a Leap Year

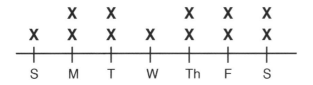

**There is no most common day.**

**Review diameter.** Show the geometric solids. See figure on the right. Holding the short cylinder, say: The distance across the circle through the center is called the *diameter*. Ask the child to find other diameters.

**Problem 3.** Tell the child to do the last problem. The solutions are below.

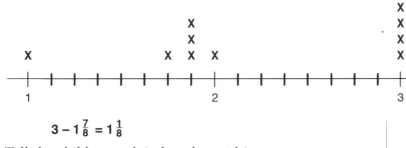

$$3 - 1\frac{7}{8} = 1\frac{1}{8}$$

Tell the child to explain how he got his answer.

**In conclusion.** Ask: In every year, do all the days of the week get a chance to start a month? [yes] What is the difference between $\frac{7}{8}$ and $1\frac{1}{8}$? [$\frac{2}{8}$, or $\frac{1}{4}$]

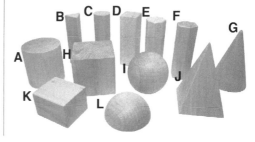

A  Large cylinder
B  Triangular prism
C  Small cylinder
D  Square prism
E  Octagonal prism
F  Hexagonal prism
G  Cone
H  Cube
I  Sphere
J  Square pyramid
K  Rectangular prism
L  Hemisphere

If there is additional time following this lesson, play the Before the Hour game, found in *Math Card Games* book, C30.

# LESSON 116: REVIEW AND GAMES 9

## OBJECTIVES:
1. To review recent topics
2. To develop skills through playing math card games

## MATERIALS:
1. Worksheet 88-A or 88-B, Review 9
2. *Math Card Games* book, P29

---

### ACTIVITIES FOR TEACHING:

**Worksheet 88-A.** Give the child the worksheet. Tell him to listen to the problems and write the answers. Read each problem twice.

$\$1.25 \times 3$          $108 - 9$          $19 \times 20$

Tell him to complete the worksheet. Solutions are below.

Write only the answers.

**$3.75**

**99**

**380**

1. After multiplying by 16, 24, 27, and 35, divide by 2, 3, 4, 5, 6, 7, 8, and 9.

```
        1 2 (3)
      × 1 6 (7)
        7 2
      1 2 0
      1 9 2 (3)
      × 2 4 (6)
        7 6 8
    3 8 4 0
    4 6 0 8 (0)
      × 2 7 (0)
    3 2 2 5 6
    9 2 1 6 0
  1 2 4 4 1 6 (0)
      × 3 5 (8)
    6 2 2 0 8 0
  3 7 3 2 4 8 0
2) 4 3 5 4 5 6 0 (0)
3) 2 1 7 7 2 8 0 (0)
4) 7 2 5 7 6 0 (0)
5) 1 8 1 4 4 0 (0)
6) 3 6 2 8 8 (0)
7) 6 0 4 8 (0)
8) 8 6 4 (0)
9) 1 0 8 (0)
        1 2
```

Write the answers.

How many oz in half a lb? (1 lb = 16 oz)= **8**

$\$4 + \$1.25 = $ **$5.25**

$(50 \times 6) - (49 \times 6) = $ **6**

2. Below are the heights of the 2016 Minnesota Lynx Women's Basketball team. What is the difference in height between the shortest and the tallest players?

**6 ft 6 in. − 5 ft 7 in. = 11 in.**

| Player | Height | Player | Height |
|---|---|---|---|
| Seimone | 6 ft 0 in. | Janel | 6 ft 2 in. |
| Rebekkah | 6 ft 2 in. | Renee | 5 ft 7 in. |
| Sylvia | 6 ft 6 in. | Maya | 6 ft 0 in. |
| Bashaara | 6 ft 2 in. | Jia | 5 ft 8 in. |
| Keisha | 6 ft 1 in. | Lindsay | 5 ft 9 in. |
| Natasha | 6 ft 3 in. | | |

3. Logan is serving cranberry juice to senior citizens. He has a gallon and a quart of juice. Each serving is half a cup. How many servings can he make? (1 quart = 4 cups)

**1 gal = 4 qt, so Logan has 5 qt.**
**5 qt × 4 = 20 cups**
**He can make 40 servings.**

4. Paxton wants to buy enough orange juice for each team member to have 250 milliliters to drink. There are 18 team members. How many 2-L containers does he need to buy? How much will be left over?

**Paxton needs 250 × 18 = 4500 ml. Each 2-L container has 2000 ml, so he needs 3 containers. 6000 − 4500 = 1500 ml leftover.**

### EXPLANATIONS:

Ask the child to correct any errors during the lesson.

---

## ACTIVITIES FOR TEACHING CONTINUED:

**EXPLANATIONS CONTINUED:**

*Find the Two Factors game.* Play the Find the Two Factors game found in *Math Card Games* book, P29.

*Worksheet 88-B.* Give the child the worksheet. Tell him to listen to the problems and write the answers. Read each problem twice.

$$\$0.25 \times 5 \qquad 103 - 7 \qquad 12 \times 30$$

Tell him to complete the worksheet. Solutions are below.

---

Write only the answers.

**$1.25**

**96**

**360**

1. After multiplying by 16, 24, 27, and 35, divide by 2, 3, 4, 5, 6, 7, 8, and 9.

```
                2 1 (3)
              × 1 6 (7)
              1 2 6
              2 1 0
              3 3 6 (3)
            × 2 4 (6)
          1 3 4 4
          6 7 2 0
          8 0 6 4 (0)
          × 2 7 (0)
      5 6 4 4 8
    1 6 1 2 8 0
    2 1 7 7 2 8 (0)
          × 3 5 (8)
  1 0 8 8 6 4 0
  6 5 3 1 8 4 0
2) 7 6 2 0 4 8 0 (0)
3) 3 8 1 0 2 4 0 (0)
4) 1 2 7 0 0 8 0 (0)
5) 3 1 7 5 2 0 (0)
  6) 6 3 5 0 4 (0)
  7) 1 0 5 8 4 (0)
    8) 1 5 1 2 (0)
    9) 1 8 9 (0)
        2 1
```

Write the answers.

How many oz in $\frac{1}{4}$ of a lb? (1 lb = 16 oz) = **4**

$3.65 + \$5 = **$8.65**

$(40 \times 5) - (39 \times 5) = **5**

2. Below are the heights of the 2016 New York Liberty Women's Basketball team. What is the difference in height between the shortest and the tallest players?

**6 ft 6 in. − 5 ft 9 in. = 9 in.**

| Player | Height | Player | Height |
|---|---|---|---|
| Brittany | 5 ft 9 in. | Shoni | 5 ft 9 in. |
| Adut | 6 ft 4 in. | Kiah | 6 ft 3 in. |
| Swin | 6 ft 1 in. | Carolyn | 6 ft 6 in. |
| Tina | 6 ft 4 in. | Tanisha | 5 ft 11 in. |
| Epiphanny | 5 ft 9 in. | Amanda | 6 ft 5 in. |
| Sugar | 5 ft 9 in. | Shavonte | 5 ft 10 in. |

3. Sebastian is serving pomegranate juice to senior citizens. He has a gallon and a half of juice. Each serving is half a cup. How many servings can he make? (1 quart = 4 cups)

**1 gal = 4 qt, so he has 6 qt.**
**6 qt × 4 = 24 cups**
**He can make 48 half cups.**

4. James is buying enough orange juice for each team member to have 250 milliliters to drink. There are 21 team members. How many 2-L containers does he need to buy? How much will be left over?

**James needs 250 × 21 = 5250 ml. Each 2-L container has 2000 ml, so he needs 3 containers. 6000 − 5250 = 750 ml leftover.**

---

# LESSON 117: SHAPES IN AN OCTAGON

## OBJECTIVES:

1. To make shapes in an octagon
2. To note which shapes have parallel or perpendicular lines

## MATERIALS:

1. Worksheet 89, Shapes in an Octagon
2. Geoboard and rubber bands

## ACTIVITIES FOR TEACHING:

***Warm-up.*** Ask: What do you call an angle less than 90°? [acute angle] What do you call an angle more than 90°? [obtuse angle]

Ask: How many sides does an octagon have? [8] How many sides does a trapezoid have? [4] How many sets of parallel lines does a trapezoid have? [just one]

***Shapes in an octagon.*** Give the child the worksheet, geoboard, and rubber bands. Tell him to make an octagon on the circle side of the geoboard. See the left figure below. Next tell him to tilt his geoboard so his octagon looks like a stop sign. See the right figure.

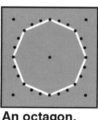

**An octagon.**

Tell him to make a square inside the octagon. Tell him to make another square, this time with a vertex at the top. See the figures below. Ask: Are the squares congruent? [yes]

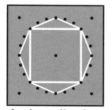 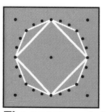

**An inscribed square.**  **The square rotated.**

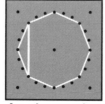 

**An obtuse triangle.**  **Another obtuse triangle.**

## EXPLANATIONS:

227

| ACTIVITIES FOR TEACHING CONTINUED: | EXPLANATIONS CONTINUED: |
|---|---|

Tell him to make an obtuse triangle inside the octagon on the geoboard. See the figures on the previous page.

Tell him to make several trapezoids in the octagon. Some possibilities are shown below.

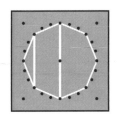 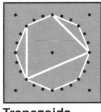 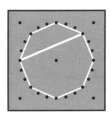

**Trapezoids.**

***Worksheet 89.*** Tell the child to complete the worksheet. The solutions are shown below.

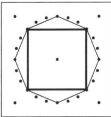 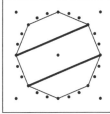 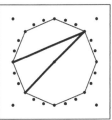

The orientations of some of the figures will vary.

Draw a square. | Draw a rectangle that is not a square. | Draw two lines to make a right triangle.

 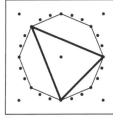 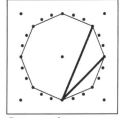

Draw an isosceles right triangle. Use the dashed line. | Draw an acute isosceles triangle. Use the dashed line. | Draw an obtuse triangle. Use the dashed line.

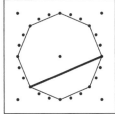 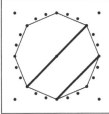

Make a trapezoid by drawing one line. | Make a trapezoid by drawing two lines.

How many of the new shapes have only one set of parallel lines? **2**
How many of the new shapes have two sets of parallel lines? **2**
How many of the new shapes have perpendicular lines? **4**

***In conclusion.*** Ask: Can a triangle have parallel lines? [no] Can a triangle have perpendicular lines? [yes] How many sets of parallel lines does a octagon have? [4]

If there is additional time following this lesson, have the child choose a game to play.

# LESSON 118: LINES OF SYMMETRY

## OBJECTIVES:
1. To identify lines of symmetry
2. To draw lines of symmetry

## MATERIALS:
1. Worksheet 90, Lines of Symmetry
2. Geoboard and rubber bands
3. Geometry reflector*

## ACTIVITIES FOR TEACHING:

**Warm-up.** Give the child the worksheet. Tell him to do just the warm-up section. The solutions are below.

$$896 \ (5)$$
$$\times 73 \ (1)$$
$$2688$$
$$62720$$
$$65,408 \ (5)$$

$$5896 \ (1)$$
$$\times 84 \ (3)$$
$$23584$$
$$471680$$
$$495,264 \ (3)$$

**Symmetry in a square.** Give the child the geoboard, rubber bands, and geometry reflector. Tell him to make a square on the array side of the geoboard three units wide. See the figure on the right.

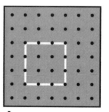
A square.

Ask: Do you see any lines of symmetry in the square? [yes] Say: A line of symmetry divides a figure in half with the halves being reflections of each other. Another way to think about reflections is to imagine cutting out the figure and folding it so the two halves exactly fit on top of each other. The fold line is the line of symmetry.

Tell the child to put his geometry reflector on a line of symmetry. Tell him to explore until all four lines of symmetry are found. See the figures below.

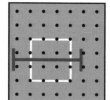  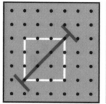 
Lines of symmetry.

**Symmetry in an octagon.** Next tell him to "chop" off the corners of the square on the geoboard to make an octagon. See the figure on right.

Ask: Is the octagon regular or irregular? [irregular] How do you know? [The

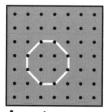
An octagon.

## EXPLANATIONS:

*If a geometry reflector is not available, a 45 triangle stood on an edge makes a satisfactory substitute.

**ACTIVITIES FOR TEACHING CONTINUED:**

**EXPLANATIONS CONTINUED:**

"diagonal" lines are longer than the horizontal or vertical lines.]

Ask: Do you see any lines of symmetry in the octagon? [yes] Say: Put your geometry reflector on a line of symmetry. Tell him to explore until all four lines of symmetry are found. See the figures below.

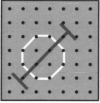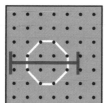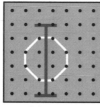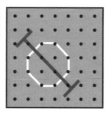

**Lines of symmetry.**

There are additional lines of symmetry in a regular octagon.

***Worksheet 90.*** Tell the child to find the symmetry of the first six figures on the worksheet. Solutions are below.

Lines of symmetry? **3**    Lines of symmetry? **4**    Lines of symmetry? **5**

Lines of symmetry? **6**    Lines of symmetry? **7**    Lines of symmetry? **8**

Then ask: What is different about the lines of symmetry in polygons with an even number of sides compared to polygons with an odd number of sides. [When the number of sides is even, the lines of symmetry are from vertex to vertex and midpoint to midpoint. When the number of sides is odd. the lines of symmetry are from vertex to midpoint.]

Tell him to complete the worksheet. Solutions are below.

If you drew a regular polygon with 12 sides, how many lines of symmetry would it have? **12**

If you drew a regular polygon with 100 angles, how many lines of symmetry would it have? **100**

If the number of sides of a regular polygon is *n*, how many lines of symmetry does it have? ***n***

 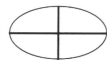  

***In conclusion.*** Ask: How many lines of symmetry does an equilateral triangle have? [3] How many lines of symmetry does an isosceles triangle have? [1] How many lines of symmetry does a scalene triangle have? [0]

If there is additional time following this lesson, play the Corners game, found in *Math Card Games* book, A9.

# LESSON 119: DRAWING REFLECTIONS

## OBJECTIVES:

1. To reflect right triangles across vertical and horizontal lines of symmetry

## MATERIALS:

1. 2 sets of tangrams
2. Geometry reflector*
3. Worksheet 91, Drawing Reflections
4. Drawing board
5. T-square
6. 45 triangle

| ACTIVITIES FOR TEACHING: | EXPLANATIONS: |
|---|---|

**ACTIVITIES FOR TEACHING:**

***Warm-up.*** Ask: What is a horizontal line? [a straight line that goes from side to side] What is a vertical line? [a line that goes straight up and down]

***Reflections with tangrams.*** Give the child the tangrams and geometry reflector. Say: You will need four right triangles from the tangrams all the same size. The size makes no difference; however, they must all be the same size.

Tell him to place the reflector horizontally along the longer side of a triangle as shown in the left figure below. Ask: What do you see in the reflector? [triangle reflected]

Tell him to replace the image with an actual tangram triangle. Say: This is reflecting the triangle vertically.

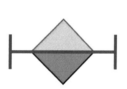
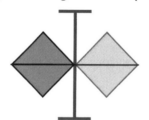

**Reflecting vertically.**          **Reflecting horizontally.**

Next tell him to place the reflector along the right edge of two triangles. See the right figure above. Say: Look at the image and replace it with two triangles. This is reflecting the figure horizontally.

***Another example.*** Tell the child to do another example. Tell him to place a triangle so the longer edge starts at the lower left and goes to the upper right as shown in the left figure on the next page.

Say: Place the reflector vertically along the right edge. Replace the image with another triangle.

**EXPLANATIONS:**

*If a geometry reflector is not available, a 45 triangle stood on an edge makes a satisfactory substitute.

Reflections are easier to see if the background surface is light-colored, especially when red tangram pieces are used.

Mathematically, to reflect vertically means the original shape is reflected about a *horizontal* line and appears vertically above or below the original image.

## ACTIVITIES FOR TEACHING CONTINUED:

## EXPLANATIONS CONTINUED:

Now tell him to place the reflector below the two triangles as shown in the right figure below. Then tell him to replace the image with triangles. Ask: How many lines of symmetry do you see in the figure? [2] Where are they? [where the reflector was placed]

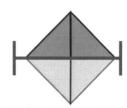

**Reflecting horizontally.** **Reflecting vertically.**

Remember, to reflect horizontally means the original shape is reflected about a *vertical* line and appears horizontally next to the original image.

***Worksheet 91.*** Give the child the worksheet and drawing tools. Tell him to tape the worksheet onto the drawing board. Say: Use your 45 triangle with this worksheet. Guessing or measuring is not allowed. Use the tangram triangles to make the reflections first, if necessary. Solutions are below.

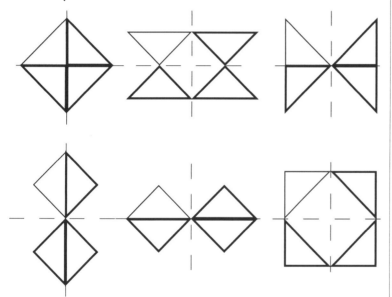

***In conclusion.*** Ask: Does it matter whether you draw the horizontal reflection first or the vertical reflection first? [no] How many lines of symmetry are in the figures that you drew? [2]

If there is additional time following this lesson, play the Corners Three game, found in *Math Card Games* book, A38.

# LESSON 120: DRAWING MORE REFLECTIONS

## OBJECTIVES:

1. To reflect figures across vertical and horizontal lines of symmetry

## MATERIALS:

1. Worksheet 92, Drawing More Reflections
2. Drawing board
3. T-square
4. 45 triangle and 30-60 triangle
5. *Math Card Games* book, P29

| ACTIVITIES FOR TEACHING: | EXPLANATIONS: |
|---|---|
| **Warm-up.** Ask: How many lines of symmetry does an equilateral triangle have? [3] How many lines of symmetry does an isosceles triangle have? [1] How many lines of symmetry does a scalene triangle have? [0] | |

Ask: How many lines of symmetry does an square have? [4] How many lines of symmetry does a regular hexagon have? [6] How many lines of symmetry does a regular octagon have? [8]

**Worksheet 92.** Give the child the worksheet, drawing board, T-square, and triangles.

**Problem 1.** Tell him to look at Problem 1, which is shown below.

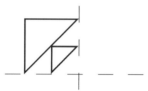

Tell him to think about how he would solve this problem; it's like a puzzle. Ask: What line would you draw first and why? [the longer diagonal line because the horizontal dashed line is a stopping point] Tell him to explain what he would do. One solution for starting the reflections is shown below.

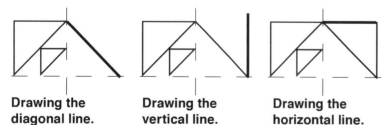

**Drawing the diagonal line.**  **Drawing the vertical line.**  **Drawing the horizontal line.**

Tell him to attach his worksheet to the drawing board and do the first problem. The solution is on the next page.

When he has completed it, ask: What is the figure? [squares inside squares] How many lines of symmetry does it have? [4]

Some children might observe that each successive smaller square is half the size of the preceding square. These squares can be made with two sets of tangrams.

233

**ACTIVITIES FOR TEACHING CONTINUED:**

**EXPLANATIONS CONTINUED:**

***Problem 2.*** Tell the child to think about how he would solve Problem 2. One solution for starting the reflections is shown below.

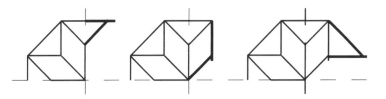

When he has completed it, ask: What figures do you see in your drawing? [8 rhombuses, 8 right triangles, 1 regular octagon]

The solutions are below.

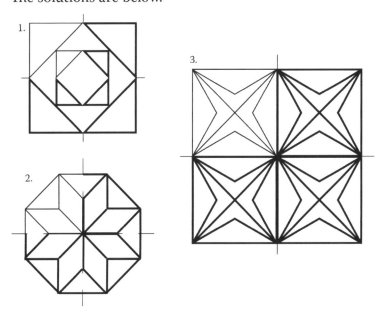

***Problem 3.*** Tell the child to do the third problem. The solution is above.

***Find the Two Factors game.*** If time remains, play the Find the Two Factors game found in *Math Card Games* book, P29. Players take five basic number cards and replace a card played after a turn.

***In conclusion.*** Ask: Do you have to plan ahead to solve this kind of drawing problem? [yes] Can you draw the reflections without any erasing? [no] Can you tell what the solution will look like before you draw it? [Answers will vary.]

As an extra challenge with Problem 3, ask: What figures do you see in your drawing? [8 rhombuses, 16 isosceles obtuse triangles, 5 squares, 32 right triangles, 4 stars] Some children may see a fifth star created by the negative space in the center.

# LESSON 121: VISUALIZING CUBES

## OBJECTIVES:
1. To learn the mathematical term *net*
2. To learn to visualize the faces of cubes

## MATERIALS:
1. Warm-up Practice 12
2. Worksheet 93, Visualizing Cubes
3. 6 squares from the geometry panels* and 5 rubber bands

## ACTIVITIES FOR TEACHING:

**Warm-up.** Give the child the warm-up practice sheet. Tell him to do only the first multivide. Solutions are on the right.

**Worksheet 93.** Give the child the worksheet and geometry panel squares. Tell him that today he will learn about *nets*. Explain that a *net* of a solid is the connected faces laid flat.

**Problem 1.** Tell him to read the directions for Problem 1. Then ask: Why do you think A for the word *aft*, which means the back of a ship, aircraft, or spacecraft, is used for the back of the cube? [because the letters, B for back and R for rear, are already used]

Tell him to make the net then fold it into a cube. Tell him to label the remaining faces of the panels on his worksheet. See the left figure below.

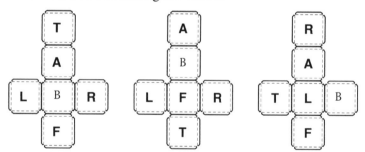

For the next two nets, tell him to try first to fold up the net mentally and label as many faces as he can before checking with the geometry panels. Solutions are above. Ask: Which one was hardest to fold mentally? [Answers will vary, although probably the third net.]

**Problem 2.** Tell him to read the directions and do Problem 2. Ask: What is different about this net? [It doesn't make a cube; it has two fronts.] See the solution on the next page.

## EXPLANATIONS:

\* If the panels have not been used yet, the edges need to be creased. Bend the edges along the perforated lines toward the colored side. Place the panel on a hard surface and bend gently. Bending two panels at a time works well.

There may be some variations in the sequences of the labels.

```
        14 (5)
      × 96 (6)
        84
      1 260
      1 344 (3)
      × 90 (0)
    120 960 (0)
      × 42 (6)
    241 920
  4 838 400
9)5 080 320 (0)
  8)564 480 (0)
  7)70 560 (0)
  6)10 080 (0)
  5)1 680 (6)
    4)336 (3)
    3)84 (3)
    2)28 (1)
      14
```

**ACTIVITIES FOR TEACHING CONTINUED:**

**EXPLANATIONS CONTINUED:**

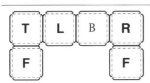

This net does not make a cube.
It does not have a back.

**Problem 3.** Tell him to complete the worksheet. The solutions are below.

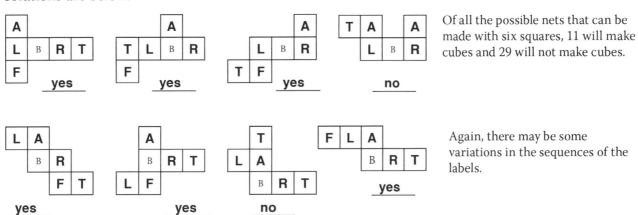

Of all the possible nets that can be made with six squares, 11 will make cubes and 29 will not make cubes.

Again, there may be some variations in the sequences of the labels.

**In conclusion.** Tell the child this story: A young man lost his job and wasn't sure what kind of work he wanted to do. A friend of his who worked with sheet metal asked him if he might want to become a sheet metal worker. Sheet metal is used, for example, to make ducts for heating and air conditioning. The man was interested, so his friend told him to practice rotating a cube in his mind until he could see all its sides. The man learned to rotate the cube and became a good sheet metal worker. Ask: Do you think you could rotate a cube in your mind to see all sides? [Answers will vary.]

If there is additional time following this lesson, play the Card Exchange game, found in *Math Card Games* book, P27.

# LESSON 122: ISOMETRIC DRAWINGS

## OBJECTIVES:
1. To introduce isometric drawing
2. To practice visualizing objects
3. To make some simple isometric drawings

## MATERIALS:
1. Warm-up Practice 12
2. Worksheet 94, Isometric Drawings
3. 35 centimeter cubes
4. Drawing board
5. T-square and 30-60 triangle
6. 10 tiles

## ACTIVITIES FOR TEACHING:

***Warm-up.*** Give the child the warm-up practice sheet. Tell him to do the second multivide on the page. Solutions are on the right.

***Worksheet 94.*** Give the child the worksheet, centimeter cubes, drawing board, T-square, triangle, and tiles. Tell him to tape the worksheet to his drawing board.

***Problem 1.*** Tell the child to read the instructions on the worksheet for Problem 1 then to use his triangle to find the angles of the lines. [90° and 30°]

Explain that the word "isometric" (i-so-MET-ric) comes from two Greek words, "iso" meaning "equal" and "metric" meaning "measure." Ask: What other mathematical word starts with "iso"? [isosceles] What does isosceles mean? [equal legs]

Ask: What small figures makes up the background for the isometric drawings? [equilateral triangles] What is special about them? [All three sides are equal.] Say: This means that the units are the same in each direction. Isometric drawings are a way to show three dimensions on a flat surface.

Tell the child that the terms *width*, *length*, and *height* do not have exact definitions. Sometimes *breadth* and *depth* are also used. Because of possible confusion, companies that sell boxes do not use these words to describe the dimensions of their boxes, but use drawings or just the measurements instead.

Tell him to make a cube with his centimeter cubes that measures 2 cm on a side. See the left figure on the next page. Then tell him to make another cube that measures 3 cm on a side. See the right figure. Ask: How does the length, width, and height change? [increases by 1 cm]

## EXPLANATIONS:

$$
\begin{array}{r}
16\ (7) \\
\times 90\ (0) \\
\hline
1\,440\ (0) \\
\times 56\ (2) \\
\hline
8\,640 \\
\underline{72\,000} \\
80\,640\ (0) \\
\times 72\ (0) \\
\hline
161\,280 \\
\underline{5\,644\,800} \\
\end{array}
$$

$$
\begin{array}{r}
9\,)\,5\,806\,080\ (0) \\
8\,)\,645\,120\ (0) \\
7\,)\,80\,640\ (0) \\
6\,)\,11\,520\ (0) \\
5\,)\,1\,920\ (3) \\
4\,)\,384\ (6) \\
3\,)\,96\ (6) \\
2\,)\,32\ (5) \\
16 \\
\end{array}
$$

237

Cube with 2 cm side.          Cube with 3 cm side.

Tell him to draw the 3 cm cube for Problem 1. The solution is shown below.

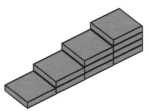

Shading isn't strictly necessary, but it makes the figure more realistic.

**Problem 2.** Tell the child to read the instructions for the second problem. Tell him to make the stairs he needs with tiles first. See the figure below.

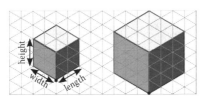

**The stairs built with tiles.**

Then tell him to draw the stairs. The solution is shown below. Tell him to explain his solution.

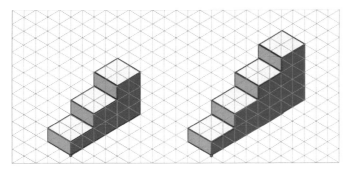

**Problems 3 and 4.** Tell him to complete the worksheet. The solutions are below.

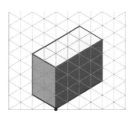 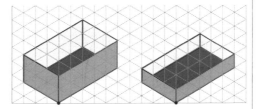

The child will need this worksheet for the next lesson.

**In conclusion.** Ask: Do you see any rectangular prisms in the room? [possibly a brick, book, picture frame, box, table top, and window glass.]

If there is additional time following this lesson, play the Card Exchange game, found in *Math Card Games* book, P27.

# LESSON 123: VIEWS OF AN OBJECT

## OBJECTIVES:

1. To practice visualizing objects
2. To introduce orthographic drawing
3. To make some simple orthographic drawings

## MATERIALS:

1. Warm-up Practice 13
2. 10 tiles
3. Worksheet 95, Views of an Object
4. Drawing board, T-square, 30-60 triangle
5. **Colored pencils, optional**
6. Worksheet 94, Isometric Drawings, from the previous lesson

## ACTIVITIES FOR TEACHING:

***Warm-up.*** Give the child the warm-up practice sheet. Tell him to do only the first multivide. Solutions are on the right.

***Naming views.*** Give the child the tiles. Tell him to make the stairs with three steps the same as he did in the previous lesson.

Now ask him to look at the stairs from the front view at eye level without seeing any tops or sides. See the left figure below. Ask: What do you see? [3 rectangles stacked on top of each other]

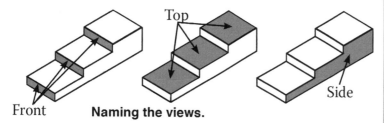

Front    **Naming the views.**    Side

Next ask him to look at the stairs from the top view See the second figure above. Ask: What do you see? [3 squares]

Next ask him to look at it from the side view. See the third figure above. Ask: What do you see? [a polygon looking like stairs]

Now ask him to visualize the figure mentally and to see the top, front, and side views. Ask: When you change to different views, do you mentally rotate the stairs or do you move yourself? [Some children will move the object and some, themselves.]

Tell him that it was an Italian, Leonardo da Vinci, who lived from 1452 to 1519, who first used these views. He was an engineer, musician, scientist, and the artist who painted the Mona Lisa.

## EXPLANATIONS:

$$
\begin{array}{r}
17\ (8) \\
\times\,72\ (0) \\
\hline
34 \\
1\,190 \\
\hline
1\,224\ (0) \\
\times\,70\ (7) \\
\hline
85\,680\ (0) \\
\times\,72\ (0) \\
\hline
171\,360 \\
5\,997\,600 \\
\hline
9\,)\,6\,168\,960\ (0) \\
8\,)\,685\,440\ (0) \\
7\,)\,85\,680\ (0) \\
6\,)\,12\,240\ (0) \\
5\,)\,2\,040\ (6) \\
4\,)\,408\ (3) \\
3\,)\,102\ (3) \\
2\,)\,34\ (7) \\
\hline
17
\end{array}
$$

**ACTIVITIES FOR TEACHING CONTINUED:**

**EXPLANATIONS CONTINUED:**

**Problem 1.** Give the child the worksheet, drawing board, T-square, 30-60 triangle, and colored pencils. Tell him to do Problem 1. The solution is shown below.

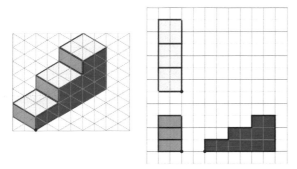

The small dots indicate the same point in all of the views.

**Visualizing the 4-stair figure.** Tell the child to look at his drawing of the 4-stair figure on the worksheet from the previous lesson. Tell him to visualize the top view. Ask: What does it look like? [4 squares] Repeat for the front view and the side view. [4 rectangles and a polygon looking like stairs] Tell him to construct the stairs with tiles. Ask: Does the model make it easier to visualize the views? [Answers will vary.]

**Problem 2.** Tell him to do Problem 2. The solution is shown below in the left figure.

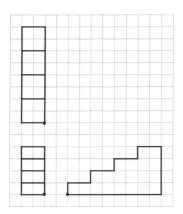

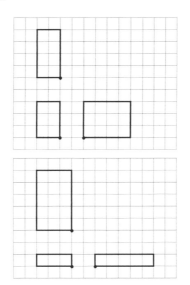

**Problems 3 and 4.** Tell him to do the last two problems. The solutions are shown above on the right.

**In conclusion.** Ask: Do you see any rectangular prisms in the room? [possibly a brick, book, picture frame, box, table top, and window glass]

If there is additional time following this lesson, play the Distribution Corners game, found in *Math Card Games* book, P37.

# LESSON 124: VIEWS OF PYRAMIDS AND CONES

## OBJECTIVES:

1. To introduce the term *truncated*
2. To visualize truncated pyramids and cones
3. To learn to draw circles with the Safe-T Compass®

## MATERIALS:

1. Warm-up Practice 13
2. Pyramids and cones from the geometric solids and one small rubber band
3. Ruler or straightedge
4. Safe-T Compass®
5. Worksheet 96, Views of Pyramids and Cones

## ACTIVITIES FOR TEACHING:

***Warm-up.*** Give the child the warm-up practice sheet. Tell him to do the second multivide on the page. Solutions are on the right.

***Views of a pyramid.*** Give the child the pyramids, cones, rubber bands, ruler, and Safe-T Compass®.

Tell the child to look at the pyramid with one side of the pyramid directly in front of him. Ask: What does the front view look like? [a triangle] What does the side view look like? [a triangle] What does the top view look like? [a square with diagonal lines] See the figures below.

**Front view.**   **Side view.**   **Top view.**

***A truncated pyramid.*** Tell the child to think about what the pyramid would look like if he chopped off the top part, leaving the new top with a flat surface parallel to the base. Tell him to place a rubber band around the pyramid to help visualize what remains. See the figure on the right. Say: The part of the pyramid that is left is called a *truncated pyramid*. Something *truncated* has been cut off or shortened.

Ask: What does the front view look like? [a trapezoid] What does the side view look like? [a trapezoid] What does the top view look like. [two squares with diagonal lines between the squares]

***Worksheet 96, Problem 1.*** Give the child the worksheet and tell him to do the first problem. Solutions are shown on the next page.

***Problem 2.*** Tell the child to read the second problem, think how he would do it, and explain it. First, he could draw the base of the pyramid, then lightly draw the sides. Measure and draw the top line. Then draw the second

## EXPLANATIONS:

```
            18 (0)
          × 42 (6)
            36
           720
           756 (0)
          × 96 (6)
          4 536 (0)
         68 040
         72 576
          × 90 (0)
     9)6 531 840 (0)
      8)725 760 (0)
      7)90 720 (0)
      6)12 960 (0)
      5)2 160 (0)
       4)432 (0)
       3)108 (0)
       2)36 (0)
          18
```

| ACTIVITIES FOR TEACHING CONTINUED: | EXPLANATIONS CONTINUED: |
|---|---|

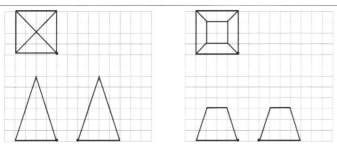

square and diagonal lines. Tell him to draw it. See the right figure above.

**Problem 3.** Tell the child he will need his Safe-T Compass® to draw the circles. The larger circle needs to be drawn with one of the little holes as shown below.

Sometimes putting a sharp point, such as a pencil, in the center allows the Safe-T Compass® to move easier than holding it with a hand.

Place the compass hole over the "×" of the circle.

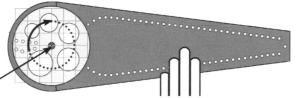

Tell him do the third problem. See the left figure below.

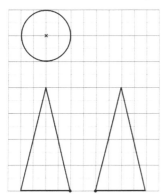 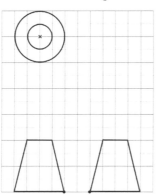

**Problem 4.** Tell the child to place the rubber band on the cone to help visualize a truncated cone. Ask: What does the top view look like? [two circles] Tell him the smaller circle needs to be drawn by tracing inside one of the larger holes on the compass. See the figure below.

Draw inside the circle on the compass.

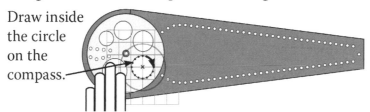

Tell him to do the problem. The solution is in the right figure above.

***In conclusion.*** Ask: Where have pyramids been constructed in the world? [Egypt and many other countries] Can you think of a treat that may be in the shape of a truncated cone? [ice cream cones]

If there is additional time following this lesson, have the child choose a game to play.

# LESSON 125: NAME THE SOLIDS FROM VIEWS

## OBJECTIVES:
1. To review the names of the geometric solids
2. To identify solids from views

## MATERIALS:
1. Warm-up Practice 14
2. Geometric solids
3. Worksheet 97, Name the Solids from Views

## ACTIVITIES FOR TEACHING:

**Warm-up.** Give the child the warm-up practice sheet. Tell him to do only the first multivide. Solutions are on the right.

**Reviewing names of the solids.** Give the child the geometric solids.

Tell the child to spread out the solids and to show the solid as you name it. See the figure below.

Then show a solid and ask: What is this one called? Continue until all the solids are identified.

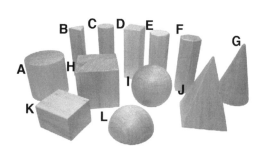

A  Large cylinder
B  Triangular prism
C  Small cylinder
D  Square prism
E  Octagonal prism
F  Hexagonal prism
G  Cone
H  Cube
I  Sphere
J  Square pyramid
K  Rectangular prism
L  Hemisphere

**Identifying solid from views.** Draw the three views of a square prism as shown in the left figure below. Tell the child to think about which solid it could be, but to pick up the solid and check the views before answering. Ask: Which solid is it? [square prism]

Repeat for views of a sphere. See the right figure below.

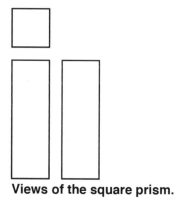

**Views of the square prism.**

**Views of the sphere.**

## EXPLANATIONS:

$$
\begin{array}{r}
19\ (1) \\
\times\,72\ (0) \\
38 \\
1\,330 \\
1\,368\ (0) \\
\times\,56\ (7) \\
8\,208\ (0) \\
68\,400 \\
76\,608\ (0) \\
\times\,90\ (0) \\
9\,)\overline{6\,894\,720}\ (0) \\
8\,)\overline{766\,080}\ (0) \\
7\,)\overline{95\,760}\ (0) \\
6\,)\overline{13\,680}\ (0) \\
5\,)\overline{2\,280}\ (3) \\
4\,)\overline{456}\ (6) \\
3\,)\overline{114}\ (6) \\
2\,)\overline{38}\ (2) \\
19
\end{array}
$$

**ACTIVITIES FOR TEACHING CONTINUED:**

**EXPLANATIONS CONTINUED:**

Draw the views of a cone on top of a cube as shown below. Tell the child these views are two solids. Ask: What are they? [cone on a cube]

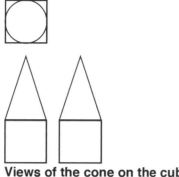

**Views of the cone on the cube.**

***Worksheet 97.*** Give the child the worksheet and tell him to complete it. The solutions are below.

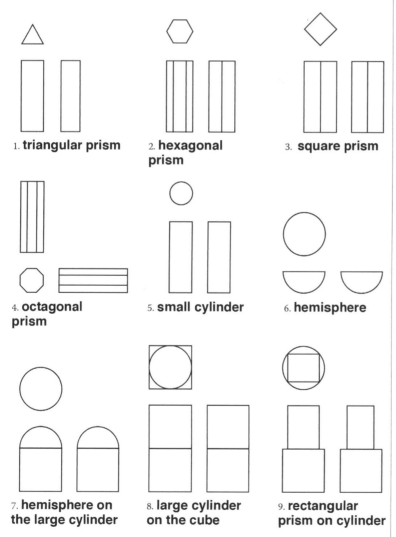

1. **triangular prism**
2. **hexagonal prism**
3. **square prism**
4. **octagonal prism**
5. **small cylinder**
6. **hemisphere**
7. **hemisphere on the large cylinder**
8. **large cylinder on the cube**
9. **rectangular prism on cylinder**

***In conclusion.*** Ask: Which geometric solids look the same in all three views? [cube and sphere] Which two solids can have triangles for two views? [pyramid and cone] Which solid can have a triangle for only one view? [triangular prism]

If there is additional time following this lesson, play the Zero Corners game, found in *Math Card Games* book, S9.

# LESSON 126: DRAWING CIRCLE DESIGNS

## OBJECTIVES:

1. To learn the terms *radius* and *concentric*
2. To learn that a circle is a set of points equidistant from a given point
3. To draw a set of concentric circles
4. To draw some circle designs

## MATERIALS:

1. Worksheets 98-1, 98-2, and 98-3, Drawing Circle Designs
2. Safe-T Compass®

## ACTIVITIES FOR TEACHING:

**Warm-up.** Ask: Do you see any rectangular prisms in the room? [possibly a brick, book, picture frame, box, table top, and window glass] Do you see any hemispheres in the room? [possibly a light bulb, door knob, bowl]

**Worksheets 98-1, 98-2, and 98-3.** Give the child the worksheets and a Safe-T Compass®.

Tell him to read and do the first problem.

**Worksheet 98-1, Problem 1.** Tell the child to do the first problem on the worksheet. The solution is below.

Ask: What does your figure look like? [a circle] Say: Mathematically, a circle is a 2D figure where all the points are the same distance from the center point. A point does not have any length or width; it has no dimensions.

Ask: Can you name a 3D figure where all the points are the same distance from the center point? [sphere] Can a sphere fit on a sheet of paper? [no] Can a circle fit on a sheet of paper? [yes]

**Problem 2.** Tell the child that to draw the circle for Problem 2 with the compass, he needs to keep the white rotator still and move the radius arm. See the figure on the right. First, position the center of the rotator over the center of the circle being drawn. Next find the hole marked 1"r and insert your pencil.

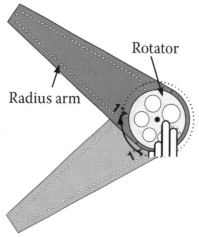

Radius arm

Rotator

## EXPLANATIONS:

If these worksheets are bound in the child's worksheets, they need to be removed.

Sometimes putting a sharp point, such as a pencil, in the center allows the Safe-T Compass® to move easier than holding it with a hand.

| ACTIVITIES FOR TEACHING CONTINUED: | EXPLANATIONS CONTINUED: |

Draw the circle in one operation, lifting the palm of your hand to complete the circle.

Tell him to do Problem 2. The solution is below.

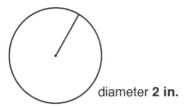

diameter **2 in.**

Ask: If you know the radius, how do find the diameter? [multiply by 2]

**Problems 3 to 5.** Tell the child to complete the worksheets. The solution to Problem 3 is below.

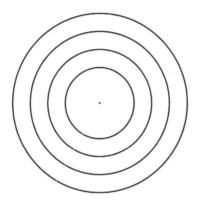

**In conclusion.** Ask: When you draw a circle, through what angle do you move the compass? [360°]

Say: Imagine a dandelion plant. Ask: What part of the plant has a 3D sphere? [the seed head] What part of the plant has a 2D circle? [the flower head] What part of the plant has a 1D line? [the stem] What part of the plant is so tiny it hardly has any dimensions? [the seed]

If there is additional time following this lesson, play the Top and Bottom Corners game, found in *Math Card Games* book, S11.

# LESSON 127: DRAWING OLYMPIC RINGS

## OBJECTIVES:

1. To learn about the Olympic rings
2. To enlarge a given model
3. To practice making circles to a given radius

## MATERIALS:

1. Worksheet 99, Drawing Olympic Rings
2. Ruler
3. Drawing board, T-square, 45 triangle
4. Safe-T Compass®
5. **Colored pencils: blue, yellow, black, green, red**

## ACTIVITIES FOR TEACHING:

***Warm-up.*** Ask: Is a photograph two dimensional, 2D, or three dimensional, 3D? [two dimensional, 2D] Is a person 2D or 3D? [3D] Is a circle 2D or 3D? [2D] Is a sphere 2D or 3D? [3D] Is a cube 2D or 3D? [3D] Is a square 2D or 3D? [2D] Is a point 2D or 3D? [it's neither]

***Worksheet 99.*** Give the child the worksheet, ruler, Safe-T Compass®, and drawing tools.

Tell him to read the instructions on the worksheet:

On the right is a model of the Olympic rings. Draw the rings below three times greater than the model.

Hint: first locate the centers of all the rings; they will be three times farther apart than the model.

Ask: What do you need to draw? [the Olympic rings] At what size? [three times larger] What do you need to draw the circles? [the center point, radius, and compass]

Ask him how he could find the point for the second circle. One way to find the point is to measure the distance between the points in the original drawing. [1 in.] Multiply that by 3 [3 in.] and place the second point 3 in. away from the first point. See the figures below. Repeat for the third point.

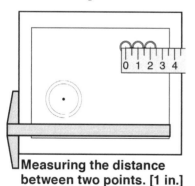

**Measuring the distance between two points. [1 in.]**

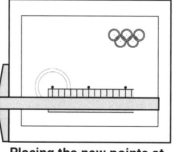

**Placing the new points at a distance 3 times greater.**

The location of the first point in the second row can be found either by measuring down and across or by measuring on the diagonal as shown on the next page. [0.7 in.] The point is 3 times 0.7 [2.1 in.] on the diagonal.

## EXPLANATIONS:

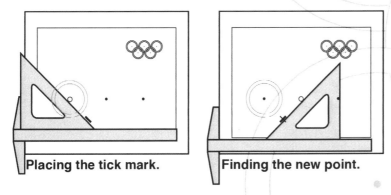

| **Measuring the distance between the points in the rows. [0.7 in.]** | **Placing the new point at a distance 3 times greater. [0.7 × 3 = 2.1 in.]** |

The fifth point is the same distance as the points in the first row.

Another way to find the first point in the second row is shown below.

| **Placing the tick mark.** | **Finding the new point.** |

With all the points located, the circles can be drawn. Use the circle given to find the correct hole on the compass.

Tell the child to draw the rings. The final rings will look like the background circles on this page.

***In conclusion.*** Ask: How many circles are in the Olympic rings? [10] How many sets of concentric circles are there? [five] What is special about the colors? [Every nation's flag has at least one of the colors.] What are the colors? [blue, yellow, black, green, and red]

There are other ways to locate the points in the second row.

If there is additional time following this lesson, play the Division War game, found in *Math Card Games* book, D12.

# LESSON 128: AREA ON THE GEOBOARD

**OBJECTIVES:**

1. To find area on the geoboard
2. To learn to use Pick's Theorem
3. To add mixed numbers with halves

**MATERIALS:**

1. Warm-up Practice 14
2. Worksheet 100, Area on the Geoboard
3. Geoboard

## ACTIVITIES FOR TEACHING:

**Warm-up.** Give the child the warm-up practice sheet. Tell him to do the second multivide on the page. Solutions are on the right.

**Worksheet 100.** Give the child the worksheet and geoboard. Explain that today he will be finding area on the geoboard and checking the area with Pick's Theorem.

**Problems 1 to 5.** Tell the child to read the instructions on his worksheet:

A square formed by four pegs on the geoboard is 1 unit of area. *Boundary points* are pegs on the perimeter of the figure. A *boundary pair* is two boundary points.

Tell him to make the first figure on the worksheet on his geoboard. See the left figure below. Ask: What is the area of the square? [1 unit] How many boundary pairs does the square have? [2] See the right figure below. Tell him to notice what is written in the table on his worksheet.

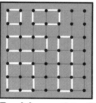

**Problems 1 to 5.**

Boundary pairs

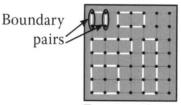

**Two pegs form a boundary pair.**

Tell him to look at the second figure. Ask: What is the area of the rectangle? [2 units] How many boundary pairs does the rectangle have? [3] Tell him to write it in the table.

Tell him to do the next two rectangles. Ask: What is the area and how many boundary pairs for the third rectangle? [3, 4] What is the area and how many boundary pairs for the fourth rectangle? [4, 5] What pattern do you see? [There is one more boundary pair than area or area is one less than the boundary pairs.]

## EXPLANATIONS:

This lesson on exploring area on the geoboard is enhanced with Pick's Theorem. This introduction to the theorem provides a hands-on approach to a higher level concept and is intended to create curiosity, pique interest, and provide another approach to calculating area.

Georg Pick (1859–1942) was an Austrian mathematician. He published his theorem in 1899, but it was not generally known until 1969.

|  | 13 | (4) |
|---|---:|---|
|  | × 72 | (0) |
|  | **26** | |
|  | **910** | |
|  | **936** | (0) |
|  | × 72 | (0) |
|  | **1 872** | (0) |
|  | **65 520** | |
|  | **67 392** | (0) |
|  | × 70 | (7) |
| 9) | 4 717 440 | (0) |
| 8) | 524 160 | (0) |
| 7) | 65 520 | (0) |
| 6) | 9 360 | (0) |
| 5) | 1 560 | (3) |
| 4) | 312 | (6) |
| 3) | 78 | (6) |
| 2) | 26 | (8) |
|  | **13** | |

Geoboards can vary in the distance between pegs, so rather than refer to the measurement in inches or centimeters, we will use "unit."

| Area in Units | Number of Pegs | |
|---|---|---|
| | Boundary Pairs | Inside |
| 1 | 2 | |
| 2 | 3 | |
| 3 | 4 | |
| 4 | 5 | |
| 4 | 4 | 1 |

| ACTIVITIES FOR TEACHING CONTINUED: | EXPLANATIONS CONTINUED: |

Now tell him to look at the fifth problem, the square. Ask: How is it different? [There is a peg inside the square.] What is the area and how many boundary pairs for the second square? [4, 4] How many pegs are inside the square? [1] Tell him to write 1 in the Inside column in the table. See the previous page.

"Inside" points are often called "interior" points.

**Problems 6 to 8.** Tell the child to do the next three problems. See the figure at the right. The solutions are in the table on the right.

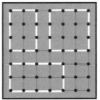

**Problems 6 to 8.**

Tell him to look at the data in his table. Ask: How does the sum of the boundary pairs and inside points compare to the area? [1 more]

| Area in Units | Number of Pegs | |
|---|---|---|
| | Boundary Pairs | Inside |
| 6 | 5 | 2 |
| 9 | 6 | 4 |
| 8 | 6 | 3 |

Tell him to watch while you show him a procedure for finding the area. Make the 2 × 3 rectangle on the geoboard. Then touch any two pegs with your non-writing hand. Count the remaining boundary pairs and continue with the inside pegs. See the figures below.

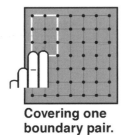

**Covering one boundary pair.**

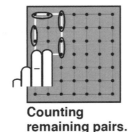

**Counting remaining pairs.**

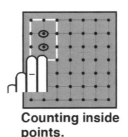

**Counting inside points.**

Memory is enhanced through engaging the muscles. Touching the pairs of pegs helps in learning.

Usually Pick's Theorem is written as:
$$A = i + \frac{b}{2} - 1$$

Tell him to try it with the three rectangles in problems 6 to 8.

**Problems 9 to 13.** Tell the child to look at the next set of figures. See the figure at the right. Ask: What is the area of the first figure? [$\frac{1}{2}$ unit] What does Pick's Theorem say? [one half of a boundary pair]

Tell the child look at the next figure. Ask: What is the area? [5] Have the child explain it. [Four whole units and two half units; $4 + \frac{1}{2} + \frac{1}{2} = 5$ units] What does Pick's Theorem say? [5]

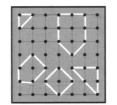

**Problems 9 to 13.**

| Area in Units | Number of Pegs | |
|---|---|---|
| | Boundary Pairs − 1 | Inside |
| $\frac{1}{2}$ | $\frac{1}{2}$ | |
| 5 | 3 | 2 |
| $2\frac{1}{2}$ | $1\frac{1}{2}$ | 1 |
| 2 | 1 | 1 |
| 2 | 2 | |

Tell him to complete the worksheet. The solutions are above at the right.

**In conclusion.** Ask: How do you use Pick's Theorem to find area? [Count boundary pairs, except for one pair, then add the inside points.]

If there is additional time following this lesson, play the Division War game, found in *Math Card Games* book, D12.

# LESSON 129: COMPARING AREAS ON THE GEOBOARD

## OBJECTIVES:

1. To find more complicated areas on the geoboard
2. To compare areas when the width and height of a figure are doubled or tripled

## MATERIALS:

1. Warm-up Practice 15
2. Worksheet 101, Comparing Areas on the Geoboard
3. Geoboard

## ACTIVITIES FOR TEACHING:

**Warm-up.** Give the child the warm-up practice sheet. Tell him to do only the first multivide. Solutions are on the right.

**Worksheet 101.** Give the child the worksheet and geoboard. Explain that today he will be finding more areas on the geoboard and using Pick's Theorem.

**Problems 1 to 4.** Tell the child to read the instructions and look at the first figure on his worksheet. See below.

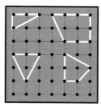
**Problems 1 to 4.**

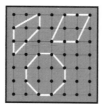
**Problems 5 to 7.**

Say: The first triangle is half of a rectangle that has an area of 2 units. Ask: What is the area of the triangle? [1 unit] Tell him that the tables on his worksheet call this "half of 2 units." Ask: What does Pick's Theorem say the area is? [The area is 1 unit; there is one boundary pair after covering a pair.] Tell him to see how the information is written in the table on his worksheet. Tell him to write the total area of the triangle. [1]

Ask: Which of the first four figures includes a unit made from half of 2 units? [They all do.] Which figure includes a one-half unit made from 1 unit? [fourth figure]

Tell the child look at the second figure. Ask: What is the area? [5] Have the child explain it. [Four whole units and one "half of 2 units" on the left; 4 + 1 = 5]

Tell him to do the next two problems. The solutions are shown in the table at the right. Tell him to explain his solutions.

**Problems 5 to 7.** Repeat for the next three problems. Solutions are shown on the right.

## EXPLANATIONS:

| | |
|---:|:---|
| 12 | **(3)** |
| × 90 | **(0)** |
| **1 080** | **(0)** |
| × 42 | **(6)** |
| **2 160** | |
| **43 200** | |
| **45 360** | **(0)** |
| × 96 | **(6)** |
| **272 160** | |
| **4 082 400** | |
| 9)**4 354 560** | **(0)** |
| 8)**483 840** | **(0)** |
| 7)**60 480** | **(0)** |
| 6)**8 640** | **(0)** |
| 5)**1 440** | **(0)** |
| 4)**288** | **(0)** |
| 3)**72** | **(0)** |
| 2)**24** | **(6)** |
| **12** | |

The triangle to the right formed by half of two units has one unit of area. It will be called "half of 2 units."

The triangle to the right formed by half of a unit has one half unit of area. It will be called a "half of 1 unit"

| Area from Whole Units | Area from Half of 1 Unit | Area from Half of 2 Units | Total Area | Area using Pick's Theorem |
|:---:|:---:|:---:|:---:|:---:|
| | | | 1 | 1 |
| 4 | | 1 | 5 | 5 |
| | | 2 | 2 | 2 |
| 1 | $\frac{1}{2}$ | 1 | $2\frac{1}{2}$ | $2\frac{1}{2}$ |
| 1 | 1 | 1 | 3 | 3 |
| 2 | | 2 | 4 | 4 |
| 5 | 2 | | 7 | 7 |

| **ACTIVITIES FOR TEACHING CONTINUED:** | **EXPLANATIONS CONTINUED:** |

**Problems 8 to 15.** Tell the child to look at the next two groups of problems. See below on the left. Ask: How are these problems different from the first two groups? [They are in sets of two with the second figure larger than the first.] How much greater is the widths and heights in the second figures compared to the first figures? [2 times greater]

Tell him to do Problems 8 to 15. The solutions are below.

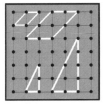

**Problems 8 to 11.**

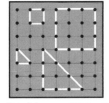

**Problems 12 to 15.**

| Area from Whole Units | Area from Half of 1 Unit | Area from Half of 2 Units | Total Area | Area using Pick's Theorem |
|---|---|---|---|---|
| | 1 | | 1 | 1 |
| 2 | 2 | | 4 | 4 |
| | | 1 | 1 | 1 |
| 2 | | 2 | 4 | 4 |
| 1 | $\frac{1}{2}$ | | $1\frac{1}{2}$ | $1\frac{1}{2}$ |
| 5 | 1 | | 6 | 6 |
| | 2 | | 2 | 2 |
| 4 | 4 | | 8 | 8 |

What happens when the width and height of a figure is doubled? **The area is 4 times greater.**

Ask: Is the area of the larger figure 4 times greater in all four examples? [yes] How many times would the smaller figures fit into the larger figures? [4 times]

**Problems 16 to 19.** Tell the child to do at the last group of problems. See below.

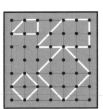

**Problems 16 to 19.**

| Area from Whole Units | Area from Half of 1 Unit | Area from Half of 2 Units | Total Area | Area using Pick's Theorem |
|---|---|---|---|---|
| 1 | | | 1 | 1 |
| 9 | | | 9 | 9 |
| | $\frac{1}{2}$ | | $\frac{1}{2}$ | $\frac{1}{2}$ |
| 3 | $1\frac{1}{2}$ | | $4\frac{1}{2}$ | $4\frac{1}{2}$ |

What happens when the width and height of a figure is 3 times greater? **The area is 9 times greater.**

Ask: How much greater is the width and height in the larger figures compared to the smaller figures? [3 times greater] How many times would the smaller figures fit into the larger figures? [9 times]

**In conclusion.** Tell the child that some people think that if you make the length and width of figure twice as much, the figure will be twice as large. Ask: Are they right? [no] How much larger will it be? [4 times]

A detailed explanation of Problem 4 from the previous page is as follows:

1. Area from a whole unit is in the lower left of the figure.

2. Area from "half of 1 unit" is in the lower right corner. There is one of these, a total of $\frac{1}{2}$ unit.

3. Area from "half of 2 units" is the upper section. Again, there is one of these, a total of 1 unit.

4. Add the areas for a total of $2\frac{1}{2}$ units.

Fitting the smaller figure into the larger figure can actually be done on the geoboard, although sometimes rotations and reflections might be needed.

If there is additional time following this lesson, play the One Half game, found in *Math Card Games* book, F8.

# LESSON 130: TRIANGLE AREAS ON THE GEOBOARD

## OBJECTIVES:

1. To explore the area of a triangle
2. To discover that when the altitude stays the same, the position of the vertex opposite the base does not affect the area
3. To discover that the area of a triangle is half the base times the height

## MATERIALS:

1. Warm-up Practice 15
2. Worksheet 102, Triangle Areas on the Geoboard
3. Geoboard

## ACTIVITIES FOR TEACHING:

***Warm-up.*** Give the child the warm-up practice sheet. Tell him to do the second multivide on the page. Solutions are on the right.

***Worksheet 102.*** Give the child the worksheet and geoboard. Explain that today he will be finding areas of triangles.

***Problems 1 to 5.*** Tell the child to look at the two geoboard figures on his worksheet. See below.

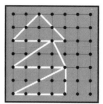 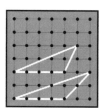

**Problems 1 to 5.**

Ask: Which of these five figures do you think has the greatest area? [Answer will vary.] Tell him to find out and write the answers on his worksheet. The solutions are below.

> Find the area of each triangle, using any method.
> 1. **4**  2. **4**  3. **4**  4. **4**  5. **4**
> What is the base of each triangle? **4**
> What is the height of each triangle? **2**

Ask: Which triangle has the greatest area? [all the same] Tell him to make the first triangle on his geoboard, then to move the rubber band from the third peg to the fourth peg, to the fifth, sixth, and seventh peg. Ask: What happens to the area? [It stays the same.] Say: This is an amazing result!

***Problems 6 to 10.*** Tell him to do the next two sets of triangles. The solutions are on the next page.

Ask: Does the area change if the base and height stay the same, but the vertex moves? [no]

## EXPLANATIONS:

```
                11 (2)
             × 56 (2)
                66
               550
               616 (4)
             × 72 (0)
             1 232 (0)
            43 120
            44 352 (0)
             × 90 (0)
        9)3 991 680 (0)
         8)443 520 (0)
          7)55 440 (0)
           6)7 920 (0)
           5)1 320 (6)
            4)264 (3)
             3)66 (3)
             2)22 (4)
               11
```

**ACTIVITIES FOR TEACHING CONTINUED:**     **EXPLANATIONS CONTINUED:**

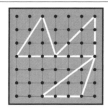 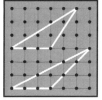

**Problems 6 to 10.**

Find the area of each triangle, using any method.
1. $4\frac{1}{2}$  2. $4\frac{1}{2}$  3. $4\frac{1}{2}$  4. $4\frac{1}{2}$  5. $4\frac{1}{2}$
What is the base of each triangle? **3**
What is the height of each triangle? **3**

**Problems 11 to 16.** Tell the child to look at the next two groups of problems. Explain that he is to fill in the table for each triangle. Tell him to do Problems 11 to 16. The solutions are below.

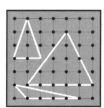 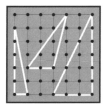

**Problems 11 to 16.**

| $b$ | $h$ | $b \times h$ | Area |
|---|---|---|---|
| 4 | 1 | 4 | 2 |
| 2 | 3 | 6 | 3 |
| 5 | 4 | 20 | 10 |
| 1 | 5 | 5 | $2\frac{1}{2}$ |
| 2 | 4 | 8 | 4 |
| 3 | 6 | 18 | 9 |

Resist the temptation to tell the child that the area of a triangle is half of the base times the height. Let him discover the relationship himself.

How is the area of a triangle related to $b \times h$?
**The area of half of $b \times h$.**

**Figures 17 to 20.** Tell the child to use the relationship he found to do the last group of problems. Explain that sometimes the base of the triangle is not at the bottom. The solutions are below.

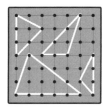

| $b$ | $h$ | $b \times h$ | Area |
|---|---|---|---|
| 3 | 2 | 6 | 3 |
| 2 | 3 | 6 | 3 |
| 5 | 3 | 15 | $7\frac{1}{2}$ |
| 3 | 1 | 3 | $1\frac{1}{2}$ |

**Problems 17 to 20.**

**In conclusion.** Ask: If you know the base and height of a triangle, how can you find the area? [multiply the base and height, then divide by 2] If the base of a triangle is 10 and the height is 4, what is the area? [20]

If there is additional time following this lesson, play the Series Solitaire game, found in *Math Card Games* book, F16.

# LESSON 131: HOW MANY SQUARES ON THE GEOBOARD

## OBJECTIVES:

1. To solve the modified checkerboard problem (how many squares) with the geoboard
2. To find other squares that can be made on the geoboard
3. To persevere in problem solving

## MATERIALS:

1. Geoboard
2. Worksheet 103, How Many Squares on the Geoboard

| ACTIVITIES FOR TEACHING: | EXPLANATIONS: |
|---|---|
| ***Warm-up.*** Ask: How do you use Pick's Theorem to find area? [Count boundary pairs, except for one pair, then add the inside points.] Will this work for triangles? [yes] | |
| Ask: If you know the base and height of a triangle, how can you find the area? [multiply the base and height, then divide by 2] | |
| ***The squares problems.*** Give the child the geoboard. Hold a geoboard with a narrow edge toward him, not favoring either side, and challenge him: If you had a thousand rubber bands, how many squares could you make on this geoboard? | Have this discussion before he sees the worksheet because the worksheet suggests the solutions. |
| Give him about five minutes to think about the challenge. Then tell him to explain it. | |
| If he does not mention it, ask: Could the squares have sides that are 45° to the edges of the geoboard? [yes] | |
| If he does not mention it, ask: Could you make squares on the circle side of the geoboard? [yes] Tell him there are three sizes of squares he can make. | The problem may not have the same answer if a different geoboard is used. |
| ***Worksheet 103.*** Give the child the worksheet and tell him to complete it. | |

***Part 1 .*** The solutions are below.

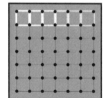 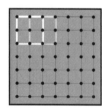 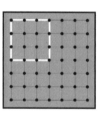

| Size of square | Number in row | Number in column | Total |
|---|---|---|---|
| 1 × 1 | 6 | 6 | 36 |
| 2 × 2 | 5 | 5 | 25 |
| 3 × 3 | 4 | 4 | 16 |
| 4 × 4 | 3 | 3 | 9 |
| 5 × 5 | 2 | 2 | 4 |
| 6 × 6 | 1 | 1 | 1 |
| | | | 91 |

## ACTIVITIES FOR TEACHING CONTINUED:

## EXPLANATIONS CONTINUED:

***Part 2.*** The solutions for the second type of squares are shown below.

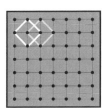 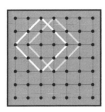 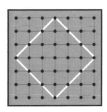

| Size of square | Number in row | Number in column | Total |
|---|---|---|---|
| **1 × 1** | **5** | **5** | **25** |
| **2 × 2** | **3** | **3** | **9** |
| **3 × 3** | **1** | **1** | **1** |
| | | | **35** |

***Parts 3 to 5.*** The solutions for the circle side of the geoboard and the totals are shown below.

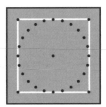 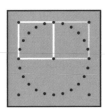 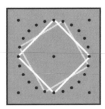

There are other squares that can be made, such as the two shown below, that are not included.

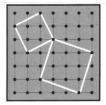

| Describe squares | Total |
|---|---|
| **Four corners** | **1** |
| **Four corners in fourths** | **4** |
| **Inside circles** | **6** |
| | **11** |

4. How many rubber bands would you need to make all these squares at the same time? **137**

5. How many different sizes of squares did you make on the geoboard for this lesson? **12**

***In conclusion.*** Ask: Did you think the number of squares on a geoboard would be so high? [Answers will vary.] Tell him there are books written with problems like these that many people solve for fun.

The classic checkerboard problem asks how many squares are on an 8 × 8 checkerboard.

If there is additional time following this lesson, have the child choose a game to play.

# LESSON 132: MIDPOINTS IN TRIANGLES

## OBJECTIVES:

1. To discover connecting the midpoints in a triangle gives four new congruent triangles each one fourth the area of original triangle
2. To discover sides of new triangle are parallel to opposite side of the original triangle
3. To discover sides of the new triangle are one half the opposite side of the original triangle

## MATERIALS:

1. Worksheet 104, Midpoints in Triangles
2. Geoboard
3. 4-in-1 ruler

## ACTIVITIES FOR TEACHING:

***Warm-up.*** Give the child the worksheet. Tell him to do just the warm-up equations. Solutions are:

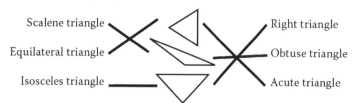

Scalene triangle — Right triangle
Equilateral triangle — Obtuse triangle
Isosceles triangle — Acute triangle

***Worksheet 109.*** Give the child the geoboard and ruler. Explain that today he will be working with triangles inside triangles.

***Midpoints.*** Tell him to look at the 6 on the inch side of his ruler and say: The 6 is the midpoint. Ask: What does that mean? [The 6 is the middle.] What number is the midpoint on the metric side of the ruler? [15]

***Problems 1 to 6.*** Tell the child to read and do the first six problems on his worksheet. The solutions are below and on the next page.

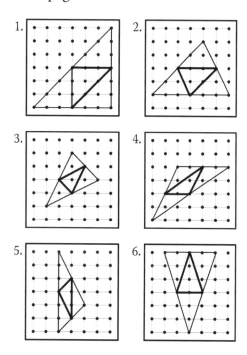

## EXPLANATIONS:

257

**ACTIVITIES FOR TEACHING CONTINUED:**

**EXPLANATIONS CONTINUED:**

| Area of large triangle | Area of small triangle | Area of parallelogram | Area of trapezoid |
|---|---|---|---|
| 18 | $4\frac{1}{2}$ | 9 | $13\frac{1}{2}$ |
| 12 | 3 | 6 | 9 |
| 6 | $1\frac{1}{2}$ | 3 | $4\frac{1}{2}$ |
| 8 | 2 | 4 | 6 |
| 6 | $1\frac{1}{2}$ | 3 | $4\frac{1}{2}$ |
| 12 | 3 | 6 | 9 |

Tell him to discuss some interesting points he notices about these triangles.

Ask questions when necessary to help him find these relationships. Observations to find:

1. Area of the new triangle is one fourth the area of the large triangle.

2. The other three triangles are congruent with the new triangle.

3. The sides of the new triangle are parallel with the large triangle.

4. There are three parallelograms.

5. Each parallelogram has half the area of the large triangle.

6. There are three trapezoids.

7. Each trapezoid has three fourths the area of the large triangle.

**Problems 7 to 14.** Tell him to complete the worksheet. The solutions are below.

7. The area of the small triangles is what fraction of the area of the large triangles? $\frac{1}{4}$

8. Are the four small triangles in the large triangle congruent? **yes**

9. Compare the length of a side of a small triangle to the opposite side of the large triangle? $\frac{1}{2}$

10. The side of a small triangle is parallel or perpendicular to the opposite side of the large triangle? **parallel**

11. How many parallelograms are in each large triangle? **3**

12. Compare the area of a parallelogram to the area of the large triangle? $\frac{1}{2}$

13. How many trapezoids are in each large triangle? **3**

14. Compare the area of a trapezoid to the area of the large triangle? $\frac{3}{4}$

**In conclusion.** Ask: What do you get when you connect the midpoints of a triangle? [a new triangle] How long are the sides of the new triangle? [half the size of the large triangle] What is its area? [one fourth the area of the large triangle]

If there is additional time following this lesson, have the child choose a game to play.

# LESSON 133: MIDPOINTS IN QUADRILATERALS

## OBJECTIVES:

1. To discover that connecting the adjacent midpoints in a quadrilateral results in a parallelogram
2. To discover that the area of that parallelogram is half the area of the quadrilateral

## MATERIALS:

1. Worksheet 105, Midpoints in Quadrilaterals
2. Geoboard
3. 4-in-1 ruler
4. **Scissors**

## ACTIVITIES FOR TEACHING:

**Warm-up.** Ask: What do you get when you connect the midpoints of a triangle? [a new triangle] How long are the sides of the new triangle? [half the size of the large triangle] What is its area? [one fourth the area of the large triangle]

**Worksheet 105.** Give the child the worksheet, geoboard, and ruler. Explain that today he will be working with quadrilaterals.

**Problem 1.** Tell the child to do Problem 1, on the top half of the worksheet. The solutions are below.

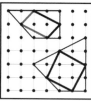

| Area of quadrilateral | Area of inside figure |
|:---:|:---:|
| 6 | 3 |
| 10 | 5 |
| 8 | 4 |
| 12 | 6 |

What figure is formed by connecting the midpoints in a quadrilateral? **parallelogram**

What is the relationship between the area of the quadrilateral and the area of the inside figure? **Area of parallelogram is half area of quadrilateral.**

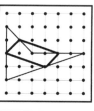

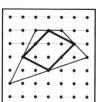

Ask: Is the new figure formed by connecting adjacent midpoints another quadrilateral? [yes] What special quadrilateral is it? [parallelogram] Are the sides of the parallelogram parallel to the quadrilateral? [no]

Ask: How does the area of the inside figure in a quadrilateral compare to the area of the inside figure of a triangle? [Quadrilateral is one half; triangle is one fourth.]

## EXPLANATIONS:

| ACTIVITIES FOR TEACHING CONTINUED: | EXPLANATIONS CONTINUED: |
|---|---|

**Problem 2.** Tell the child to read and follow the directions for Problem 2. The solutions are shown below.

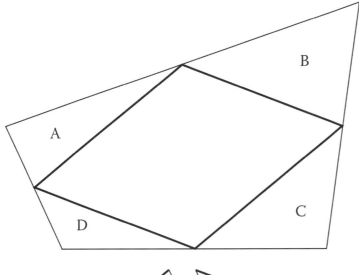

To make finding the midpoints easier, the sides of the quadrilateral are whole centimeters, Starting at the top, the sides measure 17 cm, 11 cm, 12 cm, and 6 cm.

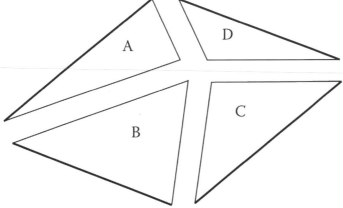

Pieces A and C are rotated 180°.

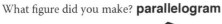
What figure did you make? **parallelogram**

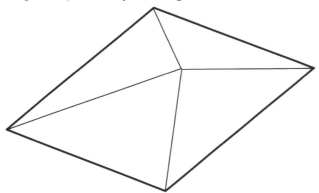

**In conclusion.** Ask: If the area of the parallelogram in a quadrilateral is 100 square centimeters, what is the total area of the four surrounding triangles? [100 square centimeters] What is the area of the entire quadrilateral? [200 square centimeters]

If there is additional time following this lesson, have the child choose a game to play.

# ENRICHMENT LESSON 134: MOBIUS STRIPS

## OBJECTIVES:

1. To introduce to another type of geometry called topology
2. To discover some unusual properties of the Mobius strip

## MATERIALS:

1. **7 strips of paper about 11" (30 cm) × 1" (2 to 3 cm) wide**
2. **Scissors**
3. **Tape**

## ACTIVITIES FOR TEACHING:

***Mobius strips.*** Give the child the strips, scissors, and tape. Tell him that today's lesson deals with another type of geometry, called topology, which deals with changing surfaces.

***Cylinder.*** Tell the child to take one of his strips and tape the ends together securely without overlapping. Taping the back may be beneficial. See the figures below.

**Taping the edges together, covering the entire seam.**

**A cylinder.**

Ask: What figure do you have now? [cylinder] How many surfaces does it have? [two, inside and outside] Could you color the surfaces two different colors? [yes] Tell him to run his finger around the edges. How many edges does it have? [two] See above.

***Making a Mobius strip.*** Tell the child to take another strip, twist one end 180°, and tape it to the other end. See the figures below.

**A Mobius strip.**

**A Mobius strip twisted the opposite direction.**

Then tell him to draw a line in the middle of the strip as far as he can. Ask: What happened? [The line continues back to the beginning.] Could you color the surface different colors? [no] Could that happen with the cylinder? [no] Say: This is called a Mobius (MOE-bee-us) strip. The Mobius strip has only one surface!

Tell him to start at the seam and run his fingers along the top edge. Ask: What happened? [ended where he started] How many edges does the strip have? [one] Say: A Mobius strip has only one surface and one edge!

## EXPLANATIONS:

* The child could cut these strips himself. Accuracy is not necessary.

## ACTIVITIES FOR TEACHING CONTINUED:

Tell him this strip is named after Augustus Ferdinand Mobius (1790-1868), a German mathematician, who discovered it in 1858.

***Mobius strip cut in half.*** Tell the child to make another Mobius strip. Next tell him to cut in the middle of the strip all the way to the end. See figure on the right.

Ask: What happened? [one strip twice as long with two full twists] Say: It is not a Mobius strip. Discuss why it is not a Mobius strip. [It has two sides and two edges.]

***Mobius strip cut at one third.*** Ask the child to make a third Mobius strip. Then ask him to cut on a line one third, rather than one half, the distance from an edge. See figure on the right. Ask: What happened? [two connected strips, one short and one long]

Ask: Is one a Mobius strip? [yes, the shorter one]

***Two cylinders.*** Tell the child to take another strip and make a second cylinder. Then tell him to turn the cylinder 90° and tape it securely to the first cylinder. Use tape on both sides. See the left figure below.

**Two cylinders at 90°.**

**The "headphones."**

Next tell him to cut all the way through the center of one of the cylinders. The results will look like headphones. See the right figure above.

Lastly, cut through the center of the remaining wide strip. Ask: What did you get? [a square]

**A square.**

***Two Mobius strips.*** Tell the child to make two Mobius strips. Say: It is important that you make one strip by twisting 180° to the left and make the other strip by twisting 180° to the right. Then tell him to turn one Mobius strip 90° and tape it securely to the other Mobius strip. See figure on the right.

**Two Mobius strips at 90°.**

Next tell him to cut all the way through the centers of the Mobius strips to get two interlocking hearts. See figure on the right.

***In conclusion.*** Ask: What is special about a Mobius strip? [It has only one side and one edge.]

## EXPLANATIONS CONTINUED:

Mobius Motors is an African automaker in Nairobi, Kenya, which started in 2009.

**A Mobius strip cut in half.**

**A Mobius strip cut in thirds.**

If the Mobius strips are made with identical twists, the project will fail.

**Two interlocking hearts.**

# LESSON 135: WHOLE NUMBER REVIEW

**OBJECTIVES:**
1. To review concepts learned during the year

**MATERIALS:**
1. Worksheet 106, Whole Number Review

---

**ACTIVITIES FOR TEACHING:**

**EXPLANATIONS:**

**Worksheet 106.** Give the child the worksheet. Tell him that today will be a review for the upcoming final assessment. He will complete the worksheet, then discuss the solutions.

Tell him to listen to the problems and write the answers. Read each problem twice.

$100 - 17 \qquad 25 \times 5 \qquad 87 + 47$

Tell him to complete the worksheet. Solutions are below and on the next page.

---

1-3. Write only the answers.

**83**
**125**
**134**

4-9. Write the answers.

$718 + 265 =$ **983**
$72 \div 9 =$ **8**
$100 \times 40 =$ **4000**

$87 - 79 =$ **8**
$512 - 15 =$ **497**
$200 -$ **132** $= 68$

10. Find 30,847 + 7946.

```
 30,847 (4)
+ 7,946 (8)
 38,793 (3)
```

11. Find 8307 − 5457.

```
  8307 (0)
− 5457 (3)
  2850 (6)
```

12. Find 6392 × 26.

```
   6392 (2)
 ×  26 (8)
  38 352
 127 840
 166 192 (7)
```

13. Find 3450 ÷ 3.

```
   1150 (7)
3)3450 (3)
```

14. Find 6729 ÷ 8.

```
   841 r1
8)6729
```

15-16. Write these as numbers. Use commas to mark the periods.

27 million **27,000,000**

40 billion **40,000,000,000**

17-22. Round the populations to the nearest million.

| | | |
|---|---|---|
| Australia | 24,168,303 | **24** million |
| Canada | 36,134,016 | **36** million |
| China | 1,375,137,837 | **1375** million |
| Indonesia | 259,281,096 | **259** million |
| United Kingdom | 63,742,977 | **64** million |
| United States | 324,308,763 | **324** million |

23. Write the countries in order of population, least to greatest.

**Australia**
**Canada**
**United Kingdom**
**Indonesia**
**United States**
**China**

24. The population of the world is 7,439,454,032. Write this number in words.

**Seven billion four hundred thirty-nine million four hundred fifty-four thousand thirty-two**

---

Ask the child to discuss and correct any errors during the lesson.

This was taught in Lessons 15 and 16.

## ACTIVITIES FOR TEACHING CONTINUED:

## EXPLANATIONS CONTINUED:

25-30. Prime numbers and factors.

How do you know that 6, 15, and 24 are not primes? **Multiples of 3**

How do you know that 14, 28, and 63 are not primes? **Multiples of 7**

Which of these numbers, 1, 13, 14, 25, 87, are prime? **13**

Which of these numbers, 1, 13, 14, 25, 87, are composite? **14, 25, 87**

Name the factor pairs for 32. **1 & 32, 2 & 16, 4 & 8**

What are the factors for 32. **1, 2, 4, 8, 16, 32**

This was taught in Lesson 61.

31-34. Solve the equations.

$589 + 17 - 17 = n$

$n = \textbf{589}$

$314 + m = 815$

$m = \textbf{501}$

$(3 + p) \times 2 = 8$

$p = \textbf{1}$

$(q \times 4) + 2 = 30$

$q = \textbf{7}$

35-42. Write <, >, or = on the lines.

$30 \times 2 \underline{\textbf{=}} 3 \times 20$

$13 \times 14 \times 15 \underline{\textbf{=}} 15 \times 14 \times 13$

$46 + 57 \underline{\textbf{<}} 46 + 59$

$1 \times 1 \underline{\textbf{<}} 1 + 1$

$2 \times 2 \underline{\textbf{=}} 2 + 2$

$3 \times 3 \underline{\textbf{>}} 3 + 3$

$(8 \times 6) + (8 \times 7) \underline{\textbf{=}} (8 \times 13)$

$73 - 59 \underline{\textbf{>}} 72 - 59$

43-45. Round 8748.

| To nearest 10. | **8750** |
| To nearest 100. | **8700** |
| To nearest 1000. | **9000** |

46-48. Round 1,583,804.

| To nearest 1000. | **1,584,000** |
| To nearest 10,000. | **1,580,000** |
| To nearest 100,000. | **1,600,000** |

This was taught in Lessons 16 and 17.

49-50. Solve the problem.

Bob worked from 11:00 a.m. to 2:00 p.m. for five days. He earned $7 an hour. Then he bought a gift for a friend for $25. How much money did he have left?

**Bob worked 3 hr a day.**
**He worked 3 × 5 = 15 hr**
**He earned 15 × 7 = $105**
**He has 105 − 25 = $80 left.**

# LESSON 136: WHOLE NUMBER GAMES

## OBJECTIVES:

1. To review concepts learned during the year by playing math card games

## MATERIALS:

1. *Math Card Games* book, D7, P29, and P32
2. AL Abacus or Short Multiplication Table, Appendix p. 1, if needed

## ACTIVITIES FOR TEACHING:

***Warm-up.*** Ask: Is there more than one way to add four-digit numbers? [yes, from the right and from the left] Is there more than one way to subtract four-digit numbers? [yes, from the right, the left, and Terry's way] When something is so many times greater than something else, do you add or multiply to find the answer? [multiply]

Ask: What is 77 rounded to the nearest ten? [80] What is 258 rounded to the nearest hundred? [300] What is 2561 rounded to the nearest thousand? [3000] What is 7449 rounded to the nearest thousand? [7000]

Ask: What is $9 \times 3$? [27] What is $9 \times 3 + 3$? [30] What is $6 \times 8$? [48] What is $6 \times 8 + 3$? [51] What is $8 \times 5$? [40] What is $8 \times 5 + 3$? [43] What is $3 \times 8 + 3$? [27] What is $2 \times 4 + 4$? [12] What is $7 \times 9 + 2$? [65]

Ask: What is the smallest prime number? [2] What are the first six prime numbers? [2, 3, 5, 7, 11, and 13] Is 23 prime or composite? [prime] Is 190 prime or composite? [composite] What number is neither prime nor composite? [1]

***Quotient and Remainder game.*** Play this variation of Quotient and Remainder game from *Math Card Games* book, D7. The variation is the card layout. Place the dividend card, the multiplication card, first in the row as shown below.

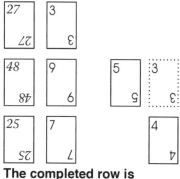

**The completed row is**
**48 ÷ 9 = 5 r3.**

## EXPLANATIONS:

This lesson is a review of concepts learned during the year by playing games. It is designed to prepare the child for the final assessment.

| ACTIVITIES FOR TEACHING CONTINUED: | EXPLANATIONS CONTINUED: |
|---|---|

**Find the Two Factors game.** Play the Find the Two Factors game found in *Math Card Games* book, P29. Players take five basic number cards and replace a card played after a turn.

**Ring around the Products game.** Play the Ring around the Products game found in the *Math Card Games* book, P32. Tell him to use the short multiplication table if he needs it.

**In conclusion.** Ask: What is opposite of addition? [subtraction] What is opposite of subtraction? [addition] What is opposite of multiplication? [division] What is opposite of division? [multiplication]

# LESSON 137: FRACTIONS, DECIMALS, AND PERCENTS REVIEW

**OBJECTIVES:**

1. To review concepts learned during the year

**MATERIALS:**

1. Worksheet 107, Fractions, Decimals, and Percents Review

---

**ACTIVITIES FOR TEACHING:**

***Worksheet 107.*** Give the child the worksheet.

Tell him that today will be a review for the upcoming final assessment. He will complete the worksheet, then discuss the solutions.

Solutions are below and on the next page.

**EXPLANATIONS:**

Ask the child to discuss and correct any errors during the lesson.

This was taught in Lesson 47.

This was taught in Lesson 56.

---

1-6. Write the non-shaded fractions on the lines.

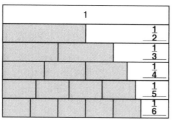

| 1 | | |
|---|---|---|
| | | $\frac{1}{2}$ |
| | | $\frac{1}{3}$ |
| | | $\frac{1}{4}$ |
| | | $\frac{1}{5}$ |
| | | $\frac{1}{6}$ |

7-13. Circle True or False.

T **(F)** A fraction is always less than one.

**(T)** F A fraction is division with the numerator divided by the denominator.

**(T)** F The numerator tells the number of parts.

**(T)** F The denominator is the divisor.

T **(F)** If the numerator equals the denominator, the fraction equals zero.

**(T)** F A fraction is improper if the numerator is greater or equal to the denominator.

**(T)** F A mixed number is a whole number and a proper fraction.

14-18. Make a small mark at the correct position on the number line and write the fraction for the following: $1\frac{1}{4}$, $\frac{2}{3}$, $1\frac{1}{2}$, $\frac{1}{2}$, and $\frac{1}{4}$.

$\frac{1}{4}$   $\frac{1}{2}$   $\frac{2}{3}$        $1\frac{1}{4}$   $1\frac{1}{2}$

0 ———————————— 1 ———————————— 2

19-30. Fill in the blanks.

12 hours is what fraction of a day? **$\frac{1}{2}$**

Four days is what fraction of a week? **$\frac{4}{7}$**

20 minutes is what fraction of a hour? **$\frac{1}{3}$**

50¢ is what fraction of a dollar? **$\frac{1}{2}$**

11 inches is what fraction of a foot? **$\frac{11}{12}$**

70 cm is what fraction of a meter? **$\frac{7}{10}$**

One third of a day is **8** hours.

Two sevenths of a week is **2** days.

A quarter of a hour is **15** minutes.

Three quarters of a dollar is **75** ¢.

Two fourths of a foot **6** inches.

Four tenths of a meter is **40** cm.

31-34. Solve the problems.

An adult giraffe weighs about 900 kg. A newborn giraffe weighs one tenth of that. What does the baby weigh? How much weight does the baby gain before becoming an adult?

**Baby weighs $\frac{1}{10}$ of 900 = 90 kg**

**Gains 900 − 90 = 810 kg**

The perimeter of each regular figure below is 15 cm. What is the length of the sides of each figure?

$s = 15 \div 4$     $s = 15 \div 8$

$s = \frac{15}{4}$ cm     $s = \frac{15}{8}$ cm

$s = 3\frac{3}{4}$ cm     $s = 1\frac{7}{8}$ cm

---

## ACTIVITIES FOR TEACHING CONTINUED:

### EXPLANATIONS CONTINUED:

35-42. Match the expressions.

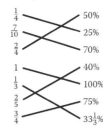

two fourths — 6
3 ÷ 2 — $\frac{1}{2}$
two thirds of 9 — $\frac{2}{3}$
$\frac{1}{2}$ of $\frac{1}{4}$ — $1\frac{1}{2}$
$\frac{1}{3} \times 2$ — $\frac{1}{8}$
$\frac{4}{10} + \frac{9}{10}$ — $1\frac{7}{10}$
2 ÷ 9 — $1\frac{3}{10}$
$2 - \frac{3}{10}$ — $\frac{2}{9}$

43-47. Write as decimals.

$\frac{4}{10}$ **.4**
$\frac{17}{100}$ **.17**
$\frac{9}{100}$ **.09**
$3\frac{7}{100}$ **3.07**
$4\frac{50}{100}$ **4.50 (4.5)**

48-52. Write as fractions.

0.7 **$\frac{7}{10}$**
.06 **$\frac{6}{100}$**
.87 **$\frac{87}{100}$**
0.95 **$\frac{95}{100}$**
2.05 **$2\frac{5}{100}$**

This was taught in Lesson 77.

53-58. Put these fractions and decimals in order from least to greatest.

| $\frac{5}{10}$ | $\frac{5}{100}$ | .04 | **.04** | **$\frac{5}{100}$** | **$\frac{5}{10}$** |
| $\frac{300}{100}$ | .03 | .33 | **.03** | **.33** | **$\frac{300}{100}$** |
| .5 | $\frac{49}{100}$ | $\frac{51}{100}$ | **$\frac{49}{100}$** | **.5** | **$\frac{51}{100}$** |
| 1.0 | $\frac{9}{10}$ | $\frac{1}{3}$ | **$\frac{1}{3}$** | **$\frac{9}{10}$** | **1.0** |
| .06 | $\frac{3}{4}$ | $\frac{50}{100}$ | **.06** | **$\frac{50}{100}$** | **$\frac{3}{4}$** |

59-65. Match the fractions and percentages.

$\frac{1}{4}$ — 50%
$\frac{7}{10}$ — 25%
$\frac{2}{4}$ — 70%
1 — 40%
$\frac{1}{3}$ — 100%
$\frac{2}{5}$ — 75%
$\frac{3}{4}$ — $33\frac{1}{3}$%

66-67. Solve the problem.

Robin is trying to decide which gift to buy. The blue one is $24 and is 15% off. The green one is $26 and is 20% off. Which one is cheaper?

**Blue: 24 × 15% off = 3.60**
**24 − 3.60 = $20.40**
**Green: 26 × 20% off = 5.20**
**26 − 5.20 = $20.80**
**Blue is cheaper.**

This was taught in Lessons 89, 90, 91, and 94.

# LESSON 138: FRACTIONS AND PERCENTAGES GAMES

## OBJECTIVES:

1. To review concepts learned during the year by playing math card games

## MATERIALS:

1. *Math Card Games* book, F8, F22.1, and F48
2. Fraction chart, if needed
3. Math journal

| ACTIVITIES FOR TEACHING: | EXPLANATIONS: |
|---|---|
| **Warm-up.** Ask: When you divide one into two equal parts, what do you have? [one half] What is another name for one divided by two? [one half] What is another name for one divided by four? [one fourth] How many one fourths equal one half? [2] Which fraction, one half or two fourths, is in the lowest terms? [one half] Which fraction, one fourth or two eighths, is in the lowest terms? [one fourth] | This lesson is a review of concepts learned during the year by playing games. It is designed to prepare the child for the final assessment. |
| Ask: In the fraction two fifths, what is the denominator? [5] In the fraction two fifths, what number is the numerator? [2] If the denominator and numerator are the same, what does the fraction equal? [1] | |
| Ask: What do we call a fraction when the numerator is greater than the denominator? [improper] What is a fraction called when the denominator is greater than the numerator? [proper] | |
| Ask: What does a decimal point do? [It tells what part of a number is the fraction.] Which is more, 7 tenths or 7 hundredths? [7 tenths] Which is more, 7 tenths or 70 hundredths? [the same] Which is more, 7 or 7 tenths? [7] | |
| **The One Half game.** Play the One Half game, found in *Math Card Games* book, F8. Use the fraction chart if needed. | |

| ACTIVITIES FOR TEACHING CONTINUED: | EXPLANATIONS CONTINUED: |
|---|---|

***Corners™ with Eighths game.*** Play Corners™ with Eighths game, found in *Math Card Games* book, F22.1. Stress that the fractions in the scoring sums must be proper fractions. Tell him to write the scoring in his math journal.

***Percentage War game.*** Play the Percentage War game, found in *Math Card Games* book, F48.

***In conclusion.*** Ask: Fifty percent is the same as what fraction? [one half] Twenty percent is the same as what fraction? [one fifth] Ninety percent is the same as what fraction? [nine tenths]

# Lesson 139: Geometry and Measurement Review

## OBJECTIVES:
1. To review concepts learned during the year

## MATERIALS:
1. Worksheet 108, Geometry and Measurement Review
2. 4-in-1 ruler

## ACTIVITIES FOR TEACHING:

***Worksheet 108.*** Give the child the worksheet.

Tell him that today will be a review for the upcoming final assessment. He will complete the worksheet, then discuss the solutions.

Solutions are below and on the next page.

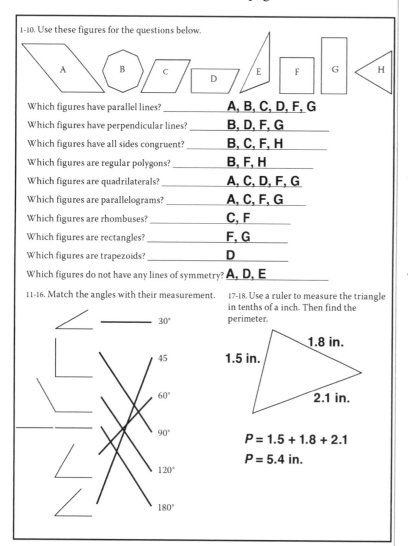

1-10. Use these figures for the questions below.

Which figures have parallel lines? **A, B, C, D, F, G**

Which figures have perpendicular lines? **B, D, F, G**

Which figures have all sides congruent? **B, C, F, H**

Which figures are regular polygons? **B, F, H**

Which figures are quadrilaterals? **A, C, D, F, G**

Which figures are parallelograms? **A, C, F, G**

Which figures are rhombuses? **C, F**

Which figures are rectangles? **F, G**

Which figures are trapezoids? **D**

Which figures do not have any lines of symmetry? **A, D, E**

11-16. Match the angles with their measurement.

30°
45
60°
90°
120°
180°

17-18. Use a ruler to measure the triangle in tenths of a inch. Then find the perimeter.

1.8 in.
1.5 in.
2.1 in.

$P = 1.5 + 1.8 + 2.1$
$P = 5.4$ in.

## EXPLANATIONS:

This was taught in Lesson 100.

These concepts were taught in Lesson 103.

This was taught in Lesson 118.

## ACTIVITIES FOR TEACHING CONTINUED:

## EXPLANATIONS CONTINUED:

19-24. Draw lines to match each triangle by sides and angles.

Scalene triangle   Right triangle

Equilateral triangle  Obtuse triangle

Isosceles triangle —— Acute triangle

25-27. Draw all the lines of symmetry in the figures below and answer the questions.

How many lines
of symmetry? **3**

How many lines
of symmetry? **4**

How many lines
of symmetry? **5**

28-41. Fill in the blanks.

How many degrees are in a circle? **360**

Name the angles in an isosceles right triangle. **45, 45, 90**

Name the angles in an equilateral triangle. **60, 60, 60**

How many angles does an octagon have? **8**

Is a square a rectangle? **yes**

Can a rhombus be a square? **yes**

Is a circle a polygon? **no**

How many inches are in a foot? **12**

How many feet are in a yard? **3**

How many centimeters are in a decimeter? **10**

How many decimeters are in a meter? **10**

How many centimeters are in a meter? **100**

How many milliliters are in a liter? **1000**

Which is longer, an inch or a centimeter? **inch**

These concepts were taught in Lesson 102.

# LESSON 140: FINAL ASSESSMENT

## OBJECTIVES:
1. To assess mastery of concepts learned during the year

## MATERIALS:
1. Worksheet 109, Final Assessment
2. 4-in-1 ruler

## ACTIVITIES FOR TEACHING:

**Worksheet 109.** Give the child the worksheets.

Tell him to listen to the problems and write the answers. Read each problem twice.

$100 - 21$        $25 \times 6$        $78 + 37$

Tell him to complete the worksheets. Solutions are below and on the next pages.

## EXPLANATIONS:

---

1-3. Write only the answers.

**79**

**150**

**115**

4-9. Write the answers.

$737 + 218 =$ **955**

$63 \div 7 =$ **9**

$100 \times 60 =$ **6000**

$94 - 86 =$ **8**

$407 - 15 =$ **392**

$200 -$ **143** $= 57$

---

10. Find $46,893 + 6827$.

**46,893 (3)**
**+ 6,827 (5)**
**53,720 (8)**

11. Find $6015 - 3837$.

**6015 (3)**
**− 3837 (3)**
**2178 (0)**

12. Find $7638 \times 36$.

**7638 (6)**
**× 36 (0)**
**45 828**
**229 140**
**274 968 (0)**

13. Find $4328 \div 4$.

**1082 (2)**
**4⟌4328 (8)**

14. Find $5847 \div 7$.

**835 r2**
**7⟌5847**

---

15-16. Write these as numbers. Use commas to mark the periods.

103 million   **103,000,000**

56 billion   **56,000,000,000**

---

17-22. Round the populations to the nearest thousand.

| Cairo, Egypt | 9,278,441 | **9,278** thousand |
| Istanbul, Turkey | 13,710,512 | **13,711** thousand |
| Lima, Peru | 8,481,415 | **8,481** thousand |
| Mumbai, India | 12,478,447 | **12,478** thousand |
| New York City, US | 8,550,405 | **8,550** thousand |
| Shanghai, China | 18,626,300 | **18,626** thousand |

23. Write the cities in order of population, least to greatest.

| **Lima** |
| **New York City** |
| **Cairo** |
| **Mumbai** |
| **Istanbul** |
| **Shanghai** |

---

24. The population of North America is 360,767,848. Write this number in words.

**Three hundred sixty million seven hundred sixty-seven thousand eight hundred forty-eight**

---

## ACTIVITIES FOR TEACHING CONTINUED:                    EXPLANATIONS CONTINUED:

25-30. Prime numbers and factors.

How do you know that 15, 25, and 50 are not primes? **Multiples of 5**

How do you know that 27, 36, and 81 are not primes? **Multiples of 9**

Which of these numbers, 1, 2, 5, 32, 53, are prime numbers? **2, 5, 53**

Which of these numbers, 1, 2, 5, 32, 53, are composite? **32**

Name the factor pairs for 20. **1 & 20, 2 & 10, 4 & 5**

What are the factors for 20. **1, 2, 4, 5, 10, 20**

31-34. Solve the equations.

$376 - 23 + 23 = n$

$n = $ **376**

$297 + m = 308$

$m = $ **11**

$(5 + p) \times 3 = 18$

$p = $ **1**

$(q \times 5) + 1 = 26$

$q = $ **5**

35-42. Write <, >, or = on the lines.

$40 \times 2$ **=** $4 \times 20$

$13 \times 14 \times 15$ **>** $15 \times 14 \times 13 \times 0$

$85 + 57$ **<** $87 + 57$

$1 + 1$ **>** $1 \times 1$

$2 + 2$ **=** $2 \times 2$

$4 + 4$ **<** $4 \times 4$

$(7 \times 10) - (7 \times 7)$ **=** $(7 \times 3)$

$37 - 19$ **>** $35 - 19$

43-45. Round 6489.

| To nearest 10. | **6490** |
|---|---|
| To nearest 100. | **6500** |
| To nearest 1000. | **6000** |

46-48. Round 3,694,758.

| To nearest 1000. | **3,695,000** |
|---|---|
| To nearest 10,000. | **3,690,000** |
| To nearest 100,000. | **3,700,000** |

49-50. Solve the problem.

Rochelle rode her bike from 9:00 a.m. to 1:00 p.m. everyday for four days. She biked 6 miles in an hour. Then she biked an extra 3 miles. How far did she bike?

**Rochelle rode 4 hr a day.**
**She rode 4 × 4 = 16 hr**
**She rode 16 × 6 = 96 miles**
**She rode 96 + 3 = 99 miles total**

The next four pages have the remaining solutions.

# LESSON 140: FINAL ASSESSMENT – CONTINUED

| ACTIVITIES FOR TEACHING: | EXPLANATIONS: |
|---|---|

51-56. Write the non-shaded fractions on the lines.

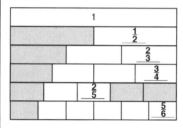

$\frac{1}{2}$

$\frac{2}{3}$

$\frac{3}{4}$

$\frac{2}{5}$

$\frac{5}{6}$

57-63. Circle True or False.

T **F** A fraction can never be greater than one.

T **F** A fraction is division with the denominator divided by the numerator.

**T** F The numerator tells the number of parts.

**T** F The denominator is the divisor.

**T** F If the numerator equals the denominator, the fraction equals one.

T **F** A fraction is proper if the numerator is more than the denominator.

T **F** A mixed number is a whole number and an improper fraction.

64-68. Make a small mark at the correct position on the number line and write the fraction for the following: $\frac{1}{3}$, $\frac{2}{3}$, $1\frac{1}{3}$, $\frac{1}{2}$, and $1\frac{3}{4}$.

$\frac{1}{3}$  $\frac{1}{2}$  $\frac{2}{3}$     $1\frac{1}{3}$     $1\frac{3}{4}$

0                    1                    2

69-80. Fill in the blanks.

90 cm is what fraction of a meter? $\frac{9}{10}\left(\frac{90}{100}\right)$

Seven days is what fraction of April? $\frac{7}{30}$

$1.25 is what fraction of a dollar? $\frac{5}{4}$

8 hours is what fraction of a day? $\frac{1}{3}$

15 minutes is what fraction of an hour? $\frac{1}{4}$

5 inches is what fraction of a foot? $\frac{5}{12}$

One half of a day is **12** hours.

One seventh of a week is **24** hours.

5 quarters of a hour is **75** minutes.

Three quarters of a dollar is **75** ¢.

Three fourths of a foot **9** inches.

One tenth of a meter is **10** cm.

81-84. Solve the problems.

An adult blue whale can be 32 ft long. At birth the baby is about one fourth that long. How long is the baby? How much longer does the baby whale grow before it is an adult?

**Baby is $\frac{1}{4}$ of 32 = 8 ft**

**Grows 32 – 8 = 24 ft**

The perimeter of each regular figure below is 13 cm. What is the length of the sides of each figure?

$s = 13 \div 3$      $s = 13 \div 6$

$s = \frac{13}{3}$ cm      $s = \frac{13}{6}$ cm

$s = 4\frac{1}{3}$ cm      $s = 2\frac{1}{6}$ cm

275

## ACTIVITIES FOR TEACHING CONTINUED:

## EXPLANATIONS CONTINUED:

85-92. Match the expressions.

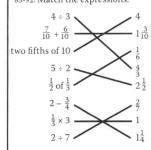

| | |
|---|---|
| $4 \div 3$ | $4$ |
| $\frac{7}{10} + \frac{6}{10}$ | $1\frac{3}{10}$ |
| two fifths of 10 | $\frac{1}{6}$ |
| $5 \div 2$ | $\frac{4}{3}$ |
| $\frac{1}{2}$ of $\frac{1}{3}$ | $2\frac{1}{2}$ |
| $2 - \frac{3}{4}$ | $\frac{2}{7}$ |
| $\frac{1}{3} \times 3$ | $1$ |
| $2 \div 7$ | $1\frac{1}{4}$ |

93-97. Write as decimals.

$\frac{3}{10}$ **.3**

$\frac{25}{100}$ **.25**

$\frac{9}{100}$ **.09**

$1\frac{59}{100}$ **1.59**

$3\frac{8}{100}$ **3.08**

98-102. Write as fractions.

0.83 **$\frac{83}{100}$**

.4 **$\frac{4}{10}$**

1.5 **$1\frac{5}{10}$**

0.01 **$\frac{1}{100}$**

2.60 **$2\frac{60}{100}$ ($2\frac{6}{10}$)**

103-108. Put these fractions and decimals in order from least to greatest.

| $\frac{9}{10}$ | $\frac{1}{9}$ | 1.0 | **$\frac{1}{9}$** | **$\frac{9}{10}$** | **1.0** |
|---|---|---|---|---|---|
| $\frac{7}{10}$ | $\frac{7}{100}$ | .06 | **.06** | **$\frac{7}{100}$** | **$\frac{7}{10}$** |
| .51 | $\frac{49}{100}$ | $\frac{52}{100}$ | **$\frac{49}{100}$** | **.51** | **$\frac{52}{100}$** |
| .01 | $\frac{5}{4}$ | $\frac{50}{100}$ | **.01** | **$\frac{50}{100}$** | **$\frac{5}{4}$** |
| .66 | $\frac{600}{100}$ | .06 | **.06** | **.66** | **$\frac{600}{100}$** |

109-115. Match the fractions and percentages.

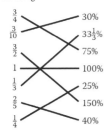

| | |
|---|---|
| $\frac{3}{4}$ | 30% |
| $\frac{3}{10}$ | $33\frac{1}{3}$% |
| $\frac{3}{2}$ | 75% |
| $1$ | 100% |
| $\frac{1}{3}$ | 25% |
| $\frac{2}{5}$ | 150% |
| $\frac{1}{4}$ | 40% |

116-117. Solve the problem.

Terry is working on a fundraiser for charity and has collected $84. Terry can keep 15%. How much does Terry earn? How much goes to the charity?

**Keeps: 84 × 15% = $12.60**

**Charity 84 − 12.60 = $71.40**

© Activities for Learning, Inc. 2016

# LESSON 140: FINAL ASSESSMENT – CONTINUED

## ACTIVITIES FOR TEACHING:

**EXPLANATIONS:**

119-128. Use these figures for the questions below.

Which figures have parallel lines? **B, C, D, E, F, G**

Which figures have perpendicular lines? **B, C, F, G**

Which figures have all sides congruent? **B, C, D, H**

Which figures are regular polygons? **B, C, H**

Which figures are quadrilaterals? **C, D, E, F, G**

Which figures are parallelograms? **C, D, E, G**

Which figures are rhombuses? **C, D**

Which figures are rectangles? **C, G**

Which figures are trapezoids? **F**

Which figures do not have any lines of symmetry? **E, F**

129-134. Match the angles with their measurement.

30°

45

60°

90°

120°

180°

135-136. Use a ruler to measure the triangle in tenths of a inch. Then find the perimeter.

2.4 in.

1.3 in.

1.9 in.

$P = 2.4 + 1.9 + 1.3$

$P = 5.6$ in.

## ACTIVITIES FOR TEACHING CONTINUED:

## EXPLANATIONS CONTINUED:

137-142. Draw lines to match each triangle by sides and angles.

Scalene triangle          Obtuse triangle

Isosceles triangle          Right triangle

Equilateral triangle          Acute triangle

143-145. Draw all the lines of symmetry in the figures below and answer the questions.

How many lines of symmetry? **3**

How many lines of symmetry? **4**

How many lines of symmetry? **6**

146-159. Fill in the blanks.

If you turn 360°, where will you end? **where you started**

Name the angles in an isosceles right triangle. **45, 45, 90**

What is special about the sides in an equilateral triangle. **equal**

How many angles does an hexagon have? **6**

Can a rectangle also be a square? **yes**

Can a parallelogram be a square? **yes**

Can a polygon have only two sides? **no**

How many inches are in 2 feet? **24**

How many yards is 6 feet? **2**

How many centimeters are in 2 decimeters? **20**

How many decimeters are in a half a meter? **5**

How many centimeters are in a meter? **100**

How many milliliters are in a liter? **1000**

Which is longer, 3 feet or 1 meter? **1 meter**

# Congratulations!

## Your child has completed RightStart™ Mathematics Level E and is now ready for Level F Second Edition.

Certificates of completion are in the back of the child's worksheets.

*Certificate of Achievement*

Presented to

_____

for completing

**RIGHTSTART™ MATHEMATICS
LEVEL E**

Second Edition

On this _____ day of_____

_____, Teacher

Joan A. Cotter, Ph.D.
Kathleen Cotter Lawler

To move on to RightStart™ Mathematics Level F Second Edition, all you need is the Level F Book Bundle. This can be purchased at RightStartMath.com or by calling 888-272-3291.

# APPENDIX

# SHORT MULTIPLICATION TABLE

| 1 | | | | | | | | | |
|----|----|----|----|----|----|----|----|----|-----|
| 2 | 4 | | | | | | | | |
| 3 | 6 | 9 | | | | | | | |
| 4 | 8 | 12 | 16 | | | | | | |
| 5 | 10 | 15 | 20 | 25 | | | | | |
| 6 | 12 | 18 | 24 | 30 | 36 | | | | |
| 7 | 14 | 21 | 28 | 35 | 42 | 49 | | | |
| 8 | 16 | 24 | 32 | 40 | 48 | 56 | 64 | | |
| 9 | 18 | 27 | 36 | 45 | 54 | 63 | 72 | 81 | |
| 10 | 20 | 30 | 40 | 50 | 60 | 70 | 80 | 90 | 100 |

Cut out the two squares at the left. Fold back on the heavy line to make the table stand up.

| 1 | | | | | | | | | |
|----|----|----|----|----|----|----|----|----|-----|
| 2 | 4 | | | | | | | | |
| 3 | 6 | 9 | | | | | | | |
| 4 | 8 | 12 | 16 | | | | | | |
| 5 | 10 | 15 | 20 | 25 | | | | | |
| 6 | 12 | 18 | 24 | 30 | 36 | | | | |
| 7 | 14 | 21 | 28 | 35 | 42 | 49 | | | |
| 8 | 16 | 24 | 32 | 40 | 48 | 56 | 64 | | |
| 9 | 18 | 27 | 36 | 45 | 54 | 63 | 72 | 81 | |
| 10 | 20 | 30 | 40 | 50 | 60 | 70 | 80 | 90 | 100 |

# SIEVE OF ERATOSTHENES PART 1

| 1 | 2 | 3 | 4 | 5 | 6 | 7 | 8 | 9 | 10 |
|---|---|---|---|---|---|---|---|---|---|
| 11 | 12 | 13 | 14 | 15 | 16 | 17 | 18 | 19 | 20 |
| 21 | 22 | 23 | 24 | 25 | 26 | 27 | 28 | 29 | 30 |
| 31 | 32 | 33 | 34 | 35 | 36 | 37 | 38 | 39 | 40 |
| 41 | 42 | 43 | 44 | 45 | 46 | 47 | 48 | 49 | 50 |
| 51 | 52 | 53 | 54 | 55 | 56 | 57 | 58 | 59 | 60 |
| 61 | 62 | 63 | 64 | 65 | 66 | 67 | 68 | 69 | 70 |
| 71 | 72 | 73 | 74 | 75 | 76 | 77 | 78 | 79 | 80 |
| 81 | 82 | 83 | 84 | 85 | 86 | 87 | 88 | 89 | 90 |
| 91 | 92 | 93 | 94 | 95 | 96 | 97 | 98 | 99 | 100 |

Total number of primes is 25.

# SIEVE OF ERATOSTHENES PART 2

| 101 | 102 | 103 | 104 | 105 | 106 | 107 | 108 | 109 | 110 |
| 111 | 112 | 113 | 114 | 115 | 116 | 117 | 118 | 119 | 120 |
| 121 | 122 | 123 | 124 | 125 | 126 | 127 | 128 | 129 | 130 |
| 131 | 132 | 133 | 134 | 135 | 136 | 137 | 138 | 139 | 140 |
| 141 | 142 | 143 | 144 | 145 | 146 | 147 | 148 | 149 | 150 |
| 151 | 152 | 153 | 154 | 155 | 156 | 157 | 158 | 159 | 160 |
| 161 | 162 | 163 | 164 | 165 | 166 | 167 | 168 | 169 | 170 |
| 171 | 172 | 173 | 174 | 175 | 176 | 177 | 178 | 179 | 180 |
| 181 | 182 | 183 | 184 | 185 | 186 | 187 | 188 | 189 | 190 |
| 191 | 192 | 193 | 194 | 195 | 196 | 197 | 198 | 199 | 200 |

Total number of primes is 21.

# Sieve of Eratosthenes Part 3

| 201 | 202 | 203 | 204 | 205 | 206 | 207 | 208 | 209 | 210 |
| 211 | 212 | 213 | 214 | 215 | 216 | 217 | 218 | 219 | 220 |
| 221 | 222 | 223 | 224 | 225 | 226 | 227 | 228 | 229 | 230 |
| 231 | 232 | 233 | 234 | 235 | 236 | 237 | 238 | 239 | 240 |
| 241 | 242 | 243 | 244 | 245 | 246 | 247 | 248 | 249 | 250 |
| 251 | 252 | 253 | 254 | 255 | 256 | 257 | 258 | 259 | 260 |
| 261 | 262 | 263 | 264 | 265 | 266 | 267 | 268 | 269 | 270 |
| 271 | 272 | 273 | 274 | 275 | 276 | 277 | 278 | 279 | 280 |
| 281 | 282 | 283 | 284 | 285 | 286 | 287 | 288 | 289 | 290 |
| 291 | 292 | 293 | 294 | 295 | 296 | 297 | 298 | 299 | 300 |

Total number of primes is 16.

| 301 | 302 | 303 | 304 | 305 | 306 | 307 | 308 | 309 | 310 |
| 311 | 312 | 313 | 314 | 315 | 316 | 317 | 318 | 319 | 320 |
| 321 | 322 | 323 | 324 | 325 | 326 | 327 | 328 | 329 | 330 |
| 331 | 332 | 333 | 334 | 335 | 336 | 337 | 338 | 339 | 340 |
| 341 | 342 | 343 | 344 | 345 | 346 | 347 | 348 | 349 | 350 |
| 351 | 352 | 353 | 354 | 355 | 356 | 357 | 358 | 359 | 360 |
| 361 | 362 | 363 | 364 | 365 | 366 | 367 | 368 | 369 | 370 |
| 371 | 372 | 373 | 374 | 375 | 376 | 377 | 378 | 379 | 380 |
| 381 | 382 | 383 | 384 | 385 | 386 | 387 | 388 | 389 | 390 |
| 391 | 392 | 393 | 394 | 395 | 396 | 397 | 398 | 399 | 400 |

Total number of primes is 16.

# SIEVE OF ERATOSTHENES PART 5

| 401 | 402 | 403 | 404 | 405 | 406 | 407 | 408 | 409 | 410 |
| 411 | 412 | 413 | 414 | 415 | 416 | 417 | 418 | 419 | 420 |
| 421 | 422 | 423 | 424 | 425 | 426 | 427 | 428 | 429 | 430 |
| 431 | 432 | 433 | 434 | 435 | 436 | 437 | 438 | 439 | 440 |
| 441 | 442 | 443 | 444 | 445 | 446 | 447 | 448 | 449 | 450 |
| 451 | 452 | 453 | 454 | 455 | 456 | 457 | 458 | 459 | 460 |
| 461 | 462 | 463 | 464 | 465 | 466 | 467 | 468 | 469 | 470 |
| 471 | 472 | 473 | 474 | 475 | 476 | 477 | 478 | 479 | 480 |
| 481 | 482 | 483 | 484 | 485 | 486 | 487 | 488 | 489 | 490 |
| 491 | 492 | 493 | 494 | 495 | 496 | 497 | 498 | 499 | 500 |

Total number of primes is 17.

# SIEVE OF ERATOSTHENES PART 6

| 501 | 502 | 503 | 504 | 505 | 506 | 507 | 508 | 509 | 510 |
|-----|-----|-----|-----|-----|-----|-----|-----|-----|-----|
| 511 | 512 | 513 | 514 | 515 | 516 | 517 | 518 | 519 | 520 |
| 521 | 522 | 523 | 524 | 525 | 526 | 527 | 528 | 529 | 530 |
| 531 | 532 | 533 | 534 | 535 | 536 | 537 | 538 | 539 | 540 |
| 541 | 542 | 543 | 544 | 545 | 546 | 547 | 548 | 549 | 550 |
| 551 | 552 | 553 | 554 | 555 | 556 | 557 | 558 | 559 | 560 |
| 561 | 562 | 563 | 564 | 565 | 566 | 567 | 568 | 569 | 570 |
| 571 | 572 | 573 | 574 | 575 | 576 | 577 | 578 | 579 | 580 |
| 581 | 582 | 583 | 584 | 585 | 586 | 587 | 588 | 589 | 590 |
| 591 | 592 | 593 | 594 | 595 | 596 | 597 | 598 | 599 | 600 |

Total number of primes is 14.

# SIEVE OF ERATOSTHENES PART 7

| | | | | | | | | | |
|---|---|---|---|---|---|---|---|---|---|
| 601 | 602 | 603 | 604 | 605 | 606 | 607 | 608 | 609 | 610 |
| 611 | 612 | 613 | 614 | 615 | 616 | 617 | 618 | 619 | 620 |
| 621 | 622 | 623 | 624 | 625 | 626 | 627 | 628 | 629 | 630 |
| 631 | 632 | 633 | 634 | 635 | 636 | 637 | 638 | 639 | 640 |
| 641 | 642 | 643 | 644 | 645 | 646 | 647 | 648 | 649 | 650 |
| 651 | 652 | 653 | 654 | 655 | 656 | 657 | 658 | 659 | 660 |
| 661 | 662 | 663 | 664 | 665 | 666 | 667 | 668 | 669 | 670 |
| 671 | 672 | 673 | 674 | 675 | 676 | 677 | 678 | 679 | 680 |
| 681 | 682 | 683 | 684 | 685 | 686 | 687 | 688 | 689 | 690 |
| 691 | 692 | 693 | 694 | 695 | 696 | 697 | 698 | 699 | 700 |

Total number of primes is 16.

# SIEVE OF ERATOSTHENES PART 8

| 701 | 702 | 703 | 704 | 705 | 706 | 707 | 708 | 709 | 710 |
| 711 | 712 | 713 | 714 | 715 | 716 | 717 | 718 | 719 | 720 |
| 721 | 722 | 723 | 724 | 725 | 726 | 727 | 728 | 729 | 730 |
| 731 | 732 | 733 | 734 | 735 | 736 | 737 | 738 | 739 | 740 |
| 741 | 742 | 743 | 744 | 745 | 746 | 747 | 748 | 749 | 750 |
| 751 | 752 | 753 | 754 | 755 | 756 | 757 | 758 | 759 | 760 |
| 761 | 762 | 763 | 764 | 765 | 766 | 767 | 768 | 769 | 770 |
| 771 | 772 | 773 | 774 | 775 | 776 | 777 | 778 | 779 | 780 |
| 781 | 782 | 783 | 784 | 785 | 786 | 787 | 788 | 789 | 790 |
| 791 | 792 | 793 | 794 | 795 | 796 | 797 | 798 | 799 | 800 |

Total number of primes is 14.

# SIEVE OF ERATOSTHENES PART 9

| | | | | | | | | | |
|---|---|---|---|---|---|---|---|---|---|
| 801 | 802 | 803 | 804 | 805 | 806 | 807 | 808 | 809 | 810 |
| 811 | 812 | 813 | 814 | 815 | 816 | 817 | 818 | 819 | 820 |
| 821 | 822 | 823 | 824 | 825 | 826 | 827 | 828 | 829 | 830 |
| 831 | 832 | 833 | 834 | 835 | 836 | 837 | 838 | 839 | 840 |
| 841 | 842 | 843 | 844 | 845 | 846 | 847 | 848 | 849 | 850 |
| 851 | 852 | 853 | 854 | 855 | 856 | 857 | 858 | 859 | 860 |
| 861 | 862 | 863 | 864 | 865 | 866 | 867 | 868 | 869 | 870 |
| 871 | 872 | 873 | 874 | 875 | 876 | 877 | 878 | 879 | 880 |
| 881 | 882 | 883 | 884 | 885 | 886 | 887 | 888 | 889 | 890 |
| 891 | 892 | 893 | 894 | 895 | 896 | 897 | 898 | 899 | 900 |

Total number of primes is 15.

# SIEVE OF ERATOSTHENES PART 10

| 901 | 902 | 903 | 904 | 905 | 906 | 907 | 908 | 909 | 910 |
|-----|-----|-----|-----|-----|-----|-----|-----|-----|------|
| 911 | 912 | 913 | 914 | 915 | 916 | 917 | 918 | 919 | 920 |
| 921 | 922 | 923 | 924 | 925 | 926 | 927 | 928 | 929 | 930 |
| 931 | 932 | 933 | 934 | 935 | 936 | 937 | 938 | 939 | 940 |
| 941 | 942 | 943 | 944 | 945 | 946 | 947 | 948 | 949 | 950 |
| 951 | 952 | 953 | 954 | 955 | 956 | 957 | 958 | 959 | 960 |
| 961 | 962 | 963 | 964 | 965 | 966 | 967 | 968 | 969 | 970 |
| 971 | 972 | 973 | 974 | 975 | 976 | 977 | 978 | 979 | 980 |
| 981 | 982 | 983 | 984 | 985 | 986 | 987 | 988 | 989 | 990 |
| 991 | 992 | 993 | 994 | 995 | 996 | 997 | 998 | 999 | 1000 |

Total number of primes is 14.

## Map of the United States

# Alphabetical List of States

| | |
|---|---|
| Alabama | Montana |
| Alaska | Nebraska |
| Arizona | Nevada |
| Arkansas | New Hampshire |
| California | New Jersey |
| Colorado | New Mexico |
| Connecticut | New York |
| Delaware | North Carolina |
| Florida | North Dakota |
| Georgia | Ohio |
| Hawaii | Oklahoma |
| Idaho | Oregon |
| Illinois | Pennsylvania |
| Indiana | Rhode Island |
| Iowa | South Carolina |
| Kansas | South Dakota |
| Kentucky | Tennessee |
| Louisiana | Texas |
| Maine | Utah |
| Maryland | Vermont |
| Massachusetts | Virginia |
| Michigan | Washington |
| Minnesota | West Virginia |
| Mississippi | Wisconsin |
| Missouri | Wyoming |

# Fraction Circles and Percent Circles

Cut out the four large circles and cut on the lines that go to the center. Then put them together as shown on the right. Be sure the 0 or 0% is on top.

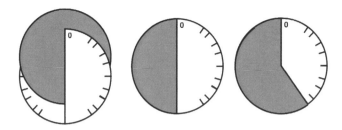

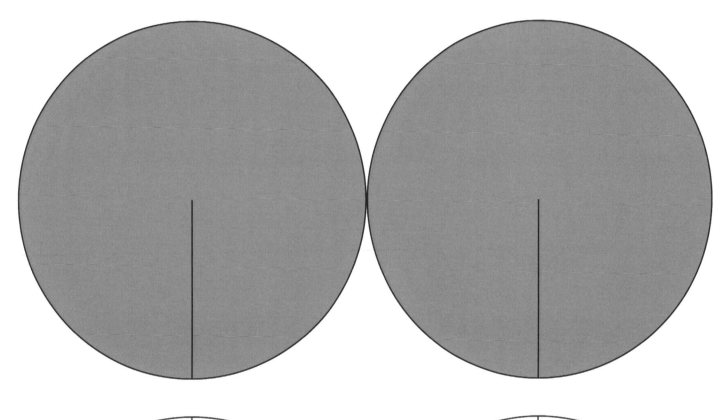

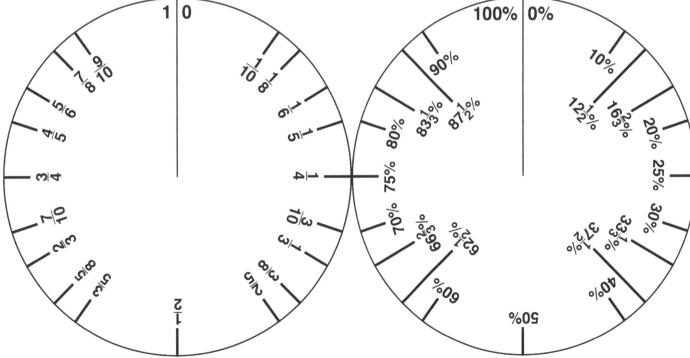

RightStart™ Mathematics, E

Cut out the large circles on the other side of this sheet of paper.

# CALENDAR

## January

| S | M | T | W | T | F | S |
|---|---|---|---|---|---|---|
| 1 | 2 | 3 | 4 | 5 | 6 | 7 |
| 8 | 9 | 10 | 11 | 12 | 13 | 14 |
| 15 | 16 | 17 | 18 | 19 | 20 | 21 |
| 22 | 23 | 24 | 25 | 26 | 27 | 28 |
| 29 | 30 | 31 | | | | |
| | | | | | | |

## February

| S | M | T | W | T | F | S |
|---|---|---|---|---|---|---|
| | | | 1 | 2 | 3 | 4 |
| 5 | 6 | 7 | 8 | 9 | 10 | 11 |
| 12 | 13 | 14 | 15 | 16 | 17 | 18 |
| 19 | 20 | 21 | 22 | 23 | 24 | 25 |
| 26 | 27 | 28 | | | | |

## March

| S | M | T | W |
|---|---|---|---|
| | | | 1 |
| 5 | 6 | 7 | 8 |
| 12 | 13 | 14 | 15 |
| 19 | 20 | 21 | 22 | 23 |
| 26 | 27 | 28 | 29 | 30 |

## April

| S | M | T | W | T | F | S |
|---|---|---|---|---|---|---|
| | | | | | | 1 |
| 2 | 3 | 4 | 5 | 6 | 7 | 8 |
| 9 | 10 | 11 | 12 | 13 | 14 | 15 |
| 16 | 17 | 18 | 19 | 20 | 21 | 22 |
| 23 | 24 | 25 | 26 | 27 | 28 | 29 |
| 30 | | | | | | |

## May

| S | M | T | W | T | F | S |
|---|---|---|---|---|---|---|
| | 1 | 2 | 3 | 4 | 5 | 6 |
| 7 | 8 | 9 | 10 | 11 | 12 | 13 |
| 14 | 15 | 16 | 17 | 18 | 19 | 20 |
| 21 | 22 | 23 | 24 | 25 | 26 | 27 |
| 28 | 29 | 30 | 31 | | | |

## June

| S | M | T | W | T | F |
|---|---|---|---|---|---|
| | | | | 1 | 2 |
| 4 | 5 | 6 | 7 | 8 | 9 |
| 11 | 12 | 13 | 14 | 15 | 16 |
| 18 | 19 | 20 | 21 | 22 | 23 |
| 25 | 26 | 27 | 28 | 29 | 30 |

## July

| S | M | T | W | T | F | S |
|---|---|---|---|---|---|---|
| | | | | | | 1 |
| 2 | 3 | 4 | 5 | 6 | 7 | 8 |
| 9 | 10 | 11 | 12 | 13 | 14 | 15 |
| 16 | 17 | 18 | 19 | 20 | 21 | 22 |
| 23 | 24 | 25 | 26 | 27 | 28 | 29 |
| 30 | 31 | | | | | |

## August

| S | M | T | W | T | F | S |
|---|---|---|---|---|---|---|
| | | 1 | 2 | 3 | 4 | 5 |
| 6 | 7 | 8 | 9 | 10 | 11 | 12 |
| 13 | 14 | 15 | 16 | 17 | 18 | 19 |
| 20 | 21 | 22 | 23 | 24 | 25 | 26 |
| 27 | 28 | 29 | 30 | 31 | | |

## September

| S | M | T | W | T | F | S |
|---|---|---|---|---|---|---|
| | | | | | 1 | 2 |
| 3 | 4 | 5 | 6 | 7 | 8 | 9 |
| 10 | 11 | 12 | 13 | 14 | 15 | 16 |
| 17 | 18 | 19 | 20 | 21 | 22 | 23 |
| 24 | 25 | 26 | 27 | 28 | 29 | 30 |

## October

| S | M | T | W | T | F | S |
|---|---|---|---|---|---|---|
| 1 | 2 | 3 | 4 | 5 | 6 | 7 |
| 8 | 9 | 10 | 11 | 12 | 13 | 14 |
| 15 | 16 | 17 | 18 | 19 | 20 | 21 |
| 22 | 23 | 24 | 25 | 26 | 27 | 28 |
| 29 | 30 | 31 | | | | |

## November

| S | M | T | W | T | F | S |
|---|---|---|---|---|---|---|
| | | | 1 | 2 | 3 | 4 |
| 5 | 6 | 7 | 8 | 9 | 10 | 11 |
| 12 | 13 | 14 | 15 | 16 | 17 | 18 |
| 19 | 20 | 21 | 22 | 23 | 24 | 25 |
| 26 | 27 | 28 | 29 | 30 | | |

## December

| S | M | T | W | T | F | S |
|---|---|---|---|---|---|---|
| | | | | | 1 | 2 |
| 3 | 4 | 5 | 6 | 7 | 8 | 9 |
| 10 | 11 | 12 | 13 | 14 | 15 | 16 |
| 17 | 18 | 19 | 20 | 21 | 22 | 23 |
| 24 | 25 | 26 | 27 | 28 | 29 | 30 |
| 31 | | | | | | |

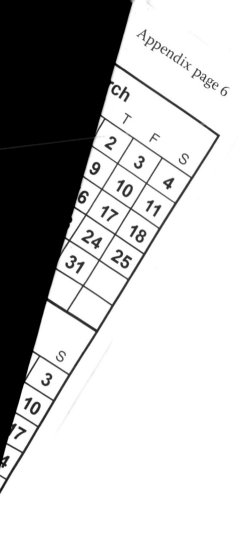

rch

| | T | F | S |
|---|---|---|---|
| | 2 | 3 | 4 |
| 9 | | 10 | 4 |
| 6 | | 17 | 11 |
| | | 24 | 18 |
| 31 | | 25 | |
| | | | |

| | | S |
|---|---|---|
| | | 3 |
| 10 | | |
| 7 | | |
| 4 | | |

# Calendar

## January

| S | M | T | W | T | F | S |
|---|---|---|---|---|---|---|
|  |  |  |  |  | 1 | 2 |
| 3 | 4 | 5 | 6 | 7 | 8 | 9 |
| 10 | 11 | 12 | 13 | 14 | 15 | 16 |
| 17 | 18 | 19 | 20 | 21 | 22 | 23 |
| 24 | 25 | 26 | 27 | 28 | 29 | 30 |
| 31 |  |  |  |  |  |  |

## February

| S | M | T | W | T | F | S |
|---|---|---|---|---|---|---|
|  | 1 | 2 | 3 | 4 | 5 | 6 |
| 7 | 8 | 9 | 10 | 11 | 12 | 13 |
| 14 | 15 | 16 | 17 | 18 | 19 | 20 |
| 21 | 22 | 23 | 24 | 25 | 26 | 27 |
| 28 | 29 |  |  |  |  |  |

## March

| S | M | T | W |
|---|---|---|---|
|  | 1 | 2 |  |
| 6 | 7 | 8 | 9 |
| 13 | 14 | 15 | 16 | 17 |
| 20 | 21 | 22 | 23 | 24 |
| 27 | 28 | 29 | 30 | 31 |

## April

| S | M | T | W | T | F | S |
|---|---|---|---|---|---|---|
|  |  |  |  |  | 1 | 2 |
| 3 | 4 | 5 | 6 | 7 | 8 | 9 |
| 10 | 11 | 12 | 13 | 14 | 15 | 16 |
| 17 | 18 | 19 | 20 | 21 | 22 | 23 |
| 24 | 25 | 26 | 27 | 28 | 29 | 30 |

## May

| S | M | T | W | T | F | S |
|---|---|---|---|---|---|---|
| 1 | 2 | 3 | 4 | 5 | 6 | 7 |
| 8 | 9 | 10 | 11 | 12 | 13 | 14 |
| 15 | 16 | 17 | 18 | 19 | 20 | 21 |
| 22 | 23 | 24 | 25 | 26 | 27 | 28 |
| 29 | 30 | 31 |  |  |  |  |

## June

| S | M | T | W | T | F |
|---|---|---|---|---|---|
|  |  |  | 1 | 2 | 3 |
| 5 | 6 | 7 | 8 | 9 | 10 |
| 12 | 13 | 14 | 15 | 16 | 17 | 18 |
| 19 | 20 | 21 | 22 | 23 | 24 | 25 |
| 26 | 27 | 28 | 29 | 30 |  |  |

## July

| S | M | T | W | T | F | S |
|---|---|---|---|---|---|---|
|  |  |  |  |  | 1 | 2 |
| 3 | 4 | 5 | 6 | 7 | 8 | 9 |
| 10 | 11 | 12 | 13 | 14 | 15 | 16 |
| 17 | 18 | 19 | 20 | 21 | 22 | 23 |
| 24 | 25 | 26 | 27 | 28 | 29 | 30 |
| 31 |  |  |  |  |  |  |

## August

| S | M | T | W | T | F | S |
|---|---|---|---|---|---|---|
|  | 1 | 2 | 3 | 4 | 5 | 6 |
| 7 | 8 | 9 | 10 | 11 | 12 | 13 |
| 14 | 15 | 16 | 17 | 18 | 19 | 20 |
| 21 | 22 | 23 | 24 | 25 | 26 | 27 |
| 28 | 29 | 30 | 31 |  |  |  |

## September

| S | M | T | W | T | F | S |
|---|---|---|---|---|---|---|
|  |  |  |  | 1 | 2 | 3 |
| 4 | 5 | 6 | 7 | 8 | 9 | 10 |
| 11 | 12 | 13 | 14 | 15 | 16 | 17 |
| 18 | 19 | 20 | 21 | 22 | 23 | 24 |
| 25 | 26 | 27 | 28 | 29 | 30 |  |

## October

| S | M | T | W | T | F | S |
|---|---|---|---|---|---|---|
|  |  |  |  |  |  | 1 |
| 2 | 3 | 4 | 5 | 6 | 7 | 8 |
| 9 | 10 | 11 | 12 | 13 | 14 | 15 |
| 16 | 17 | 18 | 19 | 20 | 21 | 22 |
| 23 | 24 | 25 | 26 | 27 | 28 | 29 |
| 30 | 31 |  |  |  |  |  |

## November

| S | M | T | W | T | F | S |
|---|---|---|---|---|---|---|
|  | 1 | 2 | 3 | 4 | 5 |  |
| 6 | 7 | 8 | 9 | 10 | 11 | 12 |
| 13 | 14 | 15 | 16 | 17 | 18 | 19 |
| 20 | 21 | 22 | 23 | 24 | 25 | 26 |
| 27 | 28 | 29 | 30 |  |  |  |

## December

| S | M | T | W | T | F | S |
|---|---|---|---|---|---|---|
|  |  |  |  | 1 | 2 | 3 |
| 4 | 5 | 6 | 7 | 8 | 9 | 10 |
| 11 | 12 | 13 | 14 | 15 | 16 | 17 |
| 18 | 19 | 20 | 21 | 22 | 23 | 24 |
| 25 | 26 | 27 | 28 | 29 | 30 | 31 |

RightStart™ Mathematics, E

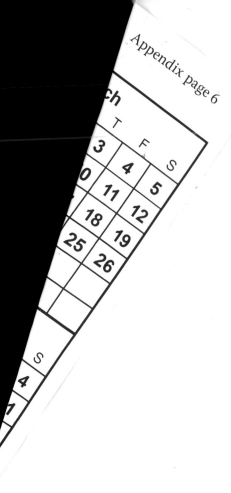

ch

| | T | F | S |
|---|---|---|---|
| 3 | | 4 | 5 |
| 0 | 11 | | 5 |
| | 18 | 12 | |
| 25 | 19 | | |
| | 26 | | |
| | | | |

| S |
|---|
| 4 |
| 1 |